HAZARDS AT WORK

TUC guide to health and safety

TUC

Working for Health and Safety

Contents

Foreword

Protecting people from the hazards of their work is an unremitting task for all active trade unionists. It requires dedication, patience, skill, determination – as well as a detailed knowledge of workplace hazards and how to overcome them. But it is also one of the most worthwhile tasks that any trade union member can undertake – for no one should ever forget the sense of anger, frustration and despair that follows a futile accident or disease at work which could have been prevented by taking simple precautions.

Since the introduction of the *Health and Safety at Work Act in 1975* and the *Safety Representatives Regulations in 1978* there has been a profound change in outlook and activity on health and safety issues throughout the whole trade union Movement. Health and safety has been pushed up the agenda and important gains have been made – despite the fact that the Government has cut back – reducing an already overstretched inspectorate and accident rates in some sectors have risen.

The inadequacy of existing arrangements has been highlighted by the tragic disasters at Zeebrugge, Kings Cross and Piper Alpha. If further progress in health and safety is to be secured, it will depend, as it always has done, on action by the trade union Movement. The TUC has recently identified what further steps need to be taken at national level if health and safety performance is to be improved over the next decade – but unless these are backed up by intensified action at the place of work, there is no certainty that lives, limbs and health will be safeguarded in the years ahead.

This guide is intended to assist in this process. I urge every active trade unionist to buy a copy, to study it carefully and to make sure the advice and guidance it contains is put into practice in order to benefit everyone at work.

Norman Willis

Norman Willis
TUC General Secretary
August 1988

Introduction

Since the introduction of the Health and Safety at Work Act in 1975, there has been a rapid and continuing expansion in demand throughout the trade union Movement for information about health and safety at work. This demand has grown steadily as trade union safety representatives have developed their skills and strengthened their organisation to tackle an ever widening range of hazard issues faced by their members. As a result, health and safety at work is now widely accepted as a major part of day to day trade union business at workplace, industry and national level.

In this process, reliable information about the nature of health and safety problems and legal and other standards that should be observed is absolutely essential – hence this Guide. Building on the success of the TUC's *Safety and Health Handbook*, which sold over 800,000 copies, it is intended as a basic information resource for all safety representatives and for anyone else concerned with the prevention of accidents and ill health at work.

The new guide has been compiled to take account not only of the latest information on hazards but recent changes in health and safety law and other relevant standards. Chapters have been included on issues such as VDUs, office safety, violence, stress, biological hazards and radiation. The aim has been to keep medical, scientific and legal technicalities to a minimum and present essential information on common sources of risk at work, the health and safety law, and the rights of workers and their representatives in a straightforward way and to give guidance on where to go for further information.

The guide does not provide all the answers to every health and safety problem but has been designed as a basic tool to help identify problems and work out solutions to them. Checklists are included at the end of each section or chapter together with suggestions for further reading. Where more detailed information is required reference should be made to the TUC's expanding range of health and safety booklets and pamphlets on specific hazard issues such as noise, dust, VDUs, asbestos etc (a full list of which is given at Appendix 3).

1: Health and safety and the law

The battle to get basic health and safety standards written into the law of the land goes back nearly two centuries. The first health and safety legislation was passed in 1802. Its main aim was to improve conditions in the textile industry. It did this by prohibiting night work; requiring ventilation; limiting hours and ensuring that apprentices were given religious instruction.

From 1802 onwards the number of industries covered by health and safety legislation gradually became more complete. Much of the pressure for change came from the trade union Movement – but laws were passed in a haphazard way. So, by 1970, specific legislation was in force covering a number of different areas of employment. These included: factories; mines and quarries; offices, shops and railway premises; agriculture; railways and building and construction.

Partly because the law had developed in such a piecemeal way, it had many weaknesses. The role of unions was limited and, other than in mines and quarries, there was no real provisions for involving workers and their union representatives in health and safety. Much of the older health and safety legislation ignored health hazards like noise and toxic risks. It only covered traditional work activities and a large number of workers were not covered by any safety legislation, for example workers in the Health Service, education and road transport. Many risk creators were left out since the old legislation concentrated on workers and employers and ignored groups like the self-employed and manufacturers and suppliers.

THE HEALTH AND SAFETY AT WORK ACT

The Health and Safety at Work etc Act 1974, which came into force in 1975, following sustained TUC pressure, was designed to overcome some of the weaknesses of earlier health and safety law. Its main aim was to ensure that all workers in all occupations were protected by safety legislation. It was designed to provide a broad framework within which health and safety could be regulated by providing for one, comprehensive, integrated system of law dealing with the health, safety and welfare of workpeople and the health and safety of the public as affected by work activities. The Act did six main jobs:

- completely overhauled and modernised the existing law dealing with safety, health and welfare at work;

- put new general duties on employers, ranging from providing and maintaining a safe place of work to consulting with their workers;

- created a new Health and Safety Commission;

- reorganised and unified the various Government inspectorates into a body called the Health and Safety Executive;

- provided new powers and penalties for the enforcement of safety laws; and

- established new methods of occupational safety and health and new ways of operating future safety regulations.

The Act itself runs to over 40,000 words and has 117 pages and 85 sections. Some of the more significant sections are outlined in the panel over page.

KEY FEATURES OF THE ACT

General duties

Because the Act is written in very general terms it contains very few specific detailed requirements. Instead the Act puts broad duties on different groups.

Section 1 states the general purpose of Part 1 of the Act, which is aimed at:

a)   maintaining or improving standards of health, safety and welfare of people at work;

b)   protecting other people against risks to health and safety arising out of work activities;

c)   controlling the storage and use of dangerous substances; and

d)   controlling certain emissions into the air from certain premises.

Section 2 puts a general duty on employers to ensure the safety, health and welfare at work of their employees; to consult them concerning arrangements for joint action on health and safety matters; and in certain circumstances, at the request of duly appointed or elected trade union safety representatives, to establish safety committees; and to prepare and publicise a written statement of their safety policy and arrangements.

Sub-section (4) of this section of the Act makes provision by regulations for the appointment of workers' safety representatives by recognised trade unions (see *Chapter 2: Safety representatives and safety committees*).

Section 3 places a general duty on employers and the self employed to ensure that their activities do not endanger anybody, and in certain circumstances, to provide information to the public about any potential hazards to health and safety.

Section 4 places a duty on anybody responsible for places of work to ensure that premises themselves, as well as plant and machinery in them, do not endanger people using them.

Section 5 Controllers of premises of a prescribed class must use the best practicable means for preventing the emission into the atmosphere of noxious or offensive substances and for rendering harmless and inoffensive such substances as may be emitted.

Section 6 places duties on anyone who designs, manufactures, imports or supplies an article or substance for use at work to ensure, so far as it is under his control, that the article or substance is safe when used in accordance with information supplied by him. The duty extends to the provision of necessary information and the carrying out of necessary testing, inspection and research. Those who install plant also have a duty to ensure that it is safely installed.

Section 7 places duties on employees to take reasonable care to ensure that they do not endanger themselves or anyone else who may be affected by their work activities; and to co-operate with employer and others in meeting statutory requirements.

Section 8 places a duty on everyone not to misuse anything provided in the interests of health or safety at work under a statutory requirement.

Section 9 provides that no employer may charge his employees for anything done or equipment provided for health or safety purposes under a statutory requirement.

Section 28 (8) requires Health and Safety Executive inspectors to supply certain information on health, safety and welfare matters affecting safety, etc, to workers or their representatives.

All these duties, except those on workers, are qualified with the words *"as far as is reasonably practicable"*. What this means is that the people to whom the duties apply can argue that the costs of a particular safety measure are not justified by the reduction in risk which the measure would produce. To see what the general duties of the Act mean in practice it is necessary to refer to other sources of health and safety law and guidance such as the old legislation (*eg* Factories Act Regulations), Regulations made under the Act or official guidance such as Approved Codes of Practice (ACOPs).

Relationship to previous health and safety law

It is intended that most of the old legislation will eventually be repealed and replaced by new Regulations and Codes of Practice made under the Act. A considerable number of new regulations and codes have been made. However, much of the old legislation remains in force, and as the table below makes clear it is still a very important source of standards.

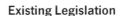

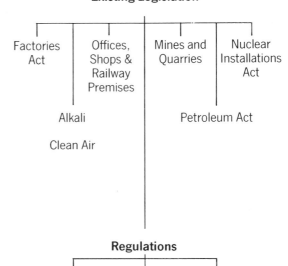

Health and Safety at Work, etc Act 1974

Existing Legislation

Factories Act	Offices, Shops & Railway Premises	Mines and Quarries	Nuclear Installations Act
Alkali		Petroleum Act	
Clean Air			

Regulations

Regulations under existing Acts, *eg* Asbestos, Abrasive Wheels, Construction, Chemicals Works	New Regulations under Health and Safety Act

Codes of Practice

Existing Codes *eg* Noise	New Codes *eg* Time off for Training

Safety policies

Section 2 (3) of the HSW Act requires any employer who employs more than five workers to prepare and keep up to date a written statement of health and safety policy and to bring the statement (and any revision of it) to the attention of her/his employees. The idea of the safety policy statement is that it should be specific to the undertaking and should set out the organisation (people) and arrangements (procedures) necessary to ensure a safe and healthy place of work. The statement, which should include a statement of intent from the employer, is important because it constitutes a basic action plan on health and safety which all employees should read, understand and follow. Quite apart from satisfying the legal requirement, a well thought out health and safety policy, that has been prepared in consultation with safety representatives, can bring real benefits. It can clarify company policy on major areas such as supervision, training, consultation and purchasing of plant, machinery and materials – it can include appendices on major sources of risk and standards and procedures that apply in particular departments – and it can make it quite clear who is responsible for ensuring health and safety throughout a work organisation.

Section 6

Section 6 of the HSW Act imposes duties on designers, manufacturers, importers and suppliers of articles and substances for use at work to ensure that these do not pose risks to health and safety. The section requires them to carry out necessary testing and examination and to provide adequate health and safety information to users – for example in the form of data sheets (see discussion of data sheets in *Chapter 5: Chemicals and toxic substances*). It is an important provision of the Act because it aims to ensure that health and safety risks are identified at the design stage and that a chain of responsibility is established to ensure that safety information reaches those who need it.

The HSE have provided guidance on complying with Section 6 in a Guidance Note GS8 "Articles and Substances for Use at Work" as well as Health and Safety at Work Series Booklet (HS (G) 17) "Substances for Use at Work: Provision of Information". These guidance documents describe the kind of information and degree of detail necessary to comply with the law, how the information should be provided and how product users can gather and use Section 6 information. There were some legal weaknesses in the interpretation of Section 6 however and these have been overcome to a large extent by amendments made by the Consumer Protection Act. Whenever safety representatives have a problem with any product which has been brought into the workplace from outside, relevant Section 6 information should always be requested and checked against HSC/E guidelines to see if it is adequate.

Enforcement

The HSW Act created a new unified enforcement body – the Health and Safety Executive – and gave health and safety inspectors new powers. Because the Act applies to all workers (except domestic servants) it can be enforced in practically all workplaces (some of these such as shops and offices are covered by local authority environmental health officers). It cannot yet be enforced in some Crown premises because of what is called 'Crown Immunity' (see below).

The Act provides for three main systems of compulsion on employers to provide and maintain a safe and healthy place of work – important notices, prohibition notices, and fines and the threat of imprisonment.

When an inspector serves an improvement notice, the employer is required to take action to put things right within a specified time. If the necessary action is not taken within the specified time, a prohibition notice may be issued stopping the particular operation which gives rise to the hazard.

An inspector also has power to issue an immediate prohibition notice stopping an operation if there is a risk of immediate danger to workers or the general public. Appeals against these notices must be made to an industrial tribunal, not to a magistrates' court. An appeal can lead to a stay of execution of an improvement notice, but there can be no delay in the implementation of a prohibition notice if the inspector is of the opinion that the risk of serious personal injury is imminent.

In cases where the inspector thinks there is no immediate risk, they may give some time for remedial action to be taken. In such cases, the prohibition notice will be called a deferred prohibition notice.

Non-compliance with these notices constitutes an offence and could lead to a maximum fine of £2,000 on conviction at a magistrates' court, or an unlimited fine or up to two years' imprisonment in the case of trial by indictment (trial at a court higher than a magistrates' court). In addition to these penalties, there could be a continuing fine of £50 per day for every day of non-compliance with the notices.

There are only about 540 HSE inspectors in the field to cover over 0.5 million workplaces. Since 1979, the Government has cut staff numbers in the HSE to pre-1974 levels meaning that some workplaces will now never receive a visit again unless there is an accident or a complaint. The TUC has been leading a major campaign against these cuts and has been pressing for a major expansion in HSC/E resources.

A full list of HSE Area Offices is given at Appendix 1.

Section 28 (8)

Section 28 (8) of the HSW Act requires HSE inspectors to give workers or their representatives certain factual information about the workplace which they have obtained by use of their powers under the Act. The purpose of this is to keep workers properly informed about matters affecting their health, safety and welfare. Inspectors must also inform employees of the action(s) they have taken or propose to take as a result of their inspection of the workplace. The same information must also be given to the employer.

Under Section 28 (8) however, inspectors are prohibited from disclosing information which may be confidential to the employer – *eg* trade secrets. This can mean that exactly what information should be provided can be a matter of judgement for inspectors. If confidential information does have to be passed on, the inspector has to explain the legal position to safety representatives who nevertheless, remain free to use such information in discussions with management and their own members. The importance of Section 28 (8) therefore is that it gives workers and their representatives a statutory right to information such as legal standards and guidance about particular hazards, the results of HSE surveys or investigations (*eg* occupational hygiene monitoring) and enforcement action by inspectors.

Crown Immunity

The parts of safety law which deal with enforcement do not apply to the Crown. This means that Government departments cannot be prosecuted and cannot have Improvement and Prohibition Notices issued against them. However, individual managers and workers in Crown employment can be prosecuted and have Improvement and Prohibition Notices issued against them.

The TUC has continued to press for abolition of Crown Immunity and this has been accepted in principle in relation to the biggest Crown employer – the National Health Service. Two interim steps have been taken to deal with the Crown Immunity problem. The *first* is the issue of "Crown Notices" – these are used in circumstances where an HSE Inspector would have normally issued an Improvement or Prohibition Notice. The HSE has stated that failure to comply with a Crown Notice will eventually result in the matter being taken up directly with the Minister responsible for the workplace concerned. The *second* is the Prosecution of individuals – but here the HSE has stated that it will not prosecute individual managers simply because it is unable to prosecute the Crown.

Health and Safety Commission (HSC)

The Health and Safety Commission was established on October 1, 1974 and is made up of a full-time, independent chairman and eight part-time commissioners. The chairman is appointed by the Secretary of State for Employment. There are three TUC members, three CBI members, two from local authorities. This body has overall responsibility for the control and development of occupational safety and health in Britain. The Commission is responsible for the activities of the Health and Safety Executive. One of the main responsibilities of the Commission is the development of new proposals for health and safety legislation and guidance. The Commission advises ministers when it has reached agreement on new measures but it in turn is advised by a series of advisory committees. These include subject advisory committees covering areas such as toxic substances, dangerous pathogens, medical matters etc and Industry Advisory Committees for specific sectors of employment. The TUC co-ordinates the work of trade union representatives in these committees to obtain improvements in health and safety law and standards.

When advisory committees have reached agreement about proposals for new Regulations, Codes or guidelines, the Commission publishes the more important of these in Consultative Documents which are circulated for comment by the TUC and CBI who in turn submit evidence based on replies received. This forms the basis of further discussions and eventually proposals are put to Ministers who propose appropriate new measures to Parliament.

USING HEALTH AND SAFETY LAW

Knowing how to use health and safety law is important in order to be able to show management and fellow workers which legal standards apply in the workplace. But the law does not always provide a ready made answer to every health and safety problem. Some health and safety laws place too much emphasis on making workers take care rather than requiring the employer to provide a safe system of work. Many safety laws are worded as broad general duties, meaning that unions need to reach agreement with management on what any laws mean in practice.

Often older health and safety legislation applies only to defined activities and excludes 'new entrants' under the HSW Act or cannot be enforced because of Crown Immunity. And even where legal standards do apply, enforcement is hampered by shortage of inspectors. Finally even when employers *are* prosecuted and taken to court, the effect of legislation tends to be undermined by the low level of fines imposed. In 1987, the average level of fines for prosecutions brought by HSE was still less than £500!

All these potential problems mean that it is very important for safety representatives to know exactly which legal standards apply to activities in a particular workplace. Several standard reference books are available which contain all the main legal standards which apply to particular industries. They have comprehensive indexes. Examples of these are:

- **Redgrave's Health and Safety in Factories:** contains the Health and Safety at Work Act, the Factories Act, the Fire Precautions Act and all the Regulations which have been made under these Acts.
- **Fife and Machin's Health and Safety at Work:** contains the Health and Safety at Work Act, the Offices, Shops and Railway Premises Act, the Fire Precautions Act, together with legislation on Shop Hours, Agricultural Safety, Railway Accident Prevention, and Offshore Safety.
- **Croner's Health and Safety at Work:** deals with the main legal standards and is updated every two months.

Reference books like these, which should be made available in the workplace, are more up to date than the officially published copies of the laws themselves. For example, the laws themselves often do not indicate where a section has been repealed.

The other clear advantage of these reference books is that their indexes can be used to home in on the standards which relate to a particular job or industry.

Figures 1.1 to 1.4 on the following pages give a rough idea of the scope of the main Acts of Parliament and Regulations made under those Acts

which cover health and safety at work. These tables and the contents page of relevant Acts and regulations should be used to work out which legal requirements apply in particular situations – or which laws are helpful in solving a specific health and safety problem. Some key questions to ask when referring to health and safety legislation include:

- who is responsible?;
- which activities and workplaces are covered?;
- what is required?; and
- are there any exemptions or qualifications?

It is important to remember that legal standards vary in their strictness. Some duties are absolute and allows no room for manoeuvre. Some apply only if 'practicable' and this gives the opportunity for the employer to argue that a requirement is not technically possible – and some are qualified by the words 'reasonably practicable'. This latter qualification means that a judgement has to be made (ultimately by a court) between risks on one hand and, on the other, the amount of time, money and effort necessary to control them. 'Reasonably practicable' duties, as well as those that are qualified by words such as 'adequate' and 'appropriate', can be harder to enforce and in such cases reference needs to be made to other sources of standards such as relevant Codes of Practice, HSE guidance notes or standards that apply in other industries or processes.

MORE INFORMATION

HSC/E leaflets on HSW Act and other legislation are free from HSE Area offices.

- **Essentials of Health and Safety at Work:** HSE guidance for small firms on basic steps to protect workers health and safety; HMSO.
- **HSE and HSC Annual Reports:** HMSO; *provide details of enforcement activities and plans for new laws.*
- **HSE Consultative Documents:** HMSO; *are used for consultation on proposals for new laws.*
- **Publications in Series:** HSE; free from HSE Library and Information Service, St Hughes House, Stanley Precinct, Bootle, Merseyside L20 3QY; *lists all current HSE publications;* includes order forms.
- **HSE Newsletter:** HSE; Room 107, St Hughes House, Stanley Precinct, Bootle, Merseyside L20 3QY; available by annual subscription; reductions for orders of more than five copies; *gives information about changes in the law and new publications from the HSE.*
- **Health and Safety at Work:** Fife and Machin, Butterworths; *reprints HSW Act, OSRP Act, Fire Precautions Act and Shops Act, with all Regulations made under these Acts; also*

includes law on agriculture and offshore installations; notes give information on interpretation and case law.

- **Redgrave's Health and Safety in Factories:** Fife and Machin, Butterworths; *includes Factories Act, Regulations made under it and other relevant laws; and contains notes and information on the laws.*

- **Croner's Health and Safety at Work:** Croner Publications, 173 Kingston Road, New Maldon, Surrey, KT3 3SS; initial cost plus annual subscription after first year; valuable loose leaf reference book with updating service; *full coverage of health and safety laws.*

Figure 1.1: Acts of Parliament

Source of Standard	Which aspects dealt with	Which jobs covered	Notes
Health and Safety at Work Act 1974	All health, safety and welfare hazards, none dealt with specifically. Enforcement. Duties of self employed people, landlords, suppliers and manufacturers.	All except domestic servants in private households and members of the armed forces.	See the Health and Safety at Work Act for more details. For Regulations made under the Act see below.
Factories Act 1961	Most health, safety and welfare hazards. Hazards which result from processes – like noise and vibration – are largely ignored. Rules controlling the employment of women and young persons (now being reviewed). Requirements to provide information to Health and Safety Inspectors and to workers.	Most manual jobs including those associated with: • manufacturing; • altering, washing, cleaning, finishing, breaking, demolition; • adapting for sale; • slaughtering animals; • shipyards and dry docks; or • repairing locomotives.	See Section 175 of the Factories Act for full details of which jobs are covered. For Regulations made under the Act, see below.
Offices, Shops and Railway Premises Act 1983	Most health, safety and welfare hazards. Hazards which result from processes – like noise and vibration – are largely ignored. Requirements to provide information to Health and Safety Inspectors and to workers.	Jobs in offices, shops and railway premises, including: • clerical work; • work in wholesale and retail establishments; • work in warehouses where no mechanical power is used; and • non-mechanical railway work.	See Section 1 of the Act for definitions of the premises to which it applies. For Regulations made under the Act, see below.
Agriculture (Poisonous Substances) Act 1952. Agriculture (Safety, Health and Welfare Provisions) Act 1956, and Regulations made under them	Most health, safety and welfare problems. Aspects dealt with by specific Regulations include: • circular saws; • accidents to children; • tractor cab design; • threshers and bailers; • pesticides; and • power take-offs.	Jobs in farming, forestry, market gardening and nurseries.	
Mines and Quarries Act 1954 and Regulations made under it	Most health, safety and welfare problems.	Jobs in mines and quarries.	
Mineral Workings (Offshore Installations) Act	Most health, safety and welfare problems.	Jobs connected with the underwater exploration for, exploitation of, mineral resources. For example: • diving; and • work on oil rigs.	See also the Diving Operations at Work Regulations 1981.

Figure 1.2: Regulations made under the HSW Act 1974

Source of Standard	*Which aspects dealt with*	*Which jobs covered*	*Notes*
Health and Safety Organisation			
Health and Safety at Work Act 1974 (Applications Outside GB) Order 1977	Extends the Health and Safety at Work Act.	Offshore installations, pipelines, mines which extend under the sea, some work on ships, diving operations.	Over 100 Regulations and Orders have been made under the Act. The vast majority of these deal with the minor modifications to the health and safety legislation which existed before the Act came into force. An up-to-date list is continued in the HSE's Publications in Series.
Safety Representatives and Safety Committees Regulations 1977	The appointment, rights and functions of safety reps, the operation of safety committees.	Jobs where unions are recognised.	
Safety Signs Regulations 1980	The design and colours of health and safety signs.	Most.	
Fire Certificates (Special Premises) Regulations 1976	Lists workplaces which require a special Fire Certificate issued by the HSE.		
Chemical and other Toxic Hazards			
	Control of Substances Hazardous to Health Regulations. Codes of practice, and Guidance Notes.	To provide a framework of principles and duties applicable to all workplaces that use hazardous substances at work.	To link with information required by CPL Regulations of 1984.
Classification, Packaging and Labelling of Dangerous Substances Regulations 1984	Rules about the design and labelling of containers for a range of dangerous substances.	Jobs in which containers of the specified dangerous substances are used.	
Health and Safety (Genetic Manipulation) Regulations 1978	Laboratories which do genetic manipulation.		

Control of Lead at Work Regulations	All aspects of work with lead or exposure to lead.	Any jobs in which workers may inhale, absorb or ingest lead, other than as a result of exposure to vehicle exhausts on a road.	These Regulations repeal the sections of the Factories Act which deal with lead and all but one of the special regulations made under the Factories Act which deal with lead.
Health and Safety (Dangerous Pathogens) Regulations 1981	Work with dangerous micro-organisms.	Laboratories, health-care and production work with micro-organisms.	
Dangerous Substances (Conveyance by Road in Road Tankers and Tank Containers) Regulations 1981	Rules about the testing, labelling of tankers, the training of drivers and the provision of information during conveyance.	Any jobs in which workers drive, load, unload or come into contact with tankers.	
Petroleum Spirit (Plastic Containers) Regulations 1982	Rules about the design and use of plastic containers for petrol.	Any jobs in which containers are used.	
Notification of Installations Handling Hazardous Substances Regulations 1982	Requirement to notify HSE of plant handling above certain quantities of toxic, flammable or explosive substances.	Applies to major hazard plant, warehousing, storage, etc.	
Notification of New Substances Regulations 1982	Requirement to provide toxicity and other data to HSE about new substances produced in quantity.	Applies to manufacturers and suppliers, etc.	

Injuries and First Aid

Reporting of Injuries, Disease and Dangerous Occurrences Regulations 1985	Rules about recording accidents and dangerous occurrences and reporting them to the Health and Safety Inspector.	All.	New regulations setting out reporting and record keeping requirements. Covers self-employed and trainees as well as employees.
Health and Safety (First Aid) Regulations 1981	All aspects of first aid provision.	Most.	See Chapter 3: *Dealing with accidents*. Replaces the first aid sections of most of the pre-HSW Act legislation.

Figure 1.3: Main regulations and orders made under the Factories Act 1981

Source of Standard	Which aspects dealt with	Notes
Abrasive Wheels Regulations	The use of abrasive wheels in nearly all situations. Substitutes for Section 14(1)a of the Factories Act. Lays down requirements on: speeds of wheels and spindles, mounting, training, guarding, machine controls, provision of rest, condition of floors.	For some jobs, Regulations made under the Factories Act 1961 are a more important source of standards than the Factories Act itself. Examples of job for which this is true include: • building and construction; • potteries; • foundries; and • shipbuilding. There is an up to date list in the HSE's Publications in Series. Redgraves' Health and Safety in Factories contains the Regulations Orders themselves and has an index.
Building Regulations 1948 and the Construction Regulations 1961-66	Cover nearly all building and construction jobs. Deal with most health, safety and welfare problems. Requirements substitute for those of the Factories Act 1961.	
Electricity Regulations 1908 and 1944	Cover the use of electricity in factories, and the carrying out of repair and maintenance work. To be replaced by Electricity at Work Regulations.	
Grinding of Metals Regulations 1908 and 1944	Cover all factories where the grinding of metals takes place. Substitutes for S63(1) of the Factories Act 1961. Most important sections are Regulation 1 on extraction and Regulation 17 on the regular testing of extraction equipment.	
Highly Flammable Liquids and Liquefied Petroleum Gases Regulations 1972	Cover all factories and most other operations. Deal with the storage and safe use of flammable liquids and LPG. Key sections are Regulations 5 and 6 on storage, Regulation 9 on sources of ignition and Regulation 10 on containment of liquids and vapours.	
Iron and Steel Foundries Regulations 1953	Cover all iron and steel foundries. Stand in addition to the Factories Act 1961, except for S63 for which they substitute.	
Non-Ferrous Metals (Melting and Founding) Regulations 1962	Cover all factories where non-ferrous castings are produced, other than lead-casting. Requirements on washing facilities, and removal of dust and fumes, substitute for the relevant sections of the Factories Act 1961.	
Power Press Regulations 1969	Cover the use and maintenance of power presses. Comprehensive and strongly worded.	
Protection of Eyes Regulations 1974	Cover all factories, and deal with the provision of eye protectors and/or guards.	
Woodworking Machinery Regulations 1974	Cover all aspects of the use of woodworking machines, including noise. Substitute for some sections of the Factories Act 1961.	

Handwritten annotation: ELECTRICITY @ WORK REGULATIONS 1989.

Figure 1.4:

Source of Standard	*Which aspects dealt with*	*Notes*
Washing Facilities Regulations 1964	Cover all office, shop and railway premises except markets. Set out the washing facilities required at workplaces of different sizes.	Only ten Regulations and Orders have been made under the OSRP Act 1963.
Sanitary Convenience Regulations 1964	Cover all office, shop and railway premises except markets and some recreation premises. Set out requirements, depending on the number employed, to provide lavatories, urinals and means to dispose of sanitary dressings.	Fife and Machin's Health and Safety at Work contains the Regulations and Orders themselves and has an index.
Prescribed Dangerous Machines Order 1964	Cover all office, shop and railway premises. Sets out the machines which should not be worked without proper training.	
Information for Employees Regulations 1965	Cover all office, shop and railway premises except markets. Require employers either to put up a copy of an official summary (abstract) of the OSRP Act 1963 and the Regulations made under it; or to provide employees with a copy of an official booklet which explains the legislation.	INFORMATION FOR EMPLOYEES REGULATIONS 1989 ?
Offices, Shops and Railway Premises (Hoists and Lifts) Regulations 1968	Cover all office, shop and railway premises except markets. Deal with safety aspects of hoists and lifts.	

2: Safety representatives and safety committees

The Safety Representatives and Safety Committees Regulations which were introduced in 1978, give trade unions the legal right to appoint workplace safety representatives. As a result there are now nearly 100,000 trade union safety representatives fighting hazards in workplaces throughout Britain.

Safety representatives now have a wide range of rights and functions. Under the 1978 Regulations safety representatives have rights to:

Representation and consultation

• represent their members' interests in relation to any matter affecting their health and safety;	Regulation 4(d)
• make representations to their employer on health, safety and welfare matters;	Regulation 4(c)
• represent their members in consultations with HSE inspectors or other enforcing authorities; and	Regulation 4(f)
• require their employer to set up a safety committee within three months and attend meeting as members.	Regulation 9 and Guidance Notes on safety committees

Inspection

• inspect designated workplace areas at least once every three months; and	Regulation (1) Guidance Notes 16-26
• make additional inspections within that time if work practices have changed or new information has come to light.	Regulation 5(21)

Investigation

• investigate potential hazards;	Regulation 4(a)
• investigate complaints by members; and	Regulation 4(b)
• investigate the causes of accidents, dangerous occurrences and causes of industrial disease.	Regulation 4(a) and (b)

Assistance, information and training

• obtain facilities and assistance for their employer to enable them to carry out inspections;	Regulation 5(3)
• receive legal and technical information from inspectors;	Regulation 4(g)
• obtain necessary information from their employer to enable them to carry out their functions; and	Regulation 7 and ACOP Para 6 and Guidance Note 27
• receive time off with pay to carry out their job as a safety representative and to undergo TUC or union approved training.	Regulation 4(2)(b) and ACOP on training

Although the law gives basic legal rights to safety representatives, in practice these rights are only put into operation through negotiation and agreement with employers. This is recognised by the official Health and Safety Commission Guidance on Safety Representatives and Safety Committees which states that employers and unions should make full and proper use of existing agreed industrial relations machinery to reach agreement on implementation of the Regulations (see ACOP paragraph 3). In many cases, good union organisation makes it possible to secure improvements which go beyond the minimum rights and entitlements in the Regulations. If however negotiations fail, there are just three instances in which the Health and Safety Commission has allowed an Inspector to intervene:

• where an employer has failed to accept the appointment of a safety representative by a recognised trade union;

- where an employer has failed to provide information and facilities; and
- where an employer has failed to discuss the establishment of a safety committee with the union following a request from two safety representatives.

WHO APPOINTS SAFETY REPRESENTATIVES?

The right to appoint safety representatives is restricted to independent trade unions who are recognised by employers for collective bargaining purposes. If the union is not recognised for negotiations at your workplace (*eg* many agricultural workplaces), it will not be able to appoint safety representatives. To have health and safety representation you must be a union member as non-union members have no such rights. Safety representatives are trade union representatives so it is up to each union to decide on their arrangements for the appointment of their representatives. It is not a matter for employers. In most cases this has meant that safety representatives are elected by the members they are to represent. Their union, of course, has to approve their election and must advise the employer in writing of their appointment.

In some unions shop stewards are appointed as safety representatives. In others, shop stewards are safety representatives only where appropriate and in some unions only lay members carry out the functions of safety representatives. In all cases, safety representatives should operate in close liaison with their trade union colleagues and ensure that they do not take decisions without the support of the members they represent. Health and safety is a trade union issue. So shop stewards, trade union committees, safety representatives and members must recognise this fact and support each other.

Union's appointing safety representatives normally provide them with credentials in accordance with special rules or through the established custom and practice arrangements for shop stewards. Employers are not involved in this matter except, of course, that they must be informed in writing of the names of safety representatives appointed and of the group or groups of employees they represent.

WHO CAN BE SAFETY REPRESENTATIVES?

The Regulations state the safety representatives must be employees employed in the workplace where they are to carry out their functions – except where they are members of the *Musicians' Union* and *Actors Equity*. For these two unions the Regulations allow their local officials to cover a number of workplaces where they are recognised.

The Regulations also state that, where reasonably practicable, safety representatives should have at least two years' employment with their present employer or two years' experience in similar employment. However, notable exceptions to this two-year rule are where:

- the employer is newly established; or
- the workplace is newly established; or
- the work is of short duration; or
- there is a high labour turnover.

HOW MANY SAFETY REPRESENTATIVES?

The Regulations do not lay down the numbers of safety representatives to be appointed, but leave it to be negotiated with unions and employers in the light of local needs and circumstances. The Health and Safety Commission's view is, however, that each safety representative should be regarded as being responsible for the interests of a clearly defined group of workers. The size of these groups will vary from union to union and from workplace to workplace and depend on factors such as the total numbers employed, variety of occupations, operation of shift systems, the type of work activity and the degree and character of workplace hazards. In general however unions have related their arrangements for the appointment of safety representatives to the arrangements which already exist for industrial relations matters.

MULTI-UNION SITUATIONS

In some areas joint union representation exists for health and safety purposes. However, this is up to the unions involved, although it has been specifically allowed for by the Health and Safety Commission in their Guidance Notes on the Regulations. The Health and Safety Commission state that the Regulations ". . . *do not preclude the possibility of a safety representative representing, by mutual agreement between the appropriate unions, more than one group or groups of employees* (eg *in a small workplace or within the organisation of a small employer when the number of recognised trade unions is high relative to the total number employed*)".

LOCAL GOVERNMENT

The TUC's Local Government Committee has recommended that, in these situations, where local joint union committees or shop steward committees exist in the local government sector, these bodies should be used to nominate safety representatives to fit their local conditions. Furthermore, local government trade union representatives and officials have been advised to set up ad hoc joint union bodies (where these do not already exist) for the express purpose of nominating safety representatives. After safety representatives have been nominated, their trade union would be expected to formally appoint them to represent those groups of workers which they are nominated to represent. Where existing or ad hoc joint union bodies have nominated safety representatives to represent groups of employees for which a safety representative's union might not be recognised for negotiation purposes, then employers have been requested by the TUC to co-operate in recognising these arrangements for health and safety purposes.

REPLACEMENT OF SAFETY REPRESENTATIVES

Under the Regulations, workers cease to be safety representatives when their trade union notifies their employer in writing that their appointment has been terminated. In addition, the appointment of a safety representative is terminated if the employer dismisses them or transfers them from the workplace or workplaces covered by the Regulations.

WHAT CAN SAFETY REPRESENTATIVES DO?

Safety representatives are health and safety problem solvers taking up any problem which relates to health and safety on behalf of employees with the employer. They are given this function by the Health and Safety at Work Act (S2 4-6) which states that the safety representatives shall represent the employees in consultation with employers with a view to promoting and developing measures to ensure the health and safety at work of the employees, and in checking the effectiveness of such measures. These functions are given in detail in Regulation 4(1) of the Safety Representatives and Safety Committee Regulations:

"**a)** *to investigate potential hazards and dangerous occurrences at the workplace (whether or not they are drawn to her/his attention by the employees s/he represents) and to examine the causes of accidents at the workplace;*

b) *to investigate complaints by any employee s/he represents relating to the employee's health, safety or welfare at work;*

c) *to make representations to the employer on matters arising out of sub-paragraphs* (a) *and* (b) *above;*

d) *to make representations to the employer on general matters affecting the health, safety or welfare at work of the employees at the workplace;*

e) *to carry out inspections in accordance with Regulations 5, 6 and 7;*

f) *to represent the employees s/he was appointed to represent in consultations at the workplace with inspectors of the Health and Safety Executive and of any other enforcing authority;*

g) *to receive information from inspectors in accordance with section 28 (8) of the 1974 Act; and*

h) *to attend meetings of safety committees where s/he attends in her/his capacity as a safety representative in connection with any of the above functions; but without prejudice to sections 7 and 8 of the 1984 Act, no function given to a safety representative by this paragraph shall be construed as imposing any duty on her/him."*

Safety representatives therefore do not merely react to problems, they have broad powers to monitor the health and safety situation and keep members' health and safety interests under review. All issues that arise can be discussed with the employer but although the employer must listen to and consult the safety representative, there is no legal means of insisting that the safety representative's advice must be acted upon. This means that to be effective, safety representatives need good union organisation and they need the backing of those they represent.

In order to give further practical advice to safety representatives the TUC has published special guidance on the regulations entitled *Know Your Rights*. This highlights the key role of trade union organisation in securing improvements in health and safety at the workplace and gives clear guidance on how to overcome some of the obstacles which safety representatives commonly face. The leaflet is accompanied by a *TUC poster* for display in workplaces drawing attention to safety representatives' rights and functions.

INSPECTIONS

A major part of the safety representatives' job is carrying out inspections. These inspections are in two main areas:

- carrying out inspections of the workplace at least once a quarter; and

- inspecting any documents the employer is required to keep by law on matters of health, safety and welfare at work.

The arrangements for three-monthly and other more frequent inspections and re-inspections will need to be agreed with employers, and these matters are often best dealt with at the workplace level. The issues to be discussed with the employer will include:

- the need for more frequent inspections of high risk or rapidly changing areas of work activity;

- the precise timing and notice to be given for formal inspections by safety representatives;

- the number of representatives taking part in any one formal inspection;
- the breaking up of plant-wide formal inspections into smaller, more manageable inspections;
- the need for different groups of safety representatives to carry out inspections of different parts of the workplace;
- the kind of inspection to be carried out, *eg* safety tours, safety sampling or safety surveys; and
- the calling in of independent technical advisers by the safety representatives.

While formal inspections are not a substitute for day by day observation, they provide a useful opportunity for safety representatives to carry out a full scale examination of all or part of the workplace, for discussions with employers' representatives about remedial action and for discussions between safety representatives. They also provide an opportunity to inspect documents required under health and safety legislation *eg* certificates concerning the testing of equipment. It should be emphasised that during inspections following notifiable accidents or dangerous occurrences, employers are not required to be present when safety representatives talk with their members. This is important since there may be occasions when safety representatives do not wish employers to be present.

Following an inspection, safety representatives should complete an Inspection report. This can be done on a special form. Briefly this records the date, time and details of an inspection. One copy of the completed Inspection Form should be sent to the employer and a copy should be retained by the safety representative for their records and for discussion in safety committees.

INVESTIGATIONS

Safety representatives are also allowed under the Regulations to investigate the following:

- potential hazards;
- dangerous occurrences;
- the causes of accidents and causes of occupational ill-health; and
- complaints from their members.

This means that imminent risks, or hazards which may affect their members can be investigated right away by the safety representative without giving formal notice of an inspection.

Following an investigation of a serious mishap, the safety representative should also complete a hazard report. Again this can be done on an official form. One copy of this should be sent to the employer

and one copy retained by the safety representative. When the employer has completed the 'remedial action or explanation' part of the form, this completed form should be returned to the safety representative by the employer and should be referred for discussion to the safety committee. Inspection and report forms can be of an agreed format or may be obtained from an HMSO Bookshop.

MAKING REPRESENTATIONS

Once safety representatives have found out about unsafe conditions or about hazards to health, the Safety Representatives Safety Committees Regulations give them the right to make representations to the employer and to the Health and Safety Executive inspector as follows:

- to the employer on behalf of members about their complaints or potential hazards;
- to the employer on behalf of all employees as regards general health, safety or welfare matters at work;
- to represent members in consultations at the workplace with Health and Safety Executive inspectors; and
- to bring to the notice of the employer their findings and complaints after inspections.

Safety representatives can also seek advice from the Employment Medical Advisory Service (EMAS) under Section 55 of the Health and Safety at Work Act (see *Chapter 29: Information*, which gives details of this service).

RECEIVING INFORMATION

Under the Regulations, safety representatives are entitled to receive full information from their employers to enable them to carry out their functions. They are also entitled to receive information from Inspectors of the Health and Safety Executive and also Local Authority Environmental Health Officers during their visits to employers' premises (fuller information about this is also contained in *Chapter 29*).

Safety representatives should note that under the Health and Safety at Work Act, 1974 – Section 28 (8) – Health and Safety Executive Inspectors have an absolute duty to disclose specific kinds of information to workers or their representatives concerning their health or safety or welfare at work. This information includes any measurements, testing, the results of sampling or monitoring, and any action which the inspector takes or proposes to take, for example prosecutions, the issue of Improvement or Prohibitions Notices, or warning letters to employers. (Full guidance from the HSC on provision of information to safety representatives is also included in the TUC booklet *Know Your Rights*.)

Safety representatives should also endeavour to see that they are informed by the employer when a factory inspector or environmental health officer is expected to visit the premises, and when they are actually in the workplace. Safety representatives should also ensure that they are given the opportunity for speaking in private, if necessary, with the inspectors during these visits.

EVERYDAY WORK OF SAFETY REPRESENTATIVES

The practical day to day work of safety representatives will entail assessment of hazards in various work areas and specific work operations. Although these are dealt with in the individual chapters of this Guide, the *Checklist* below has been designed to assist in the identification of some of the main health and safety problems that can

CHECKLIST

Housekeeping

1. Are all work areas kept clean and tidy?
2. Are accumulations of dirt and refuse removed at least daily from floors and benches?

Overcrowding

3. Is there a risk of injury from overcrowding or poor workplace layout?

Temperature

4. Is the temperature reasonable?

Lighting

5. Is the lighting sufficient and suitable?

Sanitary accommodation

6. Are there sufficient and suitable sanitary conveniences?

Guarding of dangerous machinery

7. Are dangerous parts of machines securely fenced?

Other dangerous plant

Are there any hazards or problems with:
8. cranes?
9. lifts?
10. hoists?
11. forklift trucks?
12. electrical equipment?

Training and supervision

13. Do all workers receive sufficient training in their jobs, especially where machinery is involved?
14. Are all young workers properly supervised?

Noise

15. Are there problems with noise?

Safety of floors, stairs etc

Are all floors, steps, stairs, passages and gangways:
16. soundly constructed?
17. well maintained?
18. free from obstruction?
19. free from slippery substances?

Steam plant and air receivers

20. Are all steam boilers and air receivers regularly inspected to ensure that they are safe?
21. Are all workers trained to operate them safely?

Fire

22. Has the alarm been tested in the last three months?
23. Are all the fire exits properly maintained and free from obstruction?
24. Are all flammable materials properly stored?

Welfare

Are there suitable:
25. washing facilities?
26. seating facilities?
27. places for keeping and drying clothing?
28. canteen facilities?

First aid

29. Are there adequate first-aid facilities?

Dust, fumes and substances hazardous to health

30. Are workers protected against exposure to dust and fumes and substances hazardous to health?

Eye protection

31. Are there suitable goggles or screens provided for eye protection in dangerous processes?

Lifting weights

32. Are workers expected to lift, carry or move loads that are likely to cause injury?

Recording of incidents?

33. Are all accidents, dangerous occurrences, near misses and cases of occupational disease specified and recorded?

Information

Is there adequate information provided:
34. by the employer under Section 2 (2) (c) of the Health and Safety at Work Etc. Act, 1974?
35. by the Factory Inspector under Section 28 (1) of the Act?

For detailed information see *Chapter 29: Information.*

occur at the workplace. This list however is *not* intended to be exhaustive and in the course of their work, safety representatives should aim to develop checklists tailored to the specific circumstances of their own workplaces.

ABSENCE OF LEGAL LIABILITY

Under the Safety Representatives and Safety Committees Regulations, safety representatives are given a number of legal safety functions which their employers should allow them to carry out. This means that although safety representatives are permitted to carry out their functions, they will not be legally penalised if they do not carry them out, or only partly carry them out. The Regulations state that none of the functions of a safety representative are legal duties, or responsibilities (Regulation 4). As safety representatives are not legally responsible for health, safety or welfare at work they cannot be liable in either criminal or civil law for anything they may do, or fail to do, as a safety representative under these Regulations.

This protection does not of course, absolve the safety representative of her or his general legal responsibility as an employee but merely ensures that responsibility is no greater by virtue or of their appointment as a safety representative. Thus, like all other workers, safety representatives must carry out their responsibilities under Section 7(a) and (b) of Health and Safety at Work Act if they are not to be liable for criminal prosecution by a Health and Safety Executive Inspector. These duties as an employee are to take reasonable care of one's own health and safety and that of others, and to co-operate with one's employer as far as is necessary to enable him to carry out his statutory duties.

FACILITIES FOR SAFETY REPRESENTATIVES

During formal inspections, employers are required to furnish 'facilities and assistance' to safety representatives which they may reasonably require for the purpose of carrying out inspections. Such 'facilities and assistance' are not specified in the Regulations, the Approved Code or Guidance Notes. Safety representatives are allowed to have private discussions with their members during joint inspections, although they cannot prevent employers or their representatives being present in the plant during inspections. Safety representatives should also be permitted to take samples of any substance used at work, for analysis outside the workplace, though considerable care needs to be taken in collecting samples.

Unions may consider that the following facilities which are recommended in the TUC

Handbook *Facilities for Shop Stewards* should also be made to safety representatives. These include:

a) a room and desk at the workplace;

b) facilities for storing correspondence;

c) inspection reports and other papers;

d) ready access to internal and external telephones;

e) access to typing and duplicating facilities;

f) provision of noticeboards; and

g) use of suitable room for reporting back to, and consulting with members.

Other facilities should include copies of all relevant Statutes, Regulations, Approved Codes of Practice and HSC Guidance Notes; and copies of all legal or technical standards which are relevant to the workplace as well as information on plant equipment and substances used in the workplace. Further facilities may be the subject of negotiations.

THE RIGHT TO PAID TIME OFF WORK

Under the Regulations all safety representatives have the right to paid time off work. All safety representatives have the right to:

- be paid for time taken off work in order to carry out their safety functions; and

- be paid for time taken off work to undergo union training courses for safety representatives in accordance with the "HSC Approved Code of Practice on Time Off".

Safety representatives who are refused time off either for safety functions or for training, or who are not paid for such time off after it has been taken will be able to make a complaint to an industrial tribunal. If an employer is unwilling to allow safety representatives to attend training courses or pay them for doing so, they should contact their appropriate full time official immediately.

SAFETY REPRESENTATIVES' TRAINING

All safety representatives have the right to attend a basic TUC or union approved course of health and safety training. The HSC have issued an Approved Code of Practice which gives guidance on the purposes of such training, the occasions on which, and the conditions subject to which, time off work for training should be allowed. The Regulations do not extend to safety representatives the right to demand a specified period of time off with pay. This still has to be negotiated and agreed with employers. However, the HSC Approved Code of Practice is designed to assist safety representatives in these negotiations. Safety representatives should also note that employers do have the duty under the Health and Safety at Work Act, 1974, to train *all employees* including safety representatives in basic job safety. So, in addition to their trade union training, employers should provide safety representatives with training to understand the hazards of their industry or occupation. It is also important that safety representatives have the opportunity to attend in-company training to help them understand the hazards of the jobs of those they represent.

DETAILS OF THE CODE ON TIME OFF

The HSC Code of Practice on time off advises that as soon as possible after their appointment, union safety representatives should be permitted time off with pay to attend basic training facilities approved by the TUC or by the independent union or unions which appointed them. Further training should be undertaken as and when the need arises. For example, even if safety representatives have been on a basic health and safety course they should consider whether it is time for a refresher course or further training on specific hazards such as noise, chemicals or new technology.

With regard to the length of training required the Code advises that this cannot be rigidly prescribed, but basic training should take into account the functions of safety representatives under the Regulations. In particular, training should provide an understanding of the role of union safety representatives and safety committees, and of trade union policies and practices in relation to:

- the legal requirements relating to the health and safety of persons at work, particularly the group of persons they directly represent;

- the nature and extent of workplace hazards, and the measures to eliminate or minimise them; and

- the health and safety policy of their employer and the organisation and arrangements for fulfilling that policy.

The Code goes on to explain that, when a trade union wishes a safety representative to receive training relevant to their functions, it should inform management of the course it has approved and, if the employer asks, to supply a copy of the syllabus indicating its content. It should normally give at least a few weeks' notice of the names of safety representatives it has nominated for attendance. The number of safety representatives attending training courses at any one time should be that which is reasonable in the circumstances, bearing in mind such factors as the availability of relevant courses and the operational requirements of the employer. Unions and management should endeavour to reach agreement on the appropriate

numbers and arrangements and refer any problems which may arise to the relevant agreed procedures.

Unions should use the Code as a guide to negotiating time off with pay but the aim should always be to improve on the statutory minimum rights – *not* to treat them as absolute criteria.

TUC COURSES

To meet the demand for safety representatives, the TUC has developed a highly successful training programme designed to develop basic skills and provide information on how safety representatives can carry out their job. To date, some 130,000 safety representatives have been on TUC health and safety courses. TUC courses are organised through the TUC Education Service at local Colleges of Education, Polytechnics, Workers' Education Associations and Extra-Mural Departments of Universities that have been selected by the TUC because they already provide approved courses for trade unionists. In addition to providing technical and legal information, the courses aim to help safety representatives to understand general procedures and ways of dealing with problems, if they are to cope with the wide range of hazards that may come their way. If the safety representatives are aware of the whole range of health, safety and welfare problems that can occur, and knows how to start analysing and dealing with them, then they will be a better 'watchdog' than somebody who knows only what the current work's rules say.

The TUC has recognised that where the hazards, work details and industrial relations in some industries/services may be very different, then separate courses are necessary. However, the majority of TUC courses have been aimed at the factory employment and general manufacturing. In addition a wide range of Sector courses have been run for example in construction, local government, the National Health Service and the foundry, iron and steel, engineering and motor vehicle industries. These and other sector courses have been developed in co-operation with relevant unions.

In some cases, training for safety representatives has been arranged through in-plant courses where these are approved by the unions. Often such courses can be useful but, if the course is being run in order to train the safety representatives in the specific hazards and safety organisation of that workplace, then really this should be part of the employers' training programme under Section 2 (2) (c) and Regulation 7 of the Safety Representatives' Regulations, and should be provided in addition to TUC training. Even where the course is provided by the trade union, then it is often useful to get off-the-plant courses as well. A course at a local college not only helps safety representatives to compare different standards of health and safety, and the different safety organisation of companies in an area, but also enables them to use the education facilities at the College and there is less chance of interference from work pressures.

Information on how to get on a TUC course has been widely circulated within unions and publicity about courses is always available from TUC Regional Education Officers (REOs). Those wishing to attend courses should complete the nomination form which is attached to TUC publicity materials and return it through their union to their local REO, the address of whom can be found over page.

Without proper training, a safety representative has little chance of doing a successful job. So it is absolutely essential for newly appointed safety representatives to get onto a TUC or union approved health and safety course straight away.

SAFETY COMMITTEES

Every employer, if requested in writing to do so by at least two safety representatives, must establish a safety committee within three months of the request being made.

The employer must consult with the safety representatives making the request and with representatives of recognised trade unions whose members work in any workplace in respect of which it is proposed that the committee should function. They must also post a notice, in a prominent position, stating the composition of the committee and the work areas that it covers.

Guidance Notes to the Regulations state that working out the size, shape and terms of reference of a safety committee must depend on discussion and mutual agreement between employers and unions on how best to deal with the problems of their particular workplace. Arrangements for a foundry will not suit forestry workers; neither will the demands of a construction site be those of a general hospital.

The HSC have suggested some basic objectives for safety committees including:

- analysing accidents and disease trends, safety and accident reports, inspectors' reports;

- development of safety rules;

- watching safety training; and

- advising on safety communication and publicity providing a link with HSE.

On membership, the Guidance Notes recommend:

- committees should be compact;

- that there should be 50/50 management and trade union representation; and

- safety advisers, doctors and other health and safety professionals should be ex-officio members.

The same guidance also reminds readers that safety representatives are appointed by unions and not by safety committees.

The effectiveness of safety committees depends to a large extent on how well they function as arenas in which trade unionists can actually negotiate improvements. One of the most frustrating experiences for a safety representative is to be part of a weak or poorly organised health and safety committee. Therefore safety representatives should make sure that safety committees on which they serve are properly organised in line with guidance given by the HSC. They should have the power to secure changes to improve health and safety at the workplace and should not be used as a way for employers to avoid taking action on important health and safety issues. It should also be remembered safety committees are not a substitute for safety representative's action on issues that need to be taken up immediately. Some regular agenda items for safety committees might include:

- studying accident and ill health trends;

- examining safety inspection reports;

- considering information from Health and Safety Executive inspectors, unions, employer and industry bodies;

- discussing reports from safety representatives;

- developing safe systems of work;

- examining the health and safety implications of new plant, equipment and processes;

- reviewing the health and safety content of employee training;

- monitoring the effectiveness of the employer's health and safety services; and

- reviewing the overall operation of the employer's health and safety policy and making an agreed annual assessment of health and safety performance, problems and future priorities.

The measure of a good safety committee is whether or not it can secure change. If it is only talking shop, or never takes any decisions, or the same items appear again and again on this agenda, safety representatives should take action to put it right – for example by:

- making sure meeting dates are agreed in advance and only postponed by joint agreement;

- making sure that a senior person with managerial health and safety responsibility is committed to being present (this person should be named in the employer's health and safety policy);

- seeing that the right items are regularly on the agenda;

- making sure that named people are given the responsibility for actions and are committed to a completion date; and

- making sure the minutes are issued promptly, are well displayed and reflect fairly the discussions, decisions and agreed timetables for action.

  Where appropriate trade unionists may also want to form their own safety committees, either as sub-committees of shop stewards or as sub-committees of district or regional committees.

TUC REGIONAL EDUCATION SERVICE

Scotland:
L Cairns, 16 Woodlands Terrace, Glasgow G3 6ED. 041-332 2045

Northern:
T Cook, Third Floor, Scottish Provident House, 31 Mosley Street, Newcastle-upon-Tyne. 091-232 1725

Yorkshire and Humberside:
M Ball, 1 Navigation Yard, Chantry Bridge, Wakefield, West Yorks. WF1 5PQ. 0924 375836

North West:
AJ Johnstone, Baird House, 41 Merton Road, Bootle, Merseyside L20 7AP. 051-933 4403

West Midlands:
PK Hughes, 10 Pershore Street, Birmingham B54 4HU. 021-666 6179

East Midlands and East Anglia:
D Marshall, 61 Derby Road, Nottingham NG1 5BA. 0602 47283

South East:
S Grinter, Education Department, TUC, Congress House, Great Russell Street, London WC1B 3LS. 01-636 4030

South West:
D Gover, 1 Henbury Road, Westbury-on-Trym, Bristol BS9 3HH. 0272 501989

Wales:
JF Hannaway, 1 Cathedral Road, Cardiff CF1 9SD. 0222 227449

Northern Ireland:
F Bunting, Information and Training Officer, Northern Ireland Committee, Congress House, 3 Wellington Park, Belfast BT9 6DJ. 0232 681726

USEFUL PUBLICATIONS

General

- **Safety Representatives and Safety Committees Regulations** Booklet: HMSO.
- **Time off for the Training of Safety Representatives:** *HMSO, Code of Practice Approved Under Regulation 4(2)(b) of the Regulations on Safety Representatives and Safety Committees* (SI 1977 No 500).
- **Know Your Rights:** TUC, *Guide to the Safety Representatives and Safety Committees Regulations.*
- **Hazards – Raise them with your safety representative:** TUC, *workplace poster.*

3: Dealing with accidents

Every year over 200,000 work accidents are notified to the Health and Safety Executive including almost 20,000 serious accidents. There are over 400 notifiable fatalities. Hundreds of other workers are killed in road and other transport operations. In addition, occupational disease kills over 8,000 people a year. Some workers face much greater risks than others. In any year, about one in 25 construction workers are likely to suffer a notifiable accident whereas in newspaper printing, the chances of such an accident are about ten times less. But not all accidents are reported and even those figures which are collected can never indicate the true scale of trouble, pain, loss of earnings and time off work suffered by those injured or the burden which this imposes on the rest of the community. In addition to injury accidents, there is also an enormous pool of gradual health damage caused for example through back injuries whilst lifting, injuries to tendon and joints caused by repetitive work, dermatitis, or bronchitis due to exposure to dust and fumes. Most of this goes unrecorded.

If this toll of suffering is to be reduced it is important that when accidents *do* occur they are properly recorded, notified to the authorities, analysed and lessons are learned so that new preventive action can be taken to stop similar accidents or health problems happening again in the future. Also injured workers should be afforded access to compensation through NI benefits and civil claims.

WHAT CAUSES ACCIDENTS?

It is often suggested that the majority of accidents are caused by careless workers. But this tends to divert attention away from analysis of the overall system of work and instead focuses on mistakes made by the individual. Often this approach is closely connected with disputes about liability for accidents and payment of compensation.

When accidents are properly investigated, a different story emerges. The HSE has published several reports which have analysed the causes of accidents in detail. These all conclude that carelessness is the cause of only a small proportion of accidents – while the main cause is the employer's failure to provide a safe system of work.

HSE Annual Report for Manufacturing and Service Industries

Fatal injuries in factory process 1977-81

"The table below analyses the causes of the 127 fatal accidents which took place in factory processes in 1981. In 50 per cent of the cases preventive measures were wholly under the control of management."

	Number	%
Preventive measures wholly or partly under control of:		
Management	64	50
Workpeople	23	18
Management/workpeople jointly	15	12
Others	1	1
Events unforeseeable: Reasonably practicable precautions not available	24	19
Total	127	100

Transport Kills! – a study of fatal accidents in industry 1978-1980

This extract contains some of the HSE's main conclusions about the causes of the fatal transport accidents.

"a) *Poor management organisation, failure to provide and follow a safe system of working and inadequate training, information and instruction were the most common causative factors identified.*

b) *In only 14 per cent of the deaths were reasonably practicable precautions not possible.*

c) *In only 53 of the fatalities was human error considered to be one of the causative factors."*

The report concluded: *"in many cases although the deceased may at first sight appear to have been at fault, his act or omission was very often only the last link in the chain, or one of many other failures. For example, a failure to follow a written system of work at a particular fatal instant could be an error not only by the employee. Further investigation could show that a written system was inappropriate for the particular circumstances, had fallen into general disuse, or was not known to the deceased; the system was perhaps misunderstood or not followed for some reason which was not immediately obvious. Inspectors' reports indicated a tendency for employers to stop at too early a stage in their investigations and often to blame the deceased without fully considering all the relevant circumstances."*

One hundred fatal accidents in construction

"This table apportions responsibility for 100 deaths in the construction industry:
It is not easy to apportion responsibility for these one hundred accidents, but we believe that the primary responsibility for each incident breaks down as follows:

Management	68
Deceased	18
Fellow worker	2
No clear responsibility	12"

THE LAW AND ACCIDENTS

When accidents do happen at work the law requires most of them to be reported and recorded. Safety representatives also have important legal rights to investigate accidents (see *Chapter 2: Safety representatives and safety committees*).

The Social Security (Claims and Payments) Regulations require injured workers to report accidents and employers to investigate and keep records of reported accidents. The main requirements of these regulations are as follows:

SOCIAL SECURITY (CLAIMS AND PAYMENTS) REGULATIONS 1979

Requirements on workers

Injured workers, or persons acting on their behalf, to give employer specified details of any accident for which DHSS benefits may eventually be claimed.

Regulation 24

Particulars required need be no more than:

- full name, address and occupation of injured person;
- date and time of accident;
- place where accident happened;
- cause and nature of injury; and
- name, address and occupation of person giving the notice, if other than the injured person.

Schedule 4 to Regulations

Requirements on employers

Employers to investigate the circumstances of every accident reported.

Employers with more than ten workers, or with areas covered by the Factories Act 1961, to keep an accident book of an approved form.

BI 510

Records to be kept for a minimum of three years.

Regulation 25

Accident book to be kept readily accessible.

Accidents which cause serious or fatal injuries or lead to more than a specified period off work have to be notified to the HSE under the Reporting of Injuries, Diseases and Dangerous Occurrences Regulations (RIDDOR) 1985. These require employers to notify information direct to the Health and Safety Executive, and to keep records. They also cover certain dangerous occurrences and a limited range of industrial diseases. The main requirements of the regulations are as follows:

REPORTING OF INJURIES, DISEASES AND DANGEROUS OCCURRENCES REGULATIONS 1985

Definitions

Immediately reportable accident: accident causing death or specified injury or condition.

Regulations 3 (1) and 3 (2)a

Dangerous occurrence: event specified in a Schedule.

Regulation 3 (1) Schedule 1

Reportable disease: disease specified in a Schedule.

Regulation 5 Schedule 2

Reportable accident: accident resulting in injured person unable to work for more than three consecutive days.

Regulation 3 (3)

Reporting requirements

Immediately reportable accidents and dangerous occurrences: employer to notify HSE immediately and send formal report on approved form within seven days.	Regulation 3 (1)a Regulation 3 (1)b
Reportable diseases: employer to promptly notify HSE using an approved form.	Regulation 5 (1)
Reportable accidents: employer to notify HSE on approved form within seven days.	Regulation 3 (3)

Record keeping

Employer to keep specified records of all events reportable under RIDDOR. Records to be kept for at least three years. Details specified in a Schedule.	Regulation 7 Schedule 3 3 YEARS.

Notification requirements

The following injuries and occurrences must be notified by the employer to the relevant enforcing authority by the 'quickest practicable means'. Following this a written report on form F2508 must be made within seven days.

a) The death of any person as a result of an accident arising out of or in connection with work.

b) any person suffering any of the following injuries or conditions as a result of an accident arising out of or in connection with work:

- fracture of the skull, spine or pelvis;

- fracture of any bone – in the arm or wrist, but not a bone in the hand; or in the leg or ankle, but not a bone in the foot;

- amputation of – a hand or foot; or a finger, thumb or toe, or any part thereof if the joint or bone is completely severed;

- the loss of sight of an eye, a penetrating injury to an eye, or a chemical or hot metal burn to an eye;

- either injury (including burns) requiring immediate medical treatment, or loss of consciousness, resulting in either case from an electric shock from any electrical circuit or equipment, whether or not due to direct contact;

- loss of consciousness resulting from lack of oxygen;

- decompression sickness (unless suffered during an operation to which the Diving Operations at Work Regulations 1981 apply) requiring immediate medical treatment;

- either acute illness requiring treatment, or loss of consciousness, resulting in either case from absorption of any substance by inhalation, ingestion or through the skin;

- acute illness requiring medical treatment where there is reason to believe that this resulted from exposure to a pathogen or infected material; and

- any other injury which results in the person injured being admitted immediately into hospital for more than 24 hours.

Dangerous occurrences must also be notified. These are listed in a schedule to the regulations as follows:

SCHEDULE 1 REGULATION 2(1)

Dangerous occurrences Part 1 – general

Lifting machinery, etc

1: The collapse of, the overturning of, or the failure of any load bearing part of:

a) any lift, hoist, crane, derrick or mobile powered access platform, but not any winch, teagle, pulley block, gin wheel, transporter or runway;

b) any excavator; or

c) any pile driving frame or rig having an overall height, when operating, of more than seven metres.

Passenger carrying amusement device

2: The following incidents at a fun fair (whether or not a travelling fun fair) while the relevant device is in use or under test:

a) the collapse of, or the failure of any load bearing part of, any amusement device provided as part of the fun fair which is designated to allow passengers to move or ride on it or inside it; or

b) the failure of any safety arrangement connected with such a device, which is designed to restrain or support passengers.

Pressure vessels

3: Explosion, collapse or bursting of any closed vessel, including a boiler or boiler tube, in which the internal pressure was above or below atmospheric pressure, which might have been liable to cause the death of, or any of the injuries or conditions by Regulation 3(2) to, any person, or which resulted in the stoppage of the plant involved for more than 24 hours.

Electrical short circuit

4: Electrical short circuit or overload attended by fire or explosion which resulted in the stoppage of the plant involved for more than 24 hours and which, taking into account the circumstances of the occurrence, might have been liable to cause the death of, or any of the injuries or conditions covered by Regulation 3(2) to, any person.

Explosion or fire

5: An explosion by fire occurring in any plant or place which resulted in the stoppage of that plant or suspension of normal work in that place for more than 24 hours, where such explosion or fire was due to the ignition of process materials, their by-products (including waste) or finished products.

Escape of flammable substances

6: The sudden, uncontrolled release of one tonne or more of highly flammable liquid, within the meaning of Regulation 2(2) of the Highly Flammable Liquids and Liquefied Petroleum Gases Regulations 1972, flammable gas or flammable liquid above its boiling point from any system or plant or pipe-line.

Collapse of scaffolding

7: A collapse or partial collapse of any scaffold which is more than five metres high which results in a substantial part of the scaffold falling or overturning, and where the scaffold is slung or suspended, a collapse or part collapse of the suspension arrangements (including any outrigger) which causes a working platform or cradle to fall more than five metres.

Collapse of building or structure
8: Any unintended collapse or partial collapse of:

a) any building or structure under construction, reconstruction, alteration or demolition, or of any falsework, involving a fall of more than 5 tonnes of materials; or

b) any floor or wall of any building being used as a place of work, not being a building under construction, reconstruction, alteration, or demolition.

Escape of a substance or pathogen
9: The uncontrolled or accidental release or the escape of any substance or pathogen from any apparatus, equipment, pipework, pipe-line, process plant, storage vessel, tank, in-works conveyance tanker, land-fill site, or exploratory land drilling site, which having regard to the nature of the substance or pathogen and the extent and location of the release or escape, might have been liable to cause the death of, any of the injuries of conditions covered by Regulation 3(2) to, or other damage to the health of any person.

Explosives
10: Any ignition or explosion of explosives, where the ignition or explosion was not intentional.

Freight containers
11: Failure of any freight container or failure of any load bearing part thereof while it is being raised, lowered or suspended and in this paragraph 'freight container' means a container within the meaning of Regulation 2(1) of The Freight Containers (Safety Convention) Regulations 1984.

Pipe-lines
12: Either of the following incidents in relation to a pipe-line as defined by Section 65 of the Pipe-Lines Act 1962 (b):

a) the bursting, explosion or collapse of a pipe-line or any part thereof; or

b) the unintentional ignition of anything in a pipe-line or of anything which immediately before it was ignited was in a pipe-line.

Conveyance of dangerous substances by road
13: Any incident:

a) in which a road tanker or tank container used for conveying a dangerous substance by road
(i) overturns; or
(ii) suffers serious damage to the tank in which the dangerous substance is being conveyed; or

b) in which there is in relation to such a road tanker or tank container
(i) an uncontrolled release or escape of the dangerous substance being conveyed; or
(ii) a fire which involves the dangerous substance being conveyed.

In this paragraph 'conveyance by road', 'road tanker', 'tank container' and 'dangerous substance' has in each case the meaning assigned to it by Regulation 2(1) of the Dangerous Substances (Conveyance by Road in Road Tankers and Tank Containers) Regulations 1981.

14: Any incident involving a vehicle conveying a dangerous substance by road, other than a vehicle to which paragraph 13 applies, where there is:

a) an uncontrolled release or escape from any package or container of the dangerous substance being conveyed; or

b) a fire which involves the dangerous substance being conveyed.

In this paragraph 'dangerous substance' has the meaning assigned to it by Regulation 2(1) of the Classification, Packaging and Labelling of Dangerous Substances Regulations 1984 (b).

Breathing apparatus
15: Any incident where breathing apparatus while being used to enable the wearer to breathe independently of the surrounding environment malfunctions in such a way as to be likely either to deprive the wearer of oxygen or, in the case of use in the contaminated atmosphere, to expose the wearer to the contaminant to the extent in either case of posing a danger to his health, except that this paragraph shall not apply to such apparatus while it is being:

a) used in a mine; or

b) maintained or tested.

Overhead electric lines
16: Any incident in which plant or equipment either comes into contact with any uninsulated overhead electric line in which the voltage exceeds 200 volts, or causes an electrical discharge from such an electric line by coming into close proximity to it, unless in either case the incident was intentional.

Locomotives
17: Any case of an accidental collision between a locomotive or a train and any other vehicle at a factory or at dock premises which might have been liable to cause the death of, or any of the injuries or conditions covered by Regulation 3(2) to, any person.

In some cases, it is enough to report in writing to the enforcing authority within seven days – for example, injuries caused by accidents at work resulting in more than three days incapacity for work (including non work days), or a death after a work injury where this is not immediate but happens within a year of injury.

Diseases

Diseases listed in a further schedule to the regulations must also be reported to HSE on a special form (F2508A) when a relevant diagnosis has been provided by a doctor for someone who does one of the jobs also listed in the schedule. It is most important that workers undertaking scheduled jobs understand the symptoms of notifiable diseases so that they can draw this information to the attention of their doctor if they think they are suffering from a notifiable condition.

Reportable diseases – RIDDOR Regulations, Schedule 2

Disease injuries listed in the first column have to be reported when they are diagnosed in persons employed in the occupations set against those conditions in the second column.

Poisonings

Poisonings by any of the following:

1.	Acrylamide monomer	Any activity
2.	Arsenic or one of its compounds	Any activity
3.	Benzene or a homologue of benzene	Any activity
4.	Beryllium or one of its compounds	Any activity
5.	Cadmium or one of its compounds	Any activity
6.	Carbon disulphide	Any activity
7.	Diethylene dioxide (dioxan)	Any activity
8.	Ethylene oxide	Any activity
9.	Lead or one of its compounds	Any activity
10.	Manganese or one of its compounds	Any activity
11.	Mercury or one of its compounds	Any activity
12.	Methyl bromide	Any activity
13.	Nitrochlorobenzene, or a nitro or amino or chloro-derivative of benzene or of a homologue of benzene	Any activity
14.	Oxides of nitrogen	Any activity
15.	Phosphorus or one of its compounds	Any activity

Skin diseases

16.	Chrome ulceration of a) the nose or throat, or b) the skin of the hands or forearm	Work involving exposure to chromic acid or to any other chromium compound
17.	Folliculitis	Work involving exposure to mineral oil, pitch or arsenic, work with ionising radiation
18.	Acne	
19.	Skin cancer	
20.	Inflammation, ulceration or malignant disease of the skin	

Lung diseases

21.	Occupational asthma	Work involving exposure to any of the agents listed in respect of Prescribed Disease D2 in S 1980/377
22.	Extrinsic alveolitis (including farmer's lung)	
23.	Pneumoconiosis (excluding asbestosis)	
24.	Byssinosis	
25.	Mesothelioma	
26.	Lung cancer	
27.	Asbestosis	
28.	Cancer of a bronchus or lung	

Exposure to moulds or fungal spores or heterologous proteins as a result of work in the occupations listed in respect of Prescribed Disease B6 in S1 1980/377.

Work in the occupations listed in respect of Prescribed Disease D1 in S1 1980/377.

Work in any room where any process up to and including the weaving process is performed in a factory in which the spinning or manipulation of raw or waste cotton or of flax or the weaving of cotton flax, is carried on:

a) the working or handling of asbestos or any admixture of asbestos;

b) the manufacture or repair of asbestos textiles or other articles containing or composed of asbestos;

c) the cleaning of any machinery, or plant used in any of the foregoing operations and of any chambers, fixtures and appliances for the collection of asbestos dust; or

d) substantial exposure to the dust arising from any of the foregoing operations.

Work in a factory where nickel is produced by decomposition of a gaseous nickel compound which necessitates working in or about a building or buildings where that process or any industrial process ancillary or incidental thereto is carried on.

Infections

29.	Leptospirosis	Handling animals, or work in places which are, or may be infested with rats
30.	Hepatitis	Work involving exposure to human blood products or body secretions and excretions
31.	Tuberculosis	Work with persons or animals or with human or animal remains or with any other material, which might be a source of infection
32.	Any illness caused by a pathogen which presents a hazard to human health	Any activity involving work with such a pathogen
33.	Anthrax	Any activity

Other conditions

34.	Malignant disease of the bones	Work with ionising radiations
35.	Blood dyscrasia	
36.	Cataract	Work involving exposure to electromagnetic radiation (including radiant heat).
37.	Decompression sickness	Breathing cases at increased pressure
38.	Barotrauma	
39.	Cancer of the nasal cavity or associated air sinuses	Work in occupations listed in respect of Prescribed Diseases C22(a) and D6 (ie nickel production and wood furniture and leathershoe manufacture) in S1 1980/377
40.	Angiosarcoma of the liver	Work in occupations listed in respect of Prescribed Disease C24 (ie VCM polymerisation) in S1 1980/377
41.	Cancer of the urinary tract	Work involving exposure to any of the substances listed in respect of Prescribed Disease C23 (ie beta naphthylamine, etc) in S1 1960/377
42.	Vibration white finger	Work in any of the occupations listed in respect of Prescribed Disease All in S1 1980/377

Records

Finally, under RIDDOR, employers are obliged to keep records of all notifiable injuries, dangerous occurrences and diseases and this information must be made available for Safety Representatives and Safety Committees. Particulars of records to be kept are set out in the following schedule:

SCHEDULE 3 REGULATION 7

Records – Part 1

Particulars to be kept in records of any event which is reportable under Regulation 3:

a)   date and time of accident or dangerous occurrence.

b)   the following particulars of the person affected –
      i) full name;
      ii) occupation; and
      iii) nature of injury or condition.

c)   place where the accident or dangerous occurrence happened.

d)   a brief description of the circumstances.

Records – Part II

Particulars to be kept in records of instances of any of the diseases specified in Schedule 2 and reportable under Regulation 5:

a)   date of diagnosis of the disease.

b)   occupation of the person affected.

c)   name or nature of the disease.

WHAT TO DO AFTER AN ACCIDENT

In most workplaces, particularly small ones, accidents do not occur often enough for dealing with them to become a habit, so it is important for safety representatives to remember the following essential steps.

After an accident

1:   immediately after

- get to the scene of the accident;
- see that injured members are being properly looked after; and
- make sure that nothing is moved.

2:   investigation

- take photos, sketches and measurements;
- talk to witnesses; and
- do a detailed inspection.

3:   follow up

- liaise with Health and Safety Inspector;
- check the employer's accident records;
- suggest improvements or immediate precautions; and

- advise injured members.

These steps are dealt with in turn below.

STEP 1: IMMEDIATELY AFTER

Get to the scene

The sooner safety representatives can get to the scene of the accident the better. If an accident occurs in your own work area you will know about it. But if members are dispersed over a wide area, their safety representatives may need to be told so. Make sure members know how to contact safety representatives or think about negotiating an agreement with management to inform safety representatives without delay of any accident.

Under the SRSC Regulations safety representatives have the right to do an accident inspection where it is 'reasonably practicable' for them to do so. Strictly speaking, under regulation 6(1), this right only applies to reportable accidents, diseases and dangerous occurrences. However, it may only emerge that an event is reportable as a result of making an inspection and it is not always possible to tell in advance whether the injuries caused by an accident will put a person off work for long enough to make the accident reportable. In any case, safety representatives have a right under SRSC Regulation 4(1)(a) to examine the causes of accidents and to investigate potential hazards and dangerous occurrences.

Check first aid

It is important to make sure that all injured workers get appropriate first aid treatment or medical attention and are not rushed back to work or into making a statement. Any inadequacies in the speed with which treatment is provided should be taken up with management (see *Chapter 28: First aid and welfare facilities*).

Make sure nothing is moved

It is also important to be vigilant and to prevent the scene of an accident being disturbed before an investigation has been done since it is easy for an unscrupulous employer to alter the scene of an accident before the insurance company arrives. The only acceptable reasons for moving anything are rescue and safeguarding against further hazards. This is emphasised in Guidance Notes 23 and 24 of the SRSC Regulations as follows:

"It may be necessary, following an accident or dangerous occurrence, for the employer to take urgent steps to safeguard against further hazards. If he does this, he should notify the safety representatives of the action he has taken and confirm this in writing.

"The examination must not, however, include interference with any evidence or the testing of any

machinery, plant equipment or substance which could disturb or destroy the factual evidence before any inspector from the appropriate enforcing authority has had the opportunity to investigate as thoroughly as is necessary in the circumstances of the accident or occurrence."

If things have been moved by the time safety representatives arrive on the scene, a note should be made of the changes and statements should be taken to back this up. Ideally the area should be cordoned off and somebody appointed to check that nothing is moved, either by management or workers.

STEP 2: INVESTIGATION

Photos, sketches and measurements

Following an accident details provided by photos, sketches and measurements can be of crucial importance in establishing the facts. Under Regulations 5 and 6 of the SRSC Regulations safety representatives have the right to perform periodic inspections and also to investigate notifiable accidents and dangerous occurrences in the workplace. Such inspections and investigations can include the taking of measurements, preparing of sketches and taking photographs.

Witnesses and statements

Safety representatives also need to talk to witnesses and take statements as soon as possible after an accident. This right is backed up by SRSC Regulation 6(2). Witnesses are not obliged to give statements to anyone but it is always important for members to give a statement to their union representative and sooner rather than later while it is still fresh in their mind. It is not advisable to lead a witness because they might not be able to substantiate what they say later on. The person should be put at their ease and asked to tell what happened in their own words, going slowly enough for this to be written down. If there are any points which do not make sense, they should be asked to go over these again so that it is clear what happened.

If members are called in by management to discuss, or make a statement of the circumstances of their accident, they should decline or seek the advice of their steward or safety representative. It is not unknown for the employers' solicitors or insurance company's representatives to be present, and sometimes unidentified, at such interviews.

Doing a detailed inspection

The checklist below will help with a detailed accident inspection. The results will help identify the underlying causes of an accident and will help the injured person if there is a claim for damages.

CHECKLIST: ACCIDENT INVESTIGATION

Working environment

At the place of the accident, what was the state of the:

- lighting?;
- temperature/humidity?;
- noise?;
- dust and fumes?;
- workplace layout?;
- the flooring?; and
- housekeeping?

Training, job experience and supervision

- How long had the worker been doing that job?
- What safety training had the worker received? Was it effective?
- What supervision was there?
- What safety training had the supervisor received?

What information was available to the worker on:

- safe use of plant and equipment?; and
- safe handling of materials?

Maintenance

- Was all plant and equipment maintained to standard?
- What do maintenance reports reveal about the state of any equipment?

Protective clothing

- Did protective clothing hamper communications in any way?
- If protective clothing was issued, was it suitable for the individual and the job, was it properly maintained?

Legal standards

- At the time of the accident were there any clear or possible breaches of legal standards?
- If so, list them.

Other incidents

- Are there records of other accidents or dangerous occurrences in the same work area or job?
- If so, are there any common factors that could link them?
- Is there any evidence of previous unsafe practices being allowed by management?

Role of other workers

- Were other workers involved in the accident in any way?
- If so, how?

Management investigation

- What have management done to investigate the accident?
- Do the findings of this inspection square with those on management's accident report?

STEP 3: FOLLOW UP

Liaise with the Inspector

Following an accident safety representatives should check that the Health and Safety Executive has been notified – if necessary by contacting an HSE Inspector themselves. They should make sure the Inspector knows if an investigation has been carried out and ensure he takes necessary copies of any reports. Safety representatives should always be kept fully informed of any enforcement action or advice by inspectors and should have the opportunity of discussing the implications of the accident so that preventive action can be taken if necessary.

Check management's records

There are several places to check: these include the Accident Book; the register, in which Reportable Injuries and Dangerous Occurrences must be reported; the employer's copy of Form F2508 on which a report of any Dangerous Occurrence and accident causing death or major injury should have been made and the employer's own record keeping system. It is important to make sure that all details have been properly recorded and make a note of any discrepancies.

Suggest improvements

An investigation after an accident may reveal specific problems in the workplace, for example bad lighting; lack of training or defective guards. This may mean putting specific proposals to management on dealing with these problems. This should be done in writing and members should be told about action taken. The Health and Safety Inspector should also be told about proposals made.

Advise injured members

Injured members need to be advised of their rights to pursue damages claims against their employer and to claim DHSS Disablement Benefit. They also need to be reminded that they are not obliged to make statements.

USING ACCIDENT RECORDS AND STATISTICS

As well as investigating the circumstances of accidents it is important to make full use of accident records, reports and statistics held by the employer. This kind of data can be used to:

- identify priorities for action – for example looking at incidence rates for different types of injury in particular departments or among particular groups – such as trainees or shift workers;

- compare the accident rates in the workplace with HSE or employers' association figures for an industry;

- check to see if changes in staffing levels, shift patterns or bonus, or the introduction of new machinery have affected accident rates;

- monitor improvement or deterioration in the safety record for a workplace;

- check that the remedial action decided on after an accident has been carried out; and

- find out the names of injured workers so they can be told their rights.

Safety representatives have a right of access to this kind of information under the SRSC Regulations but management is also able to raise objections. For example, where there may be legal proceedings, management may use SRSC Regulation 7(1) and 7(2)c to argue that an accident report need not be disclosed because it has been obtained to defend the employer in a compensation case. But this is only relevant where legal defence is the 'dominant purpose' of an accident report. Management may also use SRSC Regulation 7(1) and 7(2)c to argue that health records should not be revealed because they relate to the health record of an individual who can be identified. A way round this is to get the person concerned to give written consent to the information being released.

Management should also be encouraged to keep records of all incidents requiring first aid treatment – not just those which are 'notifiable' or which cause time off work and to collect information about near-miss accidents. To do this, management will need their own internal reporting system and to train staff to operate the system.

Once it has been collected, accident information has to be presented and analysed. Some official guidance is available on how to do this. For example, the extract, below, from an HSE publication – "Guidance on the collection and use of accident information in the construction industry" – explains the importance of proper analysis of accident information.

> **"10** *Accident information needs to be analysed to be of any benefit. The purpose of analysis is to identify where action is needed.*
>
> **11** *Analyses should be carried out at regular intervals. This might be monthly or quarterly, depending on the amount of information available, followed by an annual review.*
>
> **12** *Analysis could take the following forms:*
>
> **a)** *total numbers of injuries for the whole company;*
>
> **b)** *number of injuries on each company site (where size of site and duration of work warrant this);*
>
> **c)** *classification of accidents by type: for example, the number of falls from heights, struck by falling objects, electric shock; any type of accident which predominate will therefore be highlighted;*

d) *classification by materials or equipment involved may reveal undue problems being caused by, for example, ladders, scaffolds, hand tools, palletised brick bands;*

e) *classification by nature and site of injury may produce a pattern of, for example, foot injuries, eye injuries which could indicate the need for protective clothing or equipment;*

f) *classification by age group of injured person may reveal or confirm a need for training and extra supervision for younger workers; and*

g) *where contributory factors such as lack of training, supervision, environmental conditions have been recorded, significant patterns may be uncovered. Similarly, the time of day at which an accident occurs may prove to be significant."*

NEAR MISS ACCIDENTS

A near miss accident is any incident which represents a danger although it produces no injury. Research shows that for every injury accident there are several near miss accidents. So monitoring and taking action on near-miss accidents is important. Here are some examples:

- a tool falling from a height;

- dropping a heavy object like a typewriter while carrying it; and

- any event similar to – but not serious enough to qualify as – a Notifiable Dangerous Occurrence.

All workers should be encouraged to report all dangerous incidents. Management should be urged to process near-miss accidents through the normal accident reporting, recording and action system. In some cases, it can help if there is a list of types of near miss accidents which must be reported.

ILL HEALTH

Cases of ill health caused by work can be dealt with in a similar way to accidents. However, the links between work and disease are usually less obvious than between accidents and injuries and this means that different investigation techniques are required. If, for example, a link between work and disease is suspected, it is possible to do a short survey to find out if suspicions are justified.

Management may keep records which could help – such as details of ailments treated in the first aid room and sickness absence data. These sources can be used to pin-point particular problems.

It is also important that safety representatives know about any cases of Prescribed Industrial

Diseases (PID). Under RIDDOR, employers are required to keep records of such cases. When information about a PID case comes to light, safety representatives should:

- find out the possible causes of the disease;

- talk to the member and get a detailed job history with dates;

- refer to DHSS Leaflet NI 2 Prescribed Industrial Diseases for information about the links between specific jobs and particular diseases – ask questions based on this;

- for each job, draw up a description of the working conditions, and what the job involved – list those factors which could have contributed to the disease;

- check if there are, or have been, other cases of the disease and if these have been reported; and

- draw up a report based on the above findings.

IMPROVING HEALTH AND SAFETY PROCEDURES

As stressed at the beginning of this Chapter, the purpose behind investigation and analysis of accidents is to see if steps can be taken to stop them happening again and to identify weaknesses in health and safety arrangements at the workplace. This means that reports on accidents, ill health and near misses should be regularly reviewed by safety committees to see what lessons can be learned (see *Chapter 2: Safety representatives and safety committees*). It is important that such reviews should concentrate not just on the physical causes of accidents but on organisational factors such as design and management of work systems, responsibility for safety training, supervision and information for workers. In-depth analysis of most accidents will indicate weaknesses in an employer's health and safety policy or its implementation, so safety representatives should prepare suggestions on how these can be improved. Much useful information can also be gleaned from industry and national sources such as reports available from employers' federations and the HSE.

MORE INFORMATION ON ACCIDENTS

HSE guides and leaflets

- **Guide to the Reporting of Injuries, Diseases and Dangerous Occurrences Regulations 1985, 1986** (HS(R)23): *full official guidance on the regulations.*

- **Prevention of accidents, 1986** (Agricultural safety, as 12): free leaflet.

- **Reporting an Injury or a Dangerous Occurrence** (HSE 11 Revised): free from HSE; *Helpful leaflet.*

- **Reporting a Case of Disease** (HSE 17): free leaflet from HSE.

- **CONIAC Guidance:** guidance on the collection and use of accident information in the construction industry; HSE, £1.60 from HMSO; *deals with the collection, analysis and presentation of accident information and statistics.*

- **Health Services Advisory Committee:** guidance on the recording of accidents and incidents in the health services, 1986.

- **Education Services Advisory Committee:** guidance on a voluntary scheme for the collection, collation and analysis of injury, disease and dangerous occurrence data in the education sector, 1986.

HSE reports

- **One hundred fatal accidents in construction:** HSE; from HMSO.

- **Fatal accidents in construction,** 1978: HSE; from HMSO.

- **Transport kills:** HSE; from HMSO; *study of fatal accidents in industry.*

- **HSE Annual Reports and Industry Reports:** *regularly review experience and publish statistics.*

TUC Publications

- **Workplace health and safety services:** TUC; *policies on essential services at the workplace.*

4: The working environment

The term 'working environment' covers a wide variety of topics which are generally referred to as working conditions. This Chapter, however, confines itself to a number of general issues such as lighting, temperature, ventilation, overcrowding and cleanliness. These are all important in ensuring the health, safety and welfare of people at work. They are covered by a variety of standards laid down by law but often, such standards have lagged behind modern work practices and recommendations of professional technical institutions. However, many of these higher standards have now been generally accepted throughout industry and commerce as social norms – so where legal standards are inadequate, it is necessary to refer to other sources of guidance to assess environmental standards at the workplace.

LIGHTING

Inadequate lighting at work can lead to eye strain, fatigue, headaches, stress and accidents. In the long run, work in poor light can damage eyesight, and some workers (miners for example) can suffer from 'nystagmus' – rapid movement of the eyeballs caused by working in near darkness. Older workers are more affected by bad light. And the amount of light isn't the only factor – badly designed lighting systems give rise to glare. This can cause stress and headaches, as well as creating accident risks. Heavy contrasts can be dangerous – moving between bright to very dark areas can cause temporary blindness as the eyes adapt.

Apart from the health and safety aspects, poor lighting can reduce the speed and accuracy of work. The Electricity Council has published figures showing how improvements in lighting have affected output, reject rates and accident rates.

LIGHTING PROBLEMS

Some of the more common lighting problems found at work are:

- dark or unlit areas, especially near hazards such as machines or steps;
- lack of natural light because of dirty or badly placed windows;
- glare from badly positioned or poorly shaded lights, unshaded windows and reflecting surfaces;
- 'energy saving' programmes leading to cuts in lighting levels;
- workers suffering eyestrain or fatigue from bad postures caused by poor lighting;
- dirty or poorly maintained lighting, leading to light loss, and flicker;
- unsuitable decor, leading to lower light levels, excessive contrasts or too much glare; and
- security risks at night caused by poor lighting outdoors.

Lighting problems at work can be investigated in a number of ways:
- asking workers – although many people get used to bad lighting;
- using a light meter to check against standards – see below; and
- looking for glare or asking for a full lighting survey.

Measuring light
The level of light is measured in "lux". Some typical light levels are set out below. Interior levels are very much lower than outdoor natural light.

Very bright summer day	up to 100,000 lux
Overcast summer day	30,000 to 40,000 lux
'Bad light stops play'	1,000 lux
Shady room in daylight	100 lux
Street lighting	20 lux

The amount of light can be measured by a lightmeter. These are readily available, though many photographic lightmeters are not calibrated in lux. Safety representatives may want to ask management to provide suitable lightmeters for taking measurements as part of inspections (see *Chapter 2: Safety representatives and safety committees*). When using a lightmeter however check first that there is a zero reading when the light cell is covered. Leave the lightmeter in the light for five minutes to allow it to settle. A fluorescent and mercury light should be given time to warm up before readings are taken. Readings must be taken with furniture, equipment and staff in their normal positions (*eg* the light on a desk should be measured when the desk is occupied).

Lighting standards

No detailed legal standards for illumination now exist and the Illuminating Engineering Society's (IES) recommendations are generally adopted. For example, the HSE Health and Safety at Work booklet "Lighting in Offices, Shops and Railway Premises" reprinted the IES standards. The IES standards have been assessed for workers under 40 years of age. Older workers will need at least half as much again. American standards also recommend more light.

The amount of light needed obviously depends on the type of work being done. The following flow chart from the IES gives standards for different kinds of work, taking into account room decor, the consequence of errors, task duration and windows.

Recommendations for light levels from the IES Code for Interior Lighting

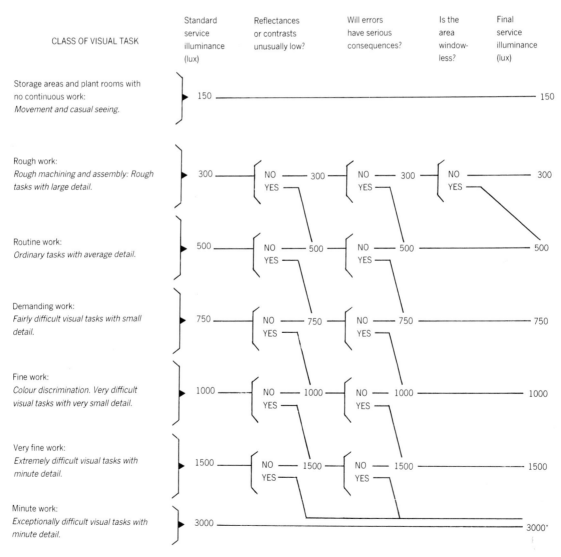

*Localised lighting, if necessary supplemented with optical aids, magnifiers, profile projectors, etc.

The Factories Act and OSRP Act contain some limited requirements as follows:

Sufficient and suitable light (natural or artificial) to be provided wherever people are working or passing	FA s5(1), OSRP Act s8(1)
Windows and skylights must be kept clean and free from obstruction unless shaded to cut out glare	FA s5(4) OSRP Act s8(3)
Light fittings must be properly maintained	OSRP Act s8(3)

The above Acts do not contain guidance on what constitutes 'sufficient' lighting. Neither do the Acts contain guidance on determining the form of lighting which is suited to different types of work. Once again, the HSE booklet "Lighting in Offices, Shops and Railway Premises" contains some advice on the correct positioning of lights and appropriate lighting for different types of work. Unfortunately, this booklet has not been updated and so many more recent lighting innovations, such as full spectrum lighting, phased flicker and indirect lighting remains unevaluated. Again, the professional bodies are a useful source of information and standards. The following table gives some general guidance on how the IES recommendations apply to specific work situations:

Machine shops

Rough work and assembly	300 lux
Medium bench and machine work	500 lux
Fine bench and machine work	1000 lux

Office work

General tasks	500 lux
More detailed work	750 lux
Very fine work	1000 lux

Stores and warehouses

Rough work	150 lux
Medium work	300 lux

Glare

Lighting levels may be adequate but glare from a direct source or light reflected off equipment or paper can cause discomfort. Glare is light in the 'wrong place' and there are three different kinds. All can cause strain and fatigue, and some may interfere with vision:

- **disability glare** can dazzle and impede vision, and so may be a cause of accidents – one example is the effect of undipped car headlamps, caused by too much light entering the eye directly;

- **discomfort glare** is more common in work situations – it can cause discomfort, strain and fatigue, especially over long periods, and is caused by direct vision of bright light source and background; and

- **reflected glare** is bright light reflected by shiny surfaces into the field of vision – its effects can be the same as those for discomfort glare.

In practice the best way to spot the effect of glare is to identify places where a light source shines directly or by reflection into the operators' vision. It can be harder to spot glare from light fittings when day light is present as well. Then see if screening, shading or fitting diffusers on lights makes any difference. More detailed studies of glare may need to be carried out by a lighting engineer.

To reduce glare the following steps should be considered:

- adjust shades, screens or reflectors to reduce direct views of light sources;

- raise the light fittings (if suspended);

- fit diffusers around the light sources (especially if fluorescent);

- check that the right size and type of bulb or tube is being used;

- use a mirror to pick out the sources of reflected glare;

- reduce the number of reflected surfaces in the workplace;

- resite the working positions to reduce glare from windows;

- redecorate to avoid heavy contrasts, especially between windows and dark walls, and ceilings and light fittings;

- fit shades or blinds to reduce glare from windows;

- alter the position of fluorescent light strips so that they are viewed end on;

- make sure that desk lamps are properly positioned and screened;

- use matt paper if light is reflected from shiny documents; and

- be careful that the light brightness is not unacceptably reduced in attempts to tackle glare – simply cutting light levels is not enough.

Design

It is important to get lighting arrangements right at the design stage – for example when new work layouts are being planned, and safety representatives should be consulted and the local Electricity Board may be able to help. Some key principles are:

- **use natural light** as much as possible; most people prefer it; windows need to be well sited and kept clean; light levels fall away rapidly as you move further from a window, so extra lighting will be needed for some parts of rooms, even in daylight.

- **position fittings carefully** to make the best use of light while avoiding glare.

- **consider room decor** – light ceilings and walls make the best use of light; avoid heavy contrasts.

- **provide local lighting** (*eg* desk lights) as needed.

- **emergency lighting** may be required by law for the workplace – it may be specified in the fire certificate; emergency lighting is powered from batteries or generators; batteries need to be placed in a well-ventilated room (see *Chapter 20: Electrical safety)* and the system must be regularly checked and tested; illuminated emergency exit signs should also be checked.

Colour

The use of colour in providing a pleasant and acceptable environment is a well accepted matter in people's homes. It is also an important factor in the decoration of shops, stores, cinemas, theatres and concert halls; even in aircraft and buses. However, it is not generally given a great deal of attention in workplaces, though the practice of giving proper attention to colour shade and light is growing in many modern office buildings. In most factory, office and warehouse situations however, little attempt is made to use colours properly. Many factories still tend to be dull places, with dark greens, browns and an occasional cream shade predominating.

If bright colours are used for walls, and contrasting colours for machinery and equipment, this can transform work surroundings, from a dull, dreary environment into one which is not only lighter and more pleasant, but safer as well. Lighter coloured objects are generally safer because these are more easily seen. This is because lighter colours reflect more light. White, for example, not surprisingly reflects 84 per cent of light against 70 per cent for cream and only 11 per cent for blue. The proper and skilful use of colours therefore is an integral part of achieving satisfactory standards for lighting at the workplace. Of course, there is little point in spending time, money and energy in painting and decorating a workplace unless it is regularly and efficiently cleaned.

Maintenance

Even well designed lighting systems will not perform properly unless well maintained. For example the IES Code indicates that dirty fittings can produce a light loss of 20 per cent. Old fluorescent tubes can lose up to half their brightness before they fail. Bulbs lose 10 per cent brightness before failure. Old light units are less economical because they use the same current to produce less light. The IES Code says that it is better to replace lamps in a group in all but small lighting systems. This can be more economic and less disruptive than

replacing individual units as and when they fail. The Code also recommends a regular cleaning programme for fittings, as the following shows:

Location	Cleaning interval (in months)		
	A	B	C
Air conditioned building	24	18	12
Country area	18	12	9
Town	12	9	6
Industrial area	9	6	4

A: recessed fittings and luminous ceilings
B: surface-mounted or pendant fittings
C: indirect fittings or cornices

OSRP Act Section 8(4) obliges employers to clean and maintain light fittings. Windows and walls should also be regularly cleaned.

Some light fittings (especially fluorescent lights) can flicker because of the alternating electrical current. In fluorescent tubes the flicker is concentrated at the ends of the tube around the electrodes. Flicker tends to increase as the tubes get older. Some workers are more affected by flicker than others, but it can give rise to headaches and fatigue. Flickering light can also create a 'stroboscopic' effect which can make moving machinery appear stationary. This can create an accident risk.

Ideas to deal with flickering are:

- screen the end of the tubes – some light fittings have built into them;

- use tubes with internal electrode shields;

- in twin-tube fittings, wiring can be arranged so that any flickers are out-of-phase and self cancelling; and

- light tubes must be replaced at the end of their recommended life, or as soon as flicker becomes noticeable; they should not be left until they break down completely – make sure there is a replacement programme for bulbs before this happens.

LIGHTING ACTION CHECKLIST

1. Draw up a checklist to help inspect the lighting at your workplace. You may want to consult other information sources.

2. Talk to members – ask them:

   - do they ever suffer eyestrain or headaches at work?;

   - do they think the lighting is adequate? If not what are the problems; and

- is the light adequate for special jobs such as cleaning or maintenance?

3. Look at accident records and any sickness records. Could any accidents or illness be linked to problems with lighting?

4. Ask management to lend safety representatives a lightmeter as part of facilities for conducting inspections. Check light levels with the meter, compare with IES standards and discuss results with your members.

5. Has management ever arranged for a proper lighting survey? If so, try to get a copy.

6. Make a list of all the areas in and around the workplace where the lighting seems inadequate. Include work areas, corridors, stairs, stores, yards and car parks.

7. Try to find out who was responsible for designing or selecting the lighting at your work. Does management have any policy or planned programme for cleaning light fittings, and replacing bulbs and tubes?

8. Draw up proposals to put to management to improve lighting in your own workplace. These could cover lighting surveys, design of lighting, amount of light, decor, maintenance and cleaning.

MORE INFORMATION ON LIGHTING

- **Lighting in Offices, Shops and Railway Premises:** HSE Health and Safety at Work Series Booklet No 39 from HMSO; *includes detailed recommendations for lighting levels.*

- **Code of Practice for Interior Lighting:** Illuminating Engineering Society, from Chartered Institute of Building Surveyors, 222 Balham High Road, London SW12; main source of detailed standards.

- **Essentials of good lighting – a simple guide for industry:** Electricity Council; from Electricity Council, 30 Millbank, London SW1P 4RD; *useful short guide.*

- **The Economics of Factory Lighting:** Electricity Council; *arguments to put to employers about benefits and costs of better lighting.*

- **Lighting systems for standby or emergency use in industrial premises:** Electricity Council Note IND 2.

HEATING AND VENTILATION

Working in unsatisfactory thermal conditions without adequate supplies of fresh air can pose problems. Unsatisfactory building design and heating systems may mean workplaces are too hot in summer or too cold in winter – leading to discomfort. Many workers have to work in cold conditions leading to respiratory problems and rheumatism – for example workers in the frozen food industry or construction or farm workers. At the other end of the scale, other workers, for example those in the iron, steel, foundry, pottery or catering industries, can be exposed to heat stress. Workplace atmospheres can be either too humid or excessively dry leading to breathing problems. Poorly designed and badly maintained air conditioning systems can lead to an allergic condition called 'humidifier fever'. All these problems mean that special attention must be paid to heating and ventilation in the workplace.

HEAT AND COLD

Some workers face extremes of temperature. Outdoor work, work in cold stores, working near bakery ovens or furnaces are examples. But for all workers, the wrong temperature at work causes problems. People will complain of discomfort if the heating cannot cope in cold weather or ventilation is bad when it is hot.

Cold snaps, heatwaves and breakdowns pose extra problems. So does moving onto a job when you are not used to it. People need time to acclimatise. It takes longer if you are older or unfit. For everyone, working in the wrong temperature can mean loss of concentration, irritability, tiredness, discomfort and increased accident risks.

Too much heat at work can mean fatigue, extra strain on the heart and lungs, dizziness and fainting, or heat cramps due to loss of water and salt through excessive sweating. Hot dry air can increase the risk of eye and throat infections. Above a blood temperature of 102°F there is a risk of heat stroke; collapse can occur above 106°F with symptoms of delirium and confusion. This condition can prove fatal and survivors may suffer from brain/kidney/liver/heart damage. Tiredness and loss of concentration can also lead to increased accident risks (*eg* burns in hot work).

Too much cold can mean chilblains and even frostbite in fingers and toes. The body keeps the blood supply to the extremities closed at lower temperatures to conserve heat. Cold conditions can also lead to fatigue since the body uses energy to keep warm. Blood vessels supplying the skin become constricted to reduce heat loss leading possibly to Reynaud's disease or white finger. There is an increased accident risk from numb fingers, obstruction by some kinds of protective clothing, slipping on ice, etc. Extreme cold for long periods can lead to hypothermia, loss of consciousness and eventual coma and, if the body temperature drops below 64°F, the heartbeat stops.

CONTROLLING HEAT HAZARDS

There are a number of basic approaches to tackling heat hazards at work. All involve reducing exposure by keeping heat away from workers. The source of the heat can be isolated. For example, fuel for boiler furnaces can be fed in by machine. Automation can be used for some very hot work. Kitchens can be redesigned to move work surfaces away from ovens. Sources of the heat can be insulated. But insulation must be properly designed and many insulation materials create hazards of their own.

Controlling heat loss can also prevent waste and may save money. The Department of Energy gives advice on how to do this.

Radiant heat can be screened by using heat reflecting shields, or water cooled heat-absorbing panels. Heat from sunlight can be shaded through large windows or glass roofs, by blinds or whitewash. To cool hot air and regulate humidity, ventilation systems can be used. Finally if there is no other way of controlling the heat then work breaks and/or job rotation can be used (see *The law and standards*, below).

In some circumstances protective clothing can be used but this should be regarded as a last resort or a temporary measure only. It is often cumbersome, uncomfortable, ineffective and can cause accidents. Thick clothing made from insulation materials can temporarily prevent heat getting through to your body. Aluminised suits and aprons give greater protection against radiant heat. Otherwise lighter clothing is better since it allows the body to be cooled by air currents and sweating.

THE LAW AND STANDARDS

The law does not include specific standards for maximum temperatures, so reliance has to be placed on the general duties in Section 2 of the HSW Act. Some regulations for textile and jute factories regulate maximum humidity. Foundries Regulations specify some protective clothing. Also pottery Regulations set a normal maximum of 75°F and, where workers must enter ovens, a maximum of 115°F. In addition, all employers in factories and offices are required to supply clean drinking water.

Some workers doing hot work have agreements with employers about rest breaks, maximum temperatures, protective clothing and rest facilities. In many cases these are based on the following guidelines published by the American Conference of Governmental Industrial Hygienists (ACGIH).

Work/Rest Regimen	Light	Work Load Moderate	Heavy
Continuous work	30.0	26.7	25.0
75% Work) each 25% Rest) hour	30.6	28.0	25.9
50% Work) each 50% Rest) hour	31.4	29.4	27.9
25% Work) each 75% Rest) hour	32.2	31.1	30.0

(Values refer to WBGT Index: see below)

The standards listed above were drawn up by the ACGIH, an American industry body. The values listed are measured using the Wet Bulb-Globe Temperature Index (WBGT) which gives a more accurate measure of heat conditions than ordinary mercury or alcohol thermometers which only measure temperature, but don't give a complete picture of humidity or radiant heat which are also important. Wet bulb globe thermometers can measure the moisture content of the air as well as temperature. At high temperatures it is important to know the humidity. For example, humid atmospheres mean sweating can't cool the body so well. Breathing in very hot conditions is more likely to hurt if the air is wet.

TACKLING THE COLD

The ideal solution is to minimise exposure to cold by reorganising work procedures so that workers are in the warm. For example, detailed preparation or prefabrication of components in workshops ensures that installation work in cold environments can be carried out more rapidly. The use of mobile workshops will allow maintenance and repair workers to carry out much of their work under cover in heated surroundings. Some work in very cold atmospheres can be automated, for example in cold stores.

If these approaches are not possible, people exposed to cold during their work should also be provided with adequate rest breaks. There should be a suitable warm area for them to go to during rest and meal breaks. Good quality hot food and drinks should be provided.

Where exposure to cold is unavoidable, workers must be provided with cold weather clothing. When the body is working the production of heat increases. To maintain a balance between heat production and heat loss, insulation must be decreased. Properly designed cold weather clothing allows the wearer to remove layers or open vents and let the excess heat escape. This prevents overheating which can be a serious problem in the cold. Sweat accumulates in the clothing and continues to evaporate during rests, chilling the body.

THE LAW AND STANDARDS

Standards for heating at work vary between somewhat outdated legal standards and other more modern practices set by professional and technical bodies. In general the law requires that a 'reasonable' temperature be maintained by a harmless method without unpleasant fumes or gases being produced.

The Factories Act specifies that where most of the work is done sitting and does not involve serious physical effort, the temperature must not be less than 60°F after the first hour. At least one thermometer should be provided in each workroom to check this.

The Offices, Shops and Railway Premises Act (OSRPA) stipulates that, after an hour's work, there should be a minimum temperature of 16°C (60.8°F) and a thermometer should be available on every floor to check this. The OSRPA minimum temperature does not apply to offices to which members of the public are admitted but employees should have access to some means of warming themselves.

The Woodworking and Jute Regulations set out minimum temperatures for certain kinds of work. There are regulations covering humidity and minimum and maximum temperatures in some textile factories. Also the Construction Regulations (Health and Welfare) require provision of warm dry rest areas, and facilities for drying clothes. Protective clothing must also be provided for work outside in wet weather.

The acceptable zone of thermal comfort for most kinds of work lies somewhere between 16°–24°C (60.8°–72.2°F). The acceptable temperatures for heavier types of work will obviously be concentrated in the lower parts of this range, whilst sedentary tasks may still be performed with reasonable comfort towards the opposite extreme and 16°C will be unpleasantly cold. The Institute of Heating and Ventilation Engineers recommend temperatures for different working areas. For example:

Factories: sedentary work	19°C
light work	16°C
heavy work	13°C
Offices	20°C
Hospital wards	18°C
Warehouses	16°C
Canteen and dining rooms	20°C
Shops and showrooms	18°C
Banking halls	20°C

When checking on compliance with these standards, care should also be taken to examine heating systems that are in use. These can cause problems of their own such as fumes, uneven temperature and draughts, dry air or too much humidity, insufficient fresh air, electrical hazards or fire hazards. Temporary heating systems are often the worst. Paraffin and gas heaters may use up oxygen and give off fumes. Electrical heaters may mean trailing wires and electrical hazards (see *Chapter 20: Electrical safety*). Often they are not checked or maintained. All types can increase fire hazards.

VENTILATION

In addition to monitoring the right temperature at work it is just as important to ensure that there is a proper supply of fresh air. Section 4 of the Factories Act states that there must be adequate fresh air ventilation. All practicable measures must be taken to protect workers against fumes, dust and other impurities. Local exhaust ventilation must be provided where required. Sections 30 and 63 also deal with fumes and dust. Section 7 of the Offices, Shops and Railway Premises Act states that effective and suitable means of ventilation shall be provided by the circulation of adequate supplies of fresh or artificially purified air.

Fresh air standards are given in the HSE Guidance Note EH22 Ventilation of Buildings: Fresh Air Requirements: This recommends that the quantity of fresh air supplied should never fall below 10 cu feet (0.28 cu metres) per person per minute in ordinary buildings. The Guide of the Institution of Heating and Ventilating Engineers suggest fresh air quantities between 10 cu feet and 30 cu feet, according to the use of the room. For these quantities of fresh air the Institution suggests between 1.5 and 7.5 air changes per hour. If fresh air is to provide ventilation, the Institution recommends that there should be 5 square feet of openable window for each 100 square feet of floor area.

In many workplaces, windows are sealed and temperature and ventilation requirements are dealt with by an air conditioning system. Heating and cooling of the air will alter its humidity. If the air becomes too dry, workers are liable to headaches and sinus troubles. For comfort, the level of humidity should be between 40 and 75 per cent. Care should be taken to ensure that humidification of the air in an air conditioning system does not create a health hazard for example from Humidifier Fever. This is the name given to the allergic reaction caused in some individuals by exposure to micro-organisms bred and circulated by a ventilation system. Careful selection of a humidifier and adequate cleaning and maintenance procedures are required to prevent this hazard as well as the possible build-up of Legionella – the organism which causes Legionnaires Disease (see also *Chapter 10: Biological hazards*). There may also be other problems with ventilation and cooling systems such as escape of coolants from plant (*eg* ammonia), draughts or dispersion of dangerous dusts (*eg* asbestos).

CHECKLIST: TEMPERATURE AND VENTILATION ACTION

1. One way of identifying a problem is by talking to your members or doing a survey. This may also help build their support for solving the problem. You could ask them:
   - do they find it too hot or too cold at work?
   - does this happen at a particular time of year?
   - do they notice any draughts at work?
   - are there any problems with heating/cooling systems?
   - do they suffer regularly from colds, catarrh, coughs, sore throats?
2. Make an inspection of temperatures and heating and cooling systems.
   Most workplaces tend to be too cold for comfortable working, particularly in winter. What is the average temperature in your workplace and is there a thermometer available to measure it? The following standards should be aimed for:
   - if the work is done sitting, between 63°F-72°F;
   - standing with wall movement, between 62°F-68°F;
   - with some physical effort between, 62°F-68°F.
3. Is the atmosphere hazy, oily, fume or dust-laiden? If so:
   - are there sufficient air movements by general ventilation (windows, doors, vents)?
   - is any provision made for mechanical ventilation by fans, exhaust ventilation or other air cleaning equipment?
   - are there maintenance and cleaning programmes for ventilation equipment?
4. Draw up a list of the main problems with heating and ventilation, hot work and cold work.
5. Draw up a leaflet about temperature and ventilation problems to start off discussions with members.
6. Prepare a draft agreement on temperature control and ventilation for your workplace.
7. Prepare a report for management. Set out your aims and a plan for action on temperature and ventilation problems.

MORE INFORMATION ON TEMPERATURE AND VENTILATION

- **Encyclopaedia of Occupational Health and Safety:** International Labour Organisation; *has useful sections on hot and cold.*

- **Hot Environments:** US Dept of Labour Publications, Nos 80-132; Dept of Health and Human Services, Robert A Taft Laboratories, 4676 Columbia Parkway, Cincinnati, Ohio, 45225, USA.

- **Cold:** Construction Industry Advisory Committee; Health Hazard Information Sheet No 2: Cold Weather.

- **Documentation of the TLV for Workroom Air:** ACGIH; PO Box 1937, Cincinnati, Ohio, 45201, USA; *gives the background to the US standards quoted on page 48.*

- **Ventilation:** HSE Guidance Note, EH 22 Ventilation of Buildings: Fresh Air Requirements, 1979.

OVERCROWDING

The provision of an adequate amount of space within which to work is essential for all workers. Overcrowding can increase health and accident risks and can be a major source of stress. Section 2 of the Factories Act states that a factory shall not be so overcrowded that it will cause risk to injury to the health of the people employed in it, and that there shall be 400 cubic feet of space allocated for each worker. When this space is being calculated, no height more than 14 feet from the floor can be taken into account. A notice must be posted in the workplace specifying the number of people who may be employed in the workroom.

The Offices, Shops and Railway Premises Act (Section 5), is not so straightforward. The Act stipulates, not only 400 cu feet per person, but also mentions 40 square feet per person. In addition, it states that when calculating this space requirement, notice should be taken, not only of the number of people working in the room, but also the space occupied by furniture, fittings, machinery, plant and equipment. For example, if a room has an adequate space requirement when empty and is then subsequently filled with filing cabinets, then it would not satisfy the requirements of the Act. Whichever way it is calculated, 40 square feet is not very much space. The International Labour Office recommends 75-90 square feet per worker.

From 1st September 1982, the Offices, Shops and Railway Premises Act was metricated. Any premises built after this date are required to provide:

Space	New standard	Substitute
Minimum floor space per person	3.7 sq metres	(40 sq ft)
Ceiling height	3 metres	(10ft)
When the ceiling is low – volume per person	11 cu metres	(400 cu feet)

These standards, which should be regarded as minimum criteria, should be used as a baseline in all discussions with management about the design and layout of workplaces. It is especially important that safety representatives are involved in planning of new work layouts since many problems connected with working space which could be difficult to remedy later, can be identified at the planning stage.

ACTION CHECKLIST: OVERCROWDING

1. Carry out an inspection to see if there is adequate space provided in all work areas.
2. Is there a notice showing the number of people allowed to work in the area?
3. Does the amount of equipment and furniture in the workplace make the area unsafe?
4. How can work layout be improved?

CLEANLINESS

The statutory, or legal requirements for keeping workplaces clean are contained in a number of different Statutory Instruments, but the principal ones are the Factories Act, Offices, Shops and Railway Premises Act and the Food Hygiene Regulations.

Section 1 of the Factories Act says that workplaces must be kept clean and free from smells. Dirt and refuse (including waste from the work), must be removed daily. Floors have to be cleaned at least once a week; inside walls and ceilings must be washed every 14 months and painted every seven years, or whitewashed or colour-washed every 14 months; see the Factories (Cleanliness of Walls) Order, 1960.

Proper observation of this section is very important as managements often neglect it, or do not see that it is carried out efficiently. An example of this is the clearing up of dust – vigorous brushing of dusty floors and benches can often cause serious problems of air pollution, so if cleaning cannot be done by a dustless method, it should be done outside normal working hours.

The Offices, Shops and Railway Premises Act is not quite so specific and Section 4 of this Act merely has two broad requirements on cleanliness. The first is that premises, furniture and fittings shall be kept clean. The second is that no dirt or refuse shall be allowed to accumulate in any part of the premises and that the floors and steps shall be cleaned not less than once a week, either by washing or, if it is effective, sweeping.

The Food Hygiene Regulations are dealt with in *Chapter 28* in relation to messrooms and canteen facilities, but it should be noted that these Regulations require arrangements to be made for regular and frequent cleaning of the premises. In this connection, safety representatives should note

the importance of ensuring that management's system of cleaning is adequate, and is carried out on a regular basis. In production areas this may often be for obvious reasons, but it may not be so diligently carried out in other areas such as canteens, messrooms, toilets, washrooms and clothing accommodation areas.

ACTION CHECKLIST: CLEANLINESS

1. How often is your workplace cleaned (*eg* walls, floors, ceilings, work area)? Who is responsible for cleaning and how and when is it carried out?
2. Are dirt and refuse allowed to accumulate in work areas? What arrangements are there for disposal? How often are dirt and refuse removed?
3. Do dirt and refuse present special hazards (hazardous dust, toxic or flammable waste products etc)?
4. How are hazardous wastes disposed of?
5. Pay special attention to areas where high standards of cleanliness are especially important (*eg* food storage), preparation and eating areas, health service premises, processes using toxic materials).

5:   Chemicals and toxic substances

Recent estimates indicate that between 15,000 and 30,000 chemicals are currently in everyday use. Hundreds of new chemicals are introduced each year. Many could be harmful or dangerous. Safety representatives need to be aware of the potential damage to health arising from use of such substances. Unlike physical hazards, where the hazard is visible and the effects immediate, the harmful effects of toxic substances are not always obvious. For thousands of workers, the 'hidden hazards' of chemicals and other toxic substances present a real threat to their health every day of their working lives.

This chapter is intended to help readers identify the possible dangers of toxic substances used at work and to assess their dangers. It also describes how safety representatives can get improvements in the way substances are used and check that control measures are being properly applied.

RISKS DUE TO CHEMICALS AND TOXIC SUBSTANCES

Although our body's defence mechanisms provide protection against attack from many chemicals, if these defences are overloaded then impairment of health may follow, ranging for example, from a slight skin rash to a malignant tumour with fatal consequences.

Under the HSW Act manufacturers, and suppliers of chemicals have duties to carry out research into the harmful effects of chemicals before they are introduced into industry. Nevertheless, the history of dangerous substances has shown that the hazard of a chemical is sometimes first recognised only when it is too late and signs of ill health begin to appear. These may take many years to develop. All chemicals therefore should be treated with caution. Particular care is needed if the chemical has been proved experimentally to be harmful to an animal species (which is one method of testing) or

when a chemical with a similar structure has been known to cause harm in man.

Risk depends upon the *toxicity* and *dose* of a chemical;

a)   *Toxicity:* the toxicity of a chemical is its potential to cause harm; this varies with each chemical, its route of entry into the body and the manner, site and speed of body response. For example, caustic soda may cause a chemical burn, silica may cause fibrosis of the lung, carbon tetrachloride may cause dermatitis by defatting the skin and, after absorption, also affect the brain, blood and liver.

b)   *Dose:* this is the amount of the chemical that is absorbed into the body, and its effect is dependent on the concentration of the substance in different organs and tissues and time over which it acts. Some chemicals can accumulate in the body and, in these cases, repetitive low doses may cause harm.

HOW CHEMICALS ENTER THE BODY

The ease with which a chemical enters the body depends on both its physical and chemical properties. Physical properties include the form of the chemical when it reaches the body, *ie* whether it is a gas or vapour, an aerosol, fume, liquid, dust or fibre. For an aerosol, dust or fibre, particle size is important as this affects how far it can travel into the lungs. Chemical properties include solubility in body fluids (*eg* water and natural oils) and reactivity with the body's own chemicals.

The most common routes of entry are:

a)   *Inhalation:* breathing in chemicals is the most common route of entry. Particles of dust and fibre can cause harm. Large particles are filtered off in the nose; smaller ones, or those breathed in through the mouth, settle on the walls of the upper respiratory tract or throat and are coughed up and either spat out or swallowed. The smallest particles of dust and fibres can be inhaled down into the lungs where they can cause local damage or can be absorbed into the blood stream. Aerosols, fumes, vapours and gases can cause harm anywhere in the respiratory system and may also be absorbed into the blood stream.

b) *Skin absorption:* the thickness of the skin together with its natural covering of sweat and grease provide some protection against chemicals, so that only a few are readily absorbed by this route, *eg* organic solvents and phenols. Chemicals can also enter the body through cuts or abrasions of the skin.

c) *Ingestion:* the swallowing of chemicals is most likely when contaminated fingers are placed in the mouth, or used to handle food or cigarettes. Inhaled particles may be coughed up and then swallowed.

RESPONSE OF THE BODY TO CHEMICALS

Not all people respond to a chemical in the same way. Some are more susceptible (*ie* respond at lower doses) than others, depending on various factors such as age, race, sex, state of health etc. People may also vary in the manner of response.

Chemicals can cause a response at various sites in the body and at different speeds. Additionally, many chemicals in their passage through the body are altered in the liver, thus changing their toxicity. They are afterwards excreted by the kidneys in the urine and, as they pass through the liver and kidneys, they can cause damage to these important organs.

Most people will react in a similar way to a chemical. The main responses of the body to exposure to chemicals are documented below:

a) *Irritation:*

- *respiratory system* – chemicals can irritate the nose and upper lung passages causing sneezing and coughing, and in some cases, bronchitis. They may also affect the surface of the respiratory system and may damage lung tissue.

- *skin and eyes* – when a chemical comes into contact with the skin, a common reaction is dermatitis, the medical name for a rash. By removing the protective oils from the skin solvents can cause it to become dry, rough and sore. Some chemicals (*eg* hydrochloric acid and caustic soda), in dilute form, may cause irritation, but in concentrated form many have a more severe effect on body cells, commonly called a chemical burn. The eye is extremely vulnerable and the effect of

contact with a chemical may vary from mild temporary discomfort to permanent damage.

b) *Sensitisation:*

- *respiratory system* – some chemicals can cause sensitisation leading to occupational asthma. Once a worker is sensitised (*eg* to an isocyanate) any further exposure, even minimal, may result in an allergic response of coughing and wheezing. Such an effect is not always immediate and can occur several hours after exposure.

- *skin* – sensitisation can also occur through contact between a particular chemical and the skin, and further contact even to minute quantities may cause itching, rashes and other discomfort.

c) *Long-term effects:*
The long term effect of greatest concern is cancer. This is a disorder of cell growth. It arises from a complex interaction between a harmful agent or agents (carcinogens) and a person's own susceptibility. There are a number of chemicals which are known to cause or are suspected of causing cancer. One example is asbestos (see *Chapter 7: Asbestos*) which, as well as being capable of causing asbestosis, can lead to cancers affecting the windpipe, the lining of the lung and the abdomen. It is known that in some cases exposure to two carcinogens may considerably enhance the probability of cancer. For example the risk of cancer increases many times for persons working with asbestos who are cigarette smokers. The effect of exposure to a carcinogen may not be seen for many years, and its early clinical identification is often difficult. The possible identification of potential carcinogens may be undertaken by 'short term tests' such as the Ames Test on single cell organisms. Recourse to lifetime studies in laboratory animals may then be indicated.

d) *Reproductive disorders:*
Other responses to chemicals could include reproductive disorders such as loss of sex drive, infertility in both men and women and foetal damage. Currently there is a lack of reliable evidence for the majority of industrial chemicals. Animal studies are often inadequate or non-existent and there is even less human evidence. A review of reproductive hazards of some industrial chemicals (Barlow and Sullivan, 1982) showed that there have been reproductive disorders in animal experiments. Until further research work is undertaken, the need for a precautionary policy is paramount, particularly where animal research shows cause for concern.

SITE OF RESPONSE

The effects of exposure to a chemical may be local or general or both. A local response is one occurring at the point of contact, whilst a general response follows absorption into the body. An example of a local effect is a burn to the skin following contact with a corrosive chemical such as sodium hydroxide. An example of a general response is headache, difficulty in breathing and dizziness following inhalation of a gas like carbon monoxide which is absorbed into the blood stream. Some chemicals can target specific organs or tissues causing specific effects on parts of the body far removed from the point of entry.

SPEED OF RESPONSE

An effect may be acute or chronic. An acute response is immediate, *eg* inhalation of chlorine causing irritation of the respiratory tract. A chronic reaction is much slower and is often cumulative following repeated exposures. The effects may build up over days or weeks, or even years before symptoms first appear, *eg* dermatitis of the hands due to repeated contact with solvents or inhalation of asbestos fibres causing cancer. Acute responses usually clear up quickly once the individual has been removed from the offending environment, but some acute and most chronic diseases require a much longer period for recovery and in some cases the effect on the body is not reversible.

The distinction between acute and chronic effects is vital to an understanding of hazards from chemicals at work. Chronic and acute effects from a particular substance may be very different and protecting against one kind of effect only may not necessarily control the hazards of the other.

Here are some examples:

- *Asbestos* – has no acute toxic effect, but chronic exposure can cause asbestosis, lung cancer and mesothelioma (cancer of the lining of the chest);

- *Vinyl chloride* – the acute effect is drowsiness but long term exposure at levels far too low to cause acute effects may cause liver damage, bone damage and cancer; and

- *Carbon monoxide* – acute effects include headaches, asphyxia and death; repeated exposure to lower concentrations is associated with heart problems and nerve damage.

FINDING OUT ABOUT HAZARDOUS SUBSTANCES

The hazards of dangerous substances are often difficult to detect so safety representatives need a strategy to help them identify potential problems *before* they occur and control chemical hazards at work *before* any damage is done. This will involve the following steps:

- getting full information on substances used at work from the employer, from suppliers, and from other sources such as the Health and Safety Executive (HSE);

- using available sources of published information to add to and check up on information from employers and suppliers;

- testing substances and monitoring the atmosphere at work; and

- controlling chemical hazards by taking steps to clean up the workplace.

Duties of employers

Under the HSW Act employers have a general duty to ensure the health, safety and welfare at work of all their employees. This duty extends to arrangements for ensuring, so far as is reasonably practicable, safety and absence of risks to health in connection with the use, handling, storage and transport of articles and substances and the provision of any necessary information, instruction, training and supervision for employees. This duty is spelled out further in other legislation under the HSW Act – for example the Control of Substances Hazardous to Health (COSHH) Regulations (see page 57).

Duties of manufacturers, importers and suppliers

Manufacturers of substances have a specific duty under Section 6 (5) of the HSW Act. They must carry out any necessary research with a view to the discovery and, so far as is reasonably practicable, the elimination or minimisation of any risks to health or safety to which the substances may give rise. Thereafter, manufacturers, importers and suppliers need to comply with the following requirements:

a) to ensure, so far as is reasonably practicable, a substance is safe and without risk to health;

b) to carry out any necessary testing and examination; and

c) to make available adequate information on the results of the tests and about the necessary conditions for safe use.

Labelling of dangerous substances

Correct labelling is a useful first source of information on chemicals. The Classification, Packaging and Labelling of Dangerous Substances Regulations 1984 (SI No 1244) and associated Approved List and Approved Code of Practice provide a comprehensive system for classifying and labelling dangerous substances, including mixtures and preparations.

These Regulations, which are based on international requirements, provide for the use of 'supply labels' and 'conveyance labels'. The prime function of supply labels is to warn/inform the user of both acute and chronic exposure hazards. The label must be on the receptacle from which the dangerous substance is to be dispensed. The prime function of 'conveyance labels' is to warn/inform the transporter, emergency services and the public. Labels must be on those layers of packaging liable to be handled during conveyance (usually the outermost layer). They need only take into account the acute risks posed by the substance.

Further advice on the purposes and compilation of labels may be found in the HSE publication HS (R) 22 "A guide to the Classification, Packaging and Labelling of Dangerous Substances Regulations 1984".

Although the label may meet the requirements of the Regulations, suppliers must make further information available to comply with Section 6 (4) (c) of the HSW Act. The HSE recommend that such additional information should be referred to on the label.

Data Sheets

Data sheets or hazard information sheets about substances should be provided by suppliers. They are a very important source of data and often the most convenient and relevant way of getting further information. On the other hand, many data sheets are incomplete and can be misleading. The HSE have drawn up a checklist of essential items which need to be considered when preparing a data sheet. These include:

1. Product name
2. Intended uses
3. Composition
4. Physical and chemical properties
5. Health hazards
6. Fire hazards
7. Storage precautions
8. Transport precautions
9. Handling use precautions – including advice on personal protective equipment
10. Emergency action – fire, spillage, first aid
11. Additional information –
    - ecological hazards
    - waste disposal
    - relevant regulations
    - references
12. Name, address and telephone number of supplier
13. Reference number, date of issue

The above advice and the *Checklist* below can be used to help decide whether the information supplied by manufacturers or suppliers (on a data sheet) is adequate. Further details on checking this information can be found in "Chemical Risk" by M Frankel Social Audit, Pluto 1982. It is also possible to check up on the hazards of particular chemicals by using well known standard reference books like Sax, Patty or Trevethick.

CHECKLIST

Composition

1. Is the substance described by proper chemical names as well as a trade name?
2. If it is a mixture, are the chemical names of each ingredient given?
3. If a mixture, are percentages given of each ingredient?
4. Are any impurities identified and their likely amounts in the substance?

Exposure routes

5. Are the different routes by which substances may affect the body fully covered, *eg*::
   - inhalation?
   - ingestion?
   - skin absorption?
   - eye contact?
   - skin contact?
6. If the substance does not affect you by one of these routes, does it say so?

Hazards

7. Are the hazards of each product, its impurities, and any decomposition products described?
8. Does it distinguish between short-term (acute) and long term (chronic) effects of a single exposure and of continual exposure?
9. If no chronic effects are mentioned, is it because none exist or because no research has been done?
10. What are the symptoms of:
    - acute over exposure?
    - chronic over exposure?

Evidence

11. Is any evidence given for any opinions about the hazard (*eg* 'little or low hazard' or 'generally not regarded as toxic')?
12. Are references made to sources of hazard information or research consulted by the supplier?

Exposure limits

13. Are you told:
    - what concentration or dose causes an ill effect?
    - what length of exposure causes an ill effect?
14. Is there a control limit specified (*eg* or Occupational Exposure Standard or Maximum Exposure Limit) and does this protect all workers from all effects?

First aid

15. What are the emergency/first aid measures for:
    - eyes?
    - skin?
    - inhalation?
    - ingestion?

Chemical reactions

16. Does the substance react to form any other chemical, under heat or pressure? If so, can the product:
    - decompose?
    - change its chemical nature in some other way?
    - what conditions, *eg* temperature, can lead to these changes?

Spills

17. Does it tell you how to safely deal with spills of the material?
18. Does it tell you how to dispose of waste?

Control methods

19. Are you told what methods the employer should use to reduce contamination of the workplace? (*eg* by local exhaust ventilation).

Personal protection

20. Does it specify what personal equipment should be used for?
    - eyes?
    - skin?
    - inhalation?

Handling, storage, transport

21. Does it specify what personal equipment should be used for?
    - correct handling methods?
    - correct storage methods?
    - correct transport methods?

Fire

22. If inflammable, are details given of:
    - extinguishing methods?
    - any special precautions needed *eg* because of toxic combustion products such as fumes from polyurethane foam?

CONTROL OF SUBSTANCES HAZARDOUS TO HEALTH (COSHH) REGULATIONS

The COSHH Regulations are the main piece of legislation covering control of risks from chemicals and toxic substances generally. The Regulations, introduced in 1988, set out, within a single legislative framework, the steps which employers must take to control exposure of workers to substances hazardous to health. The broad scope of the Regulations means that the same principles of control will be applied to all such substances (except lead, asbestos and radioactive substances where existing regulations continue to apply).

In essence, the Regulations require employers to make an assessment of the risk to health that may arise from the use of substances at the workplace, establish and maintain the necessary control measures, and, provide monitoring of exposure and health surveillance. The Regulations are supported by Approved Codes of Practice (ACoPs) and other guidance dealing with the Regulations themselves and specific substances or classes of substance.

The explanation opposite sets out the main features of COSHH and produces a step by step guide to what employers must do to comply with the regulations.

TESTING SUBSTANCES AND MONITORING THE AIR AT WORK

Carrying out tests is an essential part of identifying, assessing and controlling problems from toxic substances. Tests may tell you what substances are present, and how much contamination there is. In some cases you will be aware of what is present from knowledge of the process and information provided by suppliers. In other cases (*eg* demolishing a building which might contain asbestos) testing may be the only way of finding out what problems exist. Tests often need to be carried out by specialist industrial hygienists (though some gas detectors work like 'breathalysers' and can be used by anyone to do 'spot checks'). Even though specialists may be needed, the essential principles of monitoring the tests are easy to grasp, and there is no reason why safety representatives should not be able to ask for particular types of monitoring and receive and respond to test results.

Identification of a substance can be done in a number of ways. The substance can be mixed with other chemicals – the way it reacts may indicate what it is. Otherwise the material can be vaporised in a special machine (called a spectrometer) – light rays are shone through the vapour, and the direction and colours of the beams which emerge can be used to indicate what the substance is made of. The identification of unknown substances can normally only be done in a laboratory.

The extent of contamination by known substances can be measured in two basic ways:

- a sample of air is blown through a collector or filter, and the amount of air passing is recorded on a meter. At the end of the test, the filter is weighed or inspected with a microscope. Microscopic examination of dust samples is necessary because the size range of the particles affects the proportion of dust which can be breathed deeply into the lungs.

- after the sample is counted or weighed, the results can be compared with the air volume sampled – the result can then be expressed as 'parts per million' or 'milligrams per cubic metre' or 'fibres per cubic centimetre'.

- gases and vapours can be measured by blowing air through a chemical which changes colour when exposed to the substances in the air. The extent of the colour change shows the amount of pollution.

KEY FEATURES OF COSHH

Scope

The COSHH Regulations apply to all substances classified as being very toxic, harmful, corrosive, or irritant under the Classification, Packaging and Labelling of Dangerous Substances Regulations 1984. They also apply to all other substances hazardous to health arising from work activities, including mixtures and compounds. In addition, the Regulations apply to micro-organisms but do not cover the hazard of infection arising directly from a person suffering from a disease (except where that person is an in-patient at a hospital). Certain existing prohibitions on very dangerous substances are continued (*ie* the Carcinogenic Substances Regulations) and there will be revisions in future in line with EC Directives.

Assessment

The key provision of COSHH, from which other elements follow, is the requirement in Regulation 6 for the employer to carry out an assessment of likely risks to health to his employees arising from exposure to hazardous substances. The purpose of such an assessment, which, in all but the simplest cases needs to be in writing is to enable a decision to be made about measures necessary to control substances hazardous to health arising from any work activity. It allows the employer to show: all the factors pertinent to the work have been considered; and informed and correct judgement has been reached about the risks and the steps which need to be taken to achieve and maintain adequate control; the need for monitoring exposure at the workplace; and the need for health surveillance.

HSE guidance on assessment stresses that it should allow for a systematic review to consider which substances or types of substances workers are liable to encounter, what are the effects of those substances, where the substances are likely to be present and the ways and the extent to which any groups could potentially be exposed. Under the Regulations and the general ACoP, the degree of detail involved in its preparation has to be commensurate with the nature and degree of risk arising from the work. Key issues here, concern:

- the degree of detail and rigour appropriate to the assessment procedure in various circumstances;

- the competence and qualifications of persons carrying out the assessment;

- the degree of reliance to be placed on manufacturers' and suppliers' information;

- the need for written procedures and records; and

- consultation with trade union representatives.

Control

Once the employer has identified a potential risk to health, under Regulation 7, they must ensure that the exposure of workers is either prevented or adequately controlled. Inhalation of substances assigned a maximum exposure limit (MEL) should not exceed those limits and should be reduced below them to the greatest extent that is reasonably practicable. Inhalation of substances which have been assigned an occupational exposure standard (OES) should be reduced to that standard. If exposure exceeds the OES, control will still be deemed to be adequate provided that the employer has identified why the OES has been exceeded *and* they are taking appropriate steps to comply with OES as soon as is reasonably practicable. In all cases, prevention or adequate control of exposure should be achieved by measures other than personal protective equipment (PPE) to the greatest extent that is reasonable practicable – *ie* the use of engineering controls is the first objective.

Use of control measures

Regulation 8 requires every employer who provides any control measure to ensure that it is properly used and every worker to make full and proper use of any control measures provided.

Maintenance, examination and testing

Under Regulation 9 every employer who provides any control measure to comply with Regulation 7 (*ie* to control the exposure of workers) should ensure that it is maintained in efficient working order and in good repair. The employer should ensure that thorough examinations and tests of engineering controls are carried out; in the case of local exhaust ventilation plant this should be done at least once every 12 months. Respiratory protective equipment has to be examined at suitable intervals, and, for all control measures a record (or summary) of the examinations has to be kept for five years.

The objective of this Regulation is to ensure that all control measures which have been provided to meet the requirements of Regulation 7 (1) perform as originally intended, thereby continuing to effectively prevent or adequately control exposure. The nature and content of the thorough examination and test depend on the particular engineering controls under consideration and the nature and degree of risk posed by the hazardous substance.

Monitoring exposure

Under Regulation 10 monitoring of exposure should be carried out when it is required to ensure that exposure is adequately controlled. It is required when failure or deterioration of the control measures could result in a serious risk to health or where it is necessary to demonstrate that a MEL or OES is not exceeded. A record should be kept showing when the monitoring was done, what monitoring procedures were adopted and what the results were.

Health surveillance

Regulation 11 requires that, where it is necessary for the protection of the health of workers, the employer should ensure that they are under suitable health surveillance. Health surveillance should be treated as being appropriate where the worker is exposed to one of the substances in Schedule 6 to the Regulations which lists a range of substances where statutory medical examinations are required under existing legislation.

Health surveillance also has to be carried out where the exposure of the worker is such that an identifiable disease or adverse health effect may be related to the exposure, where there is a reasonable likelihood that the disease or effect may occur under the particular conditions of work and there are valid techniques for detecting signs of the disease or the effect. Any judgement as to the likelihood that a disease or adverse health effect may occur must be related to the nature and degree of exposure. If, following assessment, it can be shown that it is most unlikely that any disease or adverse health effect will result, then exposure can be deemed not to be significant and health surveillance is not required. Examples of health effects where health surveillance should be considered are given in the ACoP.

Information, instruction and training

Under Regulation 12 workers exposed to substances hazardous to health must be given sufficient information, instruction and training to enable them to know about the risks involved and the precautions which should be taken. They are also entitled to know the results of environmental monitoring and the collective results of any health surveillance.

Test equipment

There are different kinds of test equipment. They vary in price and accuracy – some need to be backed up by laboratory analysis of samples.

- *Personal sampler:* this is worn during work – air is sucked from the workers' breathing zone and passed through a filter. At the end of the test period the filter can be examined to show the amount of pollution in the metered sample of air.

- *Indicator tubes:* these are like breathalysers – a small hand pump is used to pump a known volume of air through a glass tube of test chemical. The extent of discolouration of the test chemical shows the amount of pollution present. You have to know what substances you are looking for to choose the right test chemical. The accuracy varies according to which substance you are testing for. The advantages of this method are cheapness, ease of use, and immediate results without the need for laboratory analysis. The most common type of pump is the 'Draeger' meter. You may want to ask management for the use of one to enable safety representatives to conduct spot checks where potential problems exist.

- *Continuous monitoring equipment:* this is sophisticated test equipment which can indicate average levels of contamination as well as recording how levels change at different times during the working day. Some types can be set to sound an alarm or to shut a process down when a pre-set level of contamination is exceeded.

  Continuous monitoring equipment is now made to detect a number of common industrial chemicals. The machine used depends on the substance being monitored. The equipment can be expensive and would normally be used for special surveys or to monitor high risk processes.

- *Dust lamps:* these do not provide precise measurements of the amount of dust. What they do is to show where invisible dust clouds are present, and how the dust flows in the air. This is very useful for checking the effectiveness of ventilation systems. They are cheap – in fact any bright light beam in a darkened room can be used.

EXPOSURE LIMITS

Official limits have been set to control exposure to air contamination by about 700 substances.

They are published by the Health and Safety Executive in Guidance Note EH 40 which is revised annually.

There are two main sorts of limit:

- **Maximum Exposure Limits (MELs).** These have been formally adopted by the HSC, and are embodied in a schedule in the COSHH Regulations. They must not be exceeded and exposure must be reduced as far as is reasonably practicable below them.

- **Recommended limits or Occupational Exposure Standards (OES),** which are recommended as 'good practice' by the HSE. Many have been 'borrowed' from other countries – particularly the USA and West Germany.

MELs and OESs replace the previous system of 'Threshold Limit Values' or TLVs, which were used until 1984. The different types of limits work in broadly the same way, and share many of the same problems which safety representatives should be aware of. The HSE in Guidance Note – EH 40, states that exposure limits should not be used as an index of relative hazard or toxicity. They are not sharp dividing lines between 'safe' and 'dangerous' concentrations.

Nor does the absence of a substance from the list indicate that it is safe. They advise that exposure limits are limits which have been judged, after detailed consideration of the available scientific and medical evidence, to be *"reasonably practicable for the whole spectrum of work activities in Great Britain"*.

They are based on good working conditions and HSE Guidance recommends that *"any factors which impose additional stress on the body, eg long hours of work, exposure to ultra-violet radiation, high temperatures and humidity, may increase the toxic response to a substance. In these circumstances, care must be exercised in the application of the exposure limits listed, as exposure may have to be adjusted to take the effects of these factors into consideration"*.

MIXTURES

Limits are set on the assumption that exposure is limited to one substance only. But many workers will tend to be exposed to a variety of chemicals, and different substances may combine to create an even greater danger. On the question of mixtures the HSE has this to say:

"Mixtures

28 *The exposure limits are applicable to airborne concentrations of single substances. Exposure to additional substances, either simultaneously or sequentially, could give rise to greater hazards to health. There is no universally applicable method for the derivation of exposure limits for mixtures from those of individual substances listed in this document. A wide range of formulae of varying degrees of complexity have been devised in recent years for dealing with mixtures; all have limitations* *and none cope with the problem of synergism (the working together of two or more substances to produce an effect greater than the sum of their individual effects)".*

From *"Occupational Exposure Limits 1984"* – EH 40

CONTROL MEASURES

Measures to control hazards should be effective, acceptable and convenient from the workers point of view. A number of measures are possible – as this list from the Code of Practice makes clear.

Means of preventing or controlling exposure can include one or more of the following:

a) elimination of the substance hazardous to health;

b) substitution of a substance hazardous to health by one that is less hazardous;

c) plant, processes, and systems of work designed to prevent the exposure to, or suppress the formation of, dust, vapour; gases or aerosol;

d) where elimination, substitution, prevention or suppression are not reasonably practicable, substances hazardous to health being contained in totally closed systems, preferably under negative pressure, or in enclosed containers such as drums or bags;

e) where totally closed systems are not reasonably practicable, partial enclosure with effective local exhaust ventilation being used;

f) where no form of enclosure is reasonably practicable, by effective local exhaust ventilation a good standard of general ventilation as close to the source of contamination as possible;

g) a good standard of general ventilation is required wherever substances hazardous to health are present; but where enclosure and local exhaust ventilation are not reasonably practicable or where they are not totally effective, effective general ventilation should be provided by the circulation of fresh air in working areas;

h) restricting the quantity of the substance used, limiting the area in the workplace in which the substance is used, limiting the number of people exposed. In appropriate cases the period of exposure should be limited, but this is not generally a desirable option if it leads to a corresponding increase in the numbers of persons exposed.

Additionally, the control of exposure should include:

i) the taking of appropriate measures to secure the cleanliness of workplaces, premises and plant;

j) avoidance of the spread of contamination;

k) where necessary, the provision of adequate and suitable personal protective equipment; and

l) the provision of adequate and suitable facilities for washing, clothing accommodation, eating, drinking and smoking.

From: Code of Practice, *Control of Substances Hazardous to Health* (COSHH).

PERSONAL PROTECTION

Safety representatives should always remember that control at source is the primary objective. But in practice it may be that personnel protection has to be used. Personal protective equipment puts a 'barrier' on the worker – it does not control the hazard at source. This kind of equipment could include:

- respirators;
- goggles;
- helmets;
- overalls;
- gloves;
- aprons; and
- boots.

Personal protection should be treated as a last resort, or as a temporary measure to deal with emergencies or other special operations. In rare cases, personal protection may offer the only answer to a problem. Usually control at source can be achieved.

More details on the use of personal protection can be found in *Chapter 17*.

MORE INFORMATION

- **From Dust To Dust:** TUC; 15p; *short introduction to dust hazards; useful for discussions with members.*

- **Handbook on Dust At Work:** TUC; *extensive handbook on dust hazards and control.*

- **Asbestos in the Workplace:** TUC pamphlet.

- **Chemical Risk:** Maurice Frankel; Pluto Press, £1.95; *essential guide to getting information and using suppliers' data sheets; contains a useful list of further sources.*

- **Dangerous Properties of Industrial Materials:** NI Sax (New York – Nostrand Reinhold); *comprehensive reference book which provides basic information on over 15,000 industrial chemicals;* it is expensive so if you cannot borrow a copy from your employer, ask your nearest public library to obtain one for its reference section.

- **Encyclopaedia of Occupational Health and Safety:** International Labour Organisation; ILO, 96-98 Marsham Street, London SW1; big two-volume reference book, containing *full information on large number of substances, as well as many other aspects of health and safety;* your employer or safety officer may already have a copy, otherwise ask your public library.

- **Documentation of Threshold Limit Values for Substances in Workroom Air**: American Conference of Government Industrial Hygienists; (PO Box 19376, Cincinnati, Ohio 45201, USA); *outlines the test and research results used to set US standards (TLVs);* it may be useful to help check some exposure limits in Britain, and as a source of information.

- **Chemical Synonyms and Trade Names**: Gardner and Cooke (London, Technical Press); *the best source to refer to if you have problems finding out proper chemical names.*

- **Patty's Industrial Hygiene and Toxicology**: John Wiley and Sons, New York; large three volume reference book.

HSE leaflets

Substances for use at Work: the Provision of Information HS/G 27

- **Guidance on the Control of Substances Hazardous to Health Regulations**: HSC; *guidance package covers the COSHH Regulations and Codes of Practice.*

- **Chemicals in Paper and Board Mills**: Paper and Board Industry Advisory Committee, HMSO.

Guidance notes

Environmental hygiene series

- EH 2 **Chromium** – health and safety precautions
- EH 4 **Aniline** – health and safety precautions
- EH 5 **Trichloroethylene** – health and safety precautions
- EH 6 **Chromic acid concentrations in air**
- EH 7 **Petroleum based adhesives in building operations**
- EH 8 **Arsenic** – health and safety precautions
- EH 9 **Spraying of highly flammable liquids**
- EH 10 **Asbestos** – control of limits and measurement of airborne dust concentrations
- EH 11 **Arsine** – health and safety precautions
- EH 12 **Stibine** – health and safety precautions
- EH 13 **Beryllium** – health and safety precautions
- EH 14 **Level of training for technicians making noise survey**
- EH 16 **Isocyanates** – toxic hazards and precautions
- EH 17 **Mercury** – health and safety precautions
- EH 18 **Toxic substances** – a precautionary policy

- EH 19 **Antimony** – health and safety precautions
- EH 20 **Phosphine** – health and safety precautions
- EH 21 **Carbon dust** – health and safety precautions
- EH 22 **Ventilation of buildings** – fresh air requirements
- EH 23 **Anthrax** – health hazards
- EH 24 **Dust accidents in malthouses**
- EH 25 **Cotton dust sampling**
- EH 26 **Occupational skin diseases** – health and safety precautions
- EH 27 **Acrylonitrile** – personal protective equipment
- EH 28 **Control of lead** – air sampling techniques and strategies
- EH 29 **Control of lead** – outside workers
- EH 30 **Control of lead** – pottery and related industries
- EH 31 **Control of exposure to polyvinyl chloride dust**
- EH 32 **Control of exposure to talc dust**
- EH 33 **Atmospheric pollution in car parks**
- EH 34 **Benzidine based dyes**
- EH 35 **Probable asbestos dust concentrations at construction processes**
- EH 36 **Work with asbestos cement**
- EH 38 **Ozone** – health hazards and precautionary measures
- EH 40 **Occupational exposure limits 1988**
- EH 42 **Monitoring strategies for toxic substances**
- EH 43 **Carbon monoxide**
- EH 44 **Dust in the workplace** – general principles of protection
- EH 45 **Carbon disulphide** – control of exposure in the viscose industry
- EH 46 **Exposure to mineral wools**

Medical series

- MS 9 **Byssinosis**
- MS 13 **Asbestosis**
- MS 15 **Welding**
- MS 18 **Health surveillance by routine procedures**
- MS 20 **Pre-employment health screening**
- MS 21 **Precautions for safe handling of cytotoxic drugs**

6: Dust

DUST HAZARDS – THE LEGACY

Dust at work has been one of the largest occupational killers of all time. It has shortened lives, and caused misery to hundreds of thousands – often after a lifetime's work in dusty conditions. Take a look at some of the damage it has caused:

- *asbestos dust* has already killed thousands of workers and will kill at least another 50,000 over the next 30 years;

- *silica dust* has killed and disabled thousands of workers in areas such as coal mines, quarries, foundries and brickworks;

- *cotton and flax dust* has disabled or killed over 30,000 textile workers;

- *lead dust* has poisoned hundreds of workers in many industries;

- *flour and cereal dust* has crippled thousands of millers and bakery workers with occupational asthma;

- *wood and leather dust* has caused nasal cancer amongst scores of workers in the furniture and shoe-making industries – many other dusts have caused bronchitis and emphysema amongst thousands of workers in other industries using dusty materials;

- *radioactive dusts* in tin, iron and fluor-spar mines have killed scores of miners with lung cancer; and

- scores of workers have been killed in *dust explosions*.

Much of this damage could have been prevented. What was lacking was not so much technical knowledge, as the commitment to safe-guard workers' health.

Safety representatives and their members can help to prevent more workers from suffering health damage from dust in the future. Remember whenever materials are handled or broken down, dust is liable to be produced. In other words **work makes dust.**

DUST IS DANGEROUS BECAUSE . . .

It can damage health. It can cause:

- lung damage, such as bronchitis, emphysema, pneumoconiosis, asthma, or even cancer;

- damage to the nose and throat, leading to colds, and other infections, or even nasal cancer;

- skin damage, leading to dermatitis, ulcers and skin cancer;

- eye damage, including conjunctivitis; and

- internal effects including damage to the brain and nervous system, blood disorders, stomach cancer, liver and kidney disease, or bladder cancer.

It can cause explosions

- Many dusts – including flour, rubber, coal dust and metal dusts such as aluminium – can explode when in confined spaces, sometimes causing destruction of whole factories. For instance, five workers were injured, two seriously in July 1983, when a factory in Anglesey handling aluminium powder exploded. The factory was almost totally destroyed.

It can also affect productivity and cause product damage

- Dusty workplaces make work more difficult and can damage products or machinery. For example, areas housing complex equipment such as computers have to be kept dust free, but human beings too need the same protection.

No dust should be regarded as 'safe'; even some alleged nuisance dusts have turned out, in the light of further research, to be a real danger to health.

HOW MUCH DUST IS TOO MUCH?

That depends on:

- the composition of each dust – for example how poisonous it can be;

- its particle size – for example whether it can get into the lungs; and

- how long you are exposed to it.

For some dusts, experts have decided the amount of the respirable fraction for each which should be regarded as too much – called the *exposure limit*. A list of exposure limits is published by HSE in a guidance note called EH40 (see *Chapter 5: Chemicals and toxic substances*), and this is revised annually. These limits are used by the HSE to assess compliance by employers with their duty to control exposure to hazardous substances under the COSHH Regulations and the Health and Safety at Work Act. There is also a shorter list of what are called 'Maximum Exposure Limits' and these must not be exceeded under any circumstances.

HOW CAN DUST BE MEASURED?

By using:

- a dust lamp (or Tyndal Beam) to show up the damaging invisible dust and where it's coming from;

- portable sampling pumps with filter heads fixed near workers' breathing zones which measure how much dust they are breathing in;

- continuous dust monitors that measure dust concentrations at any one moment continuously throughout a shift.

If the dust in your workplace is likely to be dangerous, your employer should arrange for dust level measurements to be carried out at regular intervals. HSE Inspectors can also do dust monitoring. As a safety representative you have a legal right to see the results of any dust monitoring carried out by the HSE or your employer.

WHAT ARE THE EXPOSURE LIMITS FOR DUST?

These are the maximum amounts of dust in the air that workers can be exposed to. The amount is usually averaged over eight hours.

Employers have a duty under the Health and Safety at Work Act to reduce dust levels to as far below these limits as is 'reasonably practicable', so it is not acceptable to use exposure limits as safe maximum limits. Some examples of exposure limits are:

Asbestos (chyrsotile)	0.5 fibre/ml
Dust containing silica	0.3mg/m^3 total dust
Crystalline quartz	0.1mg/m^3 respirable dust
Cotton dust	0.5mg/m^3
Lead	0.15mg/m^3
Man-made mineral fibres	5mg/m^3
PVC dust	10mg/m^3 total dust
	5mg/m^3 respirable dust
Talc dust	10mg/m^3 total dust
	1mg/m^3 respirable dust

No person should be exposed to any dust in concentrations which exceed 10mg/m^3 total dust or 5mg/m^3 respirable dust. For further information see the *TUC Handbook on Dust at Work*.

HOW CAN DUST HAZARDS BE REDUCED?

Firstly: by changing dusty raw materials to dust-suppressed pellets and pastes. For example, many rubber chemicals are now supplied in this form.

Secondly: by changing the way raw materials are handled, *eg* covered conveyors, enclosed silos. Suppliers should be persuaded to supply dusty materials in closed containers – not bags or sacks.

Thirdly: by installing Local Exhaust Ventilation wherever dust 'is liable to be injurious' (Section 63 of Factories Act). Safety representatives should make sure the system is designed, installed, inspected and properly maintained by qualified ventilation engineers (see also *Chapter 5 in the TUC Handbook on Dust at Work*).

Fourthly: if other measures will not work, by using appropriate respirators. But these should only be regarded as a temporary measure or a last resort. Safety representatives should check that respirators are of an approved type, are individually fitted, and are well maintained. They should also make sure that workers have been trained in their use. Studies of the Foundry, Asbestos Insulation, and other industries have shown that many workers get little or no protection from respirators. It is difficult to work in a respirator so it is always important to insist on getting rid of the dust instead.

TACKLING THE ARGUMENTS IN FAVOUR OF DOING NOTHING

Reducing health risks due to dust requires knowledge, commitment and determination. Often it is necessary to convince workers and management of the need for change so safety representatives should know how to overcome the arguments in favour of doing nothing; such as those shown opposite.

'There's been dust around here for years but there is no disease'

How do you know? The serious dust diseases can take 20 to 50 years to develop, and victims usually leave work before they become too ill. An epidemic of dust disease at work can go unnoticed unless a proper study of all workers and leavers is carried out by experts.

'You can see that there is not much dust here'

Can you? Remember it is the invisible dust that is dangerous – and this fine dust can be re-circulated from dust lying on ledges and window sills, etc.

'It used to be dusty here years ago, but conditions have greatly improved. There is no danger now'

Disease today is always caused by yesterday's dust, but how do you know that today's dust is safe?

Asbestos, silica, cotton dust, were thought of as 'safe' years ago. No dust is good for you and we should not be using workers' bodies to prove that again.

'We already provide respirators, but your members won't wear them'

Many respirators don't protect workers because they are badly designed, are the wrong type, are poorly maintained, are wrongly fitted, or are too uncomfortable. And they shouldn't be used unless all other attempts at dust control have been tried. Anyway, ensuring the correct use of safety devices like respirators is a management job, and it requires an ongoing programme of effective training and supervision.

'It's smoking that is killing your members, not the dusty work'

Smoking certainly does kill a lot of workers but dust at work can kill non-smokers too. What is more, it can greatly increase the risks for smokers. Workers should be persuaded to give up smoking if they can, but being killed by someone else's dust is not the same as killing yourself with cigarettes.

'It's been dusty here for ages – there's no rush to clean it up now'

Health hazards like dust are damaging workers' health all the time. A little more delay means a little more damage. In this sense, health risks are different from safety hazards, since accidents have to happen before a potential risk actually causes damage.

'Ventilation is too expensive – and we don't have to provide it'

Section 63 of the Factories Act says that employers must provide local exhaust ventilation if dust is likely to be dangerous – and the cost doesn't come into it because the legal duty is a 'practicable' one, not a 'reasonably practicable' one which does allow costs to be considered. And in any case there are often less expensive ways of dealing with dust than ventilation, such as changing materials, or work methods.

'We can't afford to remove the dust'

Not doing anything can be costly. Wasted raw materials, low productivity, high absenteeism, poor industrial relations, possible legal action from Government Inspectors and unions on behalf of diseased workers as well as bad publicity and increased insurance premiums. These are just some of the costs that can be reduced by improving dusty conditions.

CHECKLIST: DUST ACTION PLAN

- *Find out* if your members are working with dusty materials and what the hazards are. Your employer must tell you this with the help of the information which suppliers of materials must provide under Section 6 of the Health and Safety at Work Act.

- By doing a *simple survey,* find out if your members are suffering from any signs of ill-health which may have been caused by dust in the workplace (*eg* coughs, bad chests, shortness of breath, asthma, skin rashes, etc).

- *Ask your employer* (or if that fails, the HSE) to measure the dust levels at your place of work – make sure you get the results; compare them with relevant exposure limits.

- *Persuade your employer,* with the help of expert advice, to put in dust control measures – get agreement in writing on a timed programme of dust removal or control. Often a simple change in working methods can eliminate dust altogether.

- *Arm yourself* with further information by reading the *TUC Handbook on Dust at Work,* and getting on a TUC or Union approved training course.

- Also, *seek legal advice* from your Union to help any members whose health has been damaged by dust to claim compensation from the DHSS. See leaflet NI 6/ entitled "Industrial Injuries Disablement Benefit and Increases". Also leaflet NI196 entitled 'Benefit Rates' Your Union will also be able to provide legal assistance in claims against your employers.

FURTHER INFORMATION ON DUST

TUC Publications

- **TUC Handbook on Dust At Work**
- **From Dust to Dust:** *a safety representatives' guide to the hazards of dust at work*
- **Dust – are you at risk?:** TUC poster.

Specific industries

Agriculture

AS leaflets

- AS 4 **Respiratory diseases in the mushroom industry;** 1981.
- AS 5 **Farmers Lung;** 1982.

Construction Industry Advisory Committee

- Hazard information sheet 1: **Cement;** 1985
- Health hazard information sheet 4: **Lead;** 1986

Foundries Industry Advisory Committee

- **Foundry dust control:** fettling benches and small adjustable heads; second report of the sub-committee on dust and fume; 1975.
- IAC/L18 **Reducing the risk of lung cancer in the iron and steel foundries:** *an action plan and precautionary policy* (issued by the Foundries Industry Advisory Committee); 1986.

Pottery and Allied Industries, Joint Standing Committee

- **Dust extraction systems in the ceramics industry:** 1975.

Printing Industry Advisory Committee

- **Ink fly in newspaper pressrooms:** 1984.

Rubber Industry Advisory Committee

- **Control of dust and fume at two roll mills;** 1986.

Approved Codes of Practice issued under Section 16 of the Health and Safety at Work etc Act 1974

- **Control of lead at work** – approved code of practice: revised June 1985 (in support of SI 1980 No. 1248).

HSE guidance notes

- EH 21 **Carbon dust** health and safety precautions; 1979.
- EH 24 **Dust and accidents in malthouses;** 1979.
- EH 25 **Cotton dust sampling;** 1980.
- EH 28 **Control of lead** – air sampling techniques and strategies; 1986.
- EH 29 **Control of lead** – outside workers, 1981.
- EH 30 **Control of lead** – pottery and related industries; 1981.
- EH 32 **Control of exposure to talc dust;** 1982.
- EH 42 **Monitoring strategies for toxic substances;** 1984.
- EH 44 **Dust in the workplace** – general principles of protection; 1984.
- EH 46 **Exposure to mineral wools;** 1986.
- MS 4 **Organic dust surveys;** 1977.

HSE guidance booklets

- 22 **Dust explosions in factories;** 1970.

Special reports

- IR 3 **Corn starch dust explosion at General Foods Ltd,** Banbury Oxfordshire, 18 November 1981; 1983.

Safety, health and welfare leaflets

- SHW 830 **Dust explosions in factories;** 1975.

Respiratory protective equipment:

- **Certificate of Approved (Respiratory Protective Equipment)** – F2486.
- **Certificate of Approved (Breathing Apparatus)** – F2501.
- **Certificate of Approved (Blasting Helmets)** –F2500.
  (The above three are issued annually by HSE, HMSO).
- **British Standard 4275: 1974** – Recommendations for the selection, use and maintenance of respiratory protective equipment; published by the British Standards Institution.

Other

- **Industrial Ventilation:** *a manual of recommended practice;* published by ACGIH.

7:   Asbestos in the workplace

WHAT IS ASBESTOS?

Asbestos is a soft mineral rock, mined abroad and imported to asbestos manufacturing plants. From mines in Zimbabwe and Canada it finds its way into pipe and boiler insulation, sprayed coatings on structural steelwork, brake linings, ceiling tiles and wall panels, ventilation systems, fire doors and hundreds of other products. It is made of millions of light, indestructible fibres that make it a valuable but hazardous material.

There are three main types of asbestos that you may find at work:

- **crocidolite** – 'blue' asbestos
- **amosite** – 'brown' asbestos
- **chrysotile** – 'white' asbestos

WHERE MIGHT ASBESTOS BE FOUND AT WORK?

Most asbestos went into buildings or ships as pipe and boiler lagging (blue, brown and white), fire insulation panels (usually brown), and asbestos cement sheets (white). There are hundreds of other asbestos products and processes.

Here is a short list:

Insulation

- sprayed onto structures;
- fire blankets, gloves, pads;
- string, tape, paper; and
- insulation board such as Asbestolux, LDR, Turnasbestos and Marinite

Friction materials

- clutches;
- disc-brake pads; and
- brake linings

Reinforced products

- asbestos cement slabs, sheeting, pipes;
- floor tiles;
- composite board;
- roofing felt;
- underseals, paints and mastics; and
- gaskets, washers, valve-packing.

WHY IS ASBESTOS DANGEROUS?

The tiny, often invisible fibres that make asbestos so useful are harmful to the delicate cells in the human body when they are breathed in. The main diseases caused by asbestos dust are:

- **Lung damage** – lung scarred and thickened, breathing difficult, strain on the heart.
- **Asbestosis** – a type of 'pneumoconiosis' (Greek for 'dust in the lungs') caused by accumulation of dust – lungs scarred and shrunken, increasing breathlessness and pain in chest. The disease can get worse even if the sufferers are no longer exposed to asbestos dust. Further information on this can be found in the *TUC Handbook on Dust at Work*.
- **Heart failure** – workers die of heart failure or of infections that easily take hold of diseased lungs.
- **Mesothelioma** – a cancer of the lining of the stomach or lung cavity. It cannot be cured and leads to early death.
- **Lung cancer** – the disease which kills most asbestos workers.
- **Other cancers** – there is some evidence that asbestos may also cause cancer of the throat.

IS THERE A SAFE LEVEL OF ASBESTOS DUST?

Experts have agreed that there is no safe level of asbestos

HSE Guidance Note EH 10 makes the position clear:

"The control limits do not represent safe levels which once attained make further improvements in dust control unnecessary. They represent the upper levels of permitted exposure, for each form of asbestos above which the risk to health is unacceptable."

Asbestos cancers have been caused by very small amounts of dust – for example, in people who cut up asbestos panels for only a few days, or in the relatives of asbestos workers who were exposed to dust from overalls. However, like smoking, asbestos dust only affects some of those exposed to it. The more dust you breathe in the greater the risk to your health.

IS WHITE ASBESTOS DANGEROUS?

Blue, brown and white asbestos can cause asbestosis, lung cancer and mesothelioma, but blue and brown seem to cause more mesothelioma in workers exposed to the dust than white asbestos. This has led to the dangerous myth that white asbestos is 'safe'.

All types of asbestos dust are dangerous.

ARE SOME ASBESTOS PRODUCTS MORE DANGEROUS THAN OTHERS?

Those that can give off dust easily are the most dangerous, *eg* insulation lagging on pipes and boilers.

Other products like asbestos cement are much less dusty and dangerous unless they are weathered, broken up, or cut up with tools. If there's asbestos dust, there's danger.

The following panel is a rough guide to the dustiness of some of the different products *if appropriate dust control measures are not applied.*

Remember that some of these products, such as brake-linings, gaskets, etc may have dusty surfaces during manufacture because they have just been through a grinding or cutting process. Brake-linings and some other products also produce dust during use.

Range of likely dust concentrations without proper control measures (Fibres per millilitre)

Very dusty	Old lagging and sprayed asbestos insulation during dry removal.	100's to 1,000's
Dusty	Handling raw asbestos and dry mixes containing asbestos; some processes in the manufacture of asbestos textiles.	10's
Dusty when sawn or broken up	Insulation boards and ceiling tiles.	
Dusty when abraded, sawn or broken up	Brake linings, clutch linings, etc. Asbestos cement sheeting etc.	2 to 10
Slightly dusty when handled	Asbestos fabrics, rope, etc, fire blankets, aprons, suits, gloves, *if in poor condition or damaged.*	0.1 to 2
Unlikely to give rise to dust	Gaskets, sealants, mastics, paints when handled and used (but not including manufacture and abrasion which may be dusty).	Less than 0.1

DOES SMOKING INCREASE THE RISK OF LUNG CANCER?

Asbestos dust alone increases the risk of lung cancer by about five times for both smokers and non-smokers as shown below.

Group of workers	Comparative lung cancer risk
Non-smokers, not exposed to asbestos	1
Non-smokers, exposed to asbestos	5
Smokers, not exposed to asbestos	10
Smokers, exposed to asbestos	50

Source: Based on table "Asbestos Related Diseases Without Asbestos", page 14, Industrial Injuries Advisory Council, HMSO 1983.

Asbestos does cause lung cancer in non-smokers, but the risk in smokers is much greater. The mesothelioma risk is not increased by smoking. Although nothing can be done about past exposure to asbestos dust, if you are a smoker it is still worth while giving up smoking. Your lung cancer risk begins to drop almost as soon as you stop smoking.

IS THERE A LEGAL LIMIT ON HOW MUCH ASBESTOS DUST THERE SHOULD BE?

The 'Control limits' for the asbestos dust in air from August 1984, are shown below.

Asbestos type	Asbestos control limits
'Blue' (crocidolite)	0.2 fibres/ml (200,000 fibres/m³)
'Brown' (amosite)	0.2 fibres/ml (200,000 fibres/m³)
'White' (chrysotile)	0.5 fibres/ml (500,000 fibres/m³)

Source: HSE Guidance Note EH 10 Asbestos Control Limits.

Note: ml (millilitre) of air is 1 millionth of a cubic metre. m³ is 1 cubic metre of air. In the course of an average working day a worker inhales about 8 cubic metres of air.

We breathe in about one cubic metre of air every hour on average, so these control limits allow workers to breathe in a lot of asbestos dust. Most is breathed out again, but some remains in the body, causing disease in some people. Employers have a duty to reduce exposure to asbestos as far below these control limits as is reasonably practicable. However, these occupational control limits represent a compromise between costs to the *asbestos manufacturing industry* and risks to the *asbestos workers,* and are considered too high for other workers and the public who should not have to face a cancer risk from asbestos. Children, the young, old, sick, etc, are not adequately protected by these occupational control limits either, so lower limits are needed to protect them.

HOW DO I KNOW THE CONTROL LIMIT IS EXCEEDED?

If you are exposed to asbestos dust your employer should measure the air in the workplace to see if the control limits are exceeded. This measuring is done by drawing air through a filter placed near to your nose and mouth. This is called personal sampling. The asbestos fibres on the filter are then counted in a laboratory.

Sampling devices can also be fixed in one place to check background levels of dust. Personal sampling however, is more accurate as it gives an indication of dust that is actually breathed in.

Your employer must tell you the results of any sampling – if he doesn't you should ask to see them. HSE or local authority inspectors may carry out sampling at your workplace and you also have the right to see the results. Action should be taken to reduce dust levels for asbestos workers whenever results exceed half of the control limits (shown in the box opposite).

The TUC and HSE recommend action whenever results are above 0.01 fibres/ml (10,000 fibres/m³) to protect *the public* and the *non-asbestos worker* from the asbestos dust risk in buildings etc. ("Where the result exceeds this value, further action may need to be taken – for example – by means of the air extraction equipment or a vacuum cleaner fitted with a high efficiency filter"; paragraph 36 and paragraph 5 of Annex 2, from HSE Guidance Note EH 10 1984).

Do not rely on dust measurements alone to tell you whether there is a risk or not – *they can be inaccurate and misleading.* If there is the possibility of exposure to asbestos dust, there is a hazard. Remember – there is no safe level and the optical microscope used to count the fibres in the laboratory misses many hazardous fibres that are too small to be seen.

ARE THERE LAWS TO PROTECT ME FROM ASBESTOS DUST?

The Asbestos Regulations 1969 cover work with asbestos in factories and construction sites. Employers must prevent workers from being exposed to any asbestos dust by using ventilation, respirators, protective clothing etc.

The Health and Safety at Work Act, 1974, provides a similar protection for workers in all other places. The Asbestos Licensing Regulations 1983 which came into operation on August 1, 1984 and the Approved Code of Practice on Work with Asbestos Insulation etc, protect the public and workers from danger when asbestos in buildings is being sealed or removed. The Control of Asbestos at Work Regulations (effective from January 1 1987) provides a comprehensive framework for the control of asbestos in the workplace. They require the prevention or reduction of exposure to asbestos, assessment of the degree of hazards involved in the work, notification to the enforcing authority of work which is liable to be hazardous, the provision of information and training to employees, medical surveillance and the provision of effective control measures.

These laws are meant to be obeyed by employers and enforced by HSE Inspectors (factories, building sites, shipyards etc) and Environmental Health Officers (offices, shops, hotels etc). Asbestos laws have been ignored in the past, fines are low (less than £300) and there are too few Inspectors, so don't just rely on the law. Make sure your workplace is organised with union-appointed and trained safety representatives who know how to protect you from asbestos dust.

HOW CAN I AVOID THE DANGERS OF ASBESTOS?

Take it up with your union safety representatives. They should:

a) Find out if you are using or are exposed to asbestos at work by asking the employer. Suspect materials already in buildings will have to be analysed under a microscope to see if they are asbestos. Several samples will need to be examined because the type of asbestos can vary between different locations. Employers and suppliers must tell you if new materials or products used at work contain asbestos. Safety representatives are entitled to see copies of the supplier's data sheets on all products used at work. This is often called 'Section 6 HSW Act' information.

b) Ask for the use of asbestos substitutes wherever possible. Some of these, (like glass fibre) are not safe, just less risky, so work practices should be arranged to prevent you from breathing the dust in. *There are now substitutes for practically every use of asbestos* but where no substitute is available, articles should be clearly marked, preferably by having a sign stamped into the item. Safety representatives should check with other employers and safety representatives, their unions, HSE, and suppliers for availability of substitutes. If asbestos is found in the building you will also want to know:

- what kind it is;
- what state it is in; and
- how likely it is to be damaged.

  This will help employers and safety representatives to determine priorities for removal or sealing of asbestos. It may not be possible to remove all asbestos immediately in which case any asbestos or products containing asbestos should be labelled. After labelling the safety representatives should ensure that no work takes place in these areas unless strict safety procedures are observed *eg* during maintenance.

c) Make sure that members are not expected to breathe in asbestos dust. For example, if they have to work on asbestos they should be trained in how to use the *approved* asbestos respirators, protective clothing and other precautions. Only certain respirators are approved by the HSE for protection against asbestos and simple guidance on the selection of appropriate respirators has been prepared by the HSE. Clothing contaminated with asbestos should never be taken home – your employer must have them specially laundered.

  If asbestos in buildings is sealed or removed, special licensed contractors must be used. They will seal off the working area with plastic tents and take other precautions to protect people in the building.

  The *Checklist* opposite summarises the precautions you need to insist on. Asbestos dust from brake linings must be removed with special vacuum cleaners – it should never be blown away with compressed air. Asbestos dust should never be swept up – industrial vacuum cleaners with special filters should be used. Small amounts of dust can be mopped up with a *damp* cloth which should then be disposed of in a sealed plastic bag before it dries out. More advice is available from your union, employer or HSE – see further reading list.

d) Make sure that asbestos is disposed of properly in labelled plastic bags on asbestos tips licensed by the local authority.

e) Seek help and advice from your union, HSE Inspector, or Environmental Health Officer – see 'Sources of advice and information'.

WHAT SHOULD I DO IF I HAVE ALREADY WORKED WITH ASBESTOS?

- Asbestos diseases usually take many years to appear, so medical checks straight after exposure are of little use. Medical checks will not cure asbestos diseases either – they just help to identify some of them earlier. However, some workers may benefit from stopping further work with asbestos if disease is detected, and some ill-health can be helped by early detection. Regular medical check-ups must include the right kind of X-Ray and lung tests. (See EMAS leaflet MA-4). You must tell your doctor how you have been exposed to asbestos dust, where and for how long. All asbestos removal workers must be given medical checks every two years.

- If you smoke, try and stop or cut down. Your risk of lung cancer begins to drop the day you stop smoking, and it can fall by two-thirds over several years.

- Make sure your employer, your doctor and the union have a record of your asbestos exposure, and if you get any of the asbestos diseases, seek compensation. If you have had slight or accidental exposure to asbestos dust, regular medical checks are unnecessary, but make sure your exposure is recorded by your employer, doctor and union.

HOW DO I CLAIM COMPENSATION FOR ASBESTOS DISEASES?

If you have been exposed to asbestos you can claim DHSS Disablement Benefit for some asbestos diseases *eg* asbestosis, mesothelioma, lung cancer, (where there is some other medical evidence of asbestos exposure – smoking is not relevant), and pleural thickening. Complete and send off form BI 100 (pn), available from the DHSS office or union. You can also sue your employers for compensation for any of the asbestos diseases and claim DHSS benefit. Contact your union for details. If your past employers have gone out of business you can claim compensation from the Department of Employment by completing form PWC 1 (S) Ref or PWC 1(D).

CHECKLIST ON CONTRACTORS: HOW SHOULD WORK BE DONE?

Removing or sealing asbestos in buildings is an expensive job, if done properly. Cowboy contractors will try and under-cut the responsible operators. Make sure that does not happen by using the checklist below to weed them out.

The contractor

1. Is the company licensed under the Asbestos Removal Licensing Regulations which came into force in 1984?
2. Is the company a member of the Asbestos Removal Contractors Association?
3. Are the workers unionised with at least one qualified Thermal Insulation Engineer?
4. Has the company supplied copies of its Safety Policy and Work Methods with the tender? Ask for these.
5. Is the company familiar with the HSE's Approved Code of Practice on Work with Asbestos Insulation and Sprayed Coatings?
6. Has the Company good references from previous asbestos removal work? Check with the previous clients and with any safety representatives who may be there.

The work method

7. Where does the company propose to locate its de-contamination unit (ie 'dirty' and 'clean' changing rooms and shower unit)?
8. Who will do the environmental monitoring for asbestos contamination and who will do the analysis (ie fibre-counting)?
9. What limit will be used to protect people in the building?
10. If the company uses hired vacuum equipment, how do they make sure that the equipment is free of asbestos when hired and returned?
11. Are there penalty clauses in the contract for breaches of safety procedures or failure to clean up satisfactorily?

Checking the work done

12. Is the work area cordoned off and, where necessary, signposted "Asbestos – Cancer Hazard – Keep Out"?
13. Is the work area sealed up with heavy duty polythene sheeting, sealed air-tight with tapes etc? Has it been tested for leaks with a smoke bomb?
14. Is there an air lock at the entrance/exit to the work area?
15. Are the polythene sheets billowing inwards, showing that the work area is under negative air pressure from the exhaust ventilation inside the plastic tent?
16. Do the workers wear transit overalls between the decontamination unit and the work area?
17. Are the workers wearing respirators or breathing apparatus approved for asbestos removal work by the HSE – see HSE Form F.2486 (1984) updated each year?
18. Are there monitoring instruments outside the work area checking on asbestos contamination – especially if normal work is continuing?

19. Are monitoring results given to the client's supervisors and safety representatives?
20. Is waste asbestos removed in double, heavy duty plastic sacks labelled "Asbestos – Cancer Hazard"; or better still by large-diameter vacuum pipes feeding directly into sealed waste hoppers outside the building?
21. How and where is the asbestos toxic waste to be disposed? Only licensed dumps should be used.
22. Are the surfaces which were covered in asbestos and sealed, rather than removed, conspicuously labelled "Asbestos – Cancer Hazard" so that future maintenance workers are warned?
23. Is there a system for checking the safety of all asbestos that is sealed or left in good condition?

SOURCES OF ADVICE AND INFORMATION

TUC Publications

- **TUC Handbook on Dust at Work.**
- **Asbestos in the Workplace:** TUC pamphlet.

Regulations and codes

- **The Control of Asbestos at Work Regulations 1987:** HMSO.

Approved Codes of Practice

- **Work with asbestos insulation and asbestos coating:** (revised February 1985); *approved code of practice and guidance note.*

HSE guidance

The Health and Safety Executive produces much helpful guidance on asbestos. This includes:

- EH 10 **Asbestos** – control limits and measurement of airborne dust concentrations; 1984.
- EH 35 **Probable asbestos dust concentrations at construction processes;** 1984.
- EH 36 **Work with asbestos cement,** 1984.
- EH 37 **Work with asbestos insulating board;** 1984.
- EH 41 **Respiratory protective equipment for use against asbestos;** 1985.
- EH 47 **Provision, use and maintenance of hygiene facilities for work with asbestos insulation and coatings;** 1986.
- MS 13 **Asbestos;** 1977.
- HS (R) 19 **Guide to the Asbestos (Licensing) Regulations 1983;** 1984.
- **Asbestos and You:** Short HSE leaflet containing the 'Asbestos Code'.

- **Working with Asbestos:** A guide for supervisors and safety representatives.

- **HSE Certificate of Approval** (Respiratory Protection Equipment Form 2486: updated each year.

- **Guidance on Respirators.**

- **EMAS leaflet MA-4.**

Industry/Sector Guidance

Garages

- IND (S) 13 **Asbestos alert for garage workers** (pocket card); 1985.

- IND (S) 14 (P) **Asbestos alert:** beware garage dust (poster); 1985.

Health Services Advisory Committee

- IAC/L5 **Asbestos hazard in health service buildings** (pocket card).

8: Noise

THE MOST WIDESPREAD HAZARD

Noise is probably the most widespread and underestimated of industrial hazards. Between 500,000 and 1 million workers in Britain may be exposed at work every day to noise levels of about 90dB(A) for periods up to and over eight hours. As many as 2 million workers may be exposed to noise levels about 84dB(A). All workers exposed to noise levels in this range run some risk of suffering permanent noise induced hearing loss. While some workers in especially noisy trades continue to suffer from serious occupational deafness, many more people at work suffer hearing loss in less acute form, which is none the less extremely distressing, both physically and socially.

TWO IMPORTANT ASPECTS

There are two aspects of noise which are especially important in understanding noise hazards. These are *frequency* (or 'pitch') and *intensity*.

Frequency

Frequency describes the rate of fluctuation of air particles produced by a noise source. This is measured in units of cycles per second called 'hertz' (Hz).

Frequency is what gives sound its quality (or 'pitch'). The range of sound audible to the human ear lies roughly between about 20 and 16,000Hz, although it varies considerably between individuals and is affected by natural processes such as ageing and/or disease and past exposure to noise.

Intensity

The intensity of sound provides a measure of the amount of energy that vibrating air particles deliver to the ears. The amount of sound energy encountered by the ear in the industrial environment can vary enormously. Painful sound is about 10 million-million times as intense as the quietest sound that can be heard. A scale based on this vast magnitude would be impossible to handle. To make it manageable therefore a special mathematical technique is employed to produce a scale for measuring sound intensity in units called decibels (dB). This is known as a logarithmic scale. The following table gives dB values and their corresponding intensities together with examples of common noises in each part of the dB range.

Intensity	dB	Example of noise source
1	0	threshold of hearing
10	10	quiet whisper, leaves rustling
100	20	very quiet room
1,000	30	subdued speech
10,000	40	quiet office
100,000	50	normal conversation at 3 feet
1,000,000	60	office
10,000,000	70	
100,000,000	80	traffic

Noise damage starts

Intensity	dB	Example of noise source
1,000,000,000	90	lathes; typical process plant
10,000,000,000	100	foundry; pneumatic drills
100,000,000,000	110	woodworking shop
1,000,000,000,000	120	boiler shop, diesel engine room
10,000,000,000,000	130	jet engine, riveting

From the above it can be seen that a small increase in the decibel scale corresponds to a large increase in intensity. This is very important in understanding the significance of noise measurements. If the sound level increases by 10dB then the sound intensity, that is the amount of sound energy being transmitted to the ear, increases tenfold. For example 80dB is ten times the intensity of 70dB and 70dB is ten times the intensity of 60dB. Thus 80dB is one hundred times the intensity of 60dB.

Similarly just as an increase of 10dB is an increase of ten times in intensity, an increase of 3dB corresponds to a doubling of intensity. Thus 83dB is not 'just over' 80dB, but is in fact twice as intense and is capable of producing correspondingly more damage to hearing. Achieving a reduction of 3dB in the noise emitted from a particular machine means a halving of sound energy and therefore a halving of the hazard to the ears.

Decibels (dB) therefore measure the intensity of noise, (or noise pressure) and Hertz (Hz) state its frequency. You could record a single note from a flute and play it back at 50dB, 60dB, or 80dB and so on, but its frequency would still be the same even though the sound was played back with increased intensity.

At their best, human ears can hear frequencies from about 20Hz (a very low hum or rumble) to 16,000Hz (a high pitched screech or whistle). Ordinary speech covers a range of frequencies from about 500Hz to 4,000Hz. Letters like 's', 't' and 'f' would be at the top end of this range, while letters like 'o' and 'a' would be nearer the bottom end. So when you take part in a conversation you are hearing sound made up of a mixture of frequencies. If your hearing is damaged through extensive exposure to noise at work, you probably will not hear the higher frequency vocal sounds around 4,000Hz. This is why speech becomes distorted as occupational deafness sets in.

When noise is measured at work, emphasis is normally given to the frequencies which have most effect on the human ear. This is done by adjusting the noise meter to take more notice of these frequencies. The scale used is called the 'A weighted decibel scale' or dB(A). Most noise meters and survey reports will be based on the dB(A) scale. This scale works on exactly the same rules as the ordinary dB scale.

Some noises are outside the frequency range of normal human hearing – a good example is a dog whistle. The two types of noise which can't be heard are:

- **Infrasound:** is sound which has a frequency below the ability of the human ear to pick up (below 20Hz). It can cause a wide range of symptoms including headaches, nausea, giddiness, and stomach disorders. Infrasound is common around heavy machinery and lorry cabs.

- **Ultrasound:** is sound which has a frequency above the human ability to hear (above 16,000Hz). It can cause similar symptoms to infrasound and may be produced by jet engines, dentists' drills and some electronic equipment.

WHAT IS HEARING?

To understand why exposure to hazardous noise levels can lead to deafness it is necessary to understand the nature of hearing. We hear sound because pressure vibrations in the air set the ear drum vibrating. Behind the ear drum are three tiny bones, the ossicles, which transmit vibrations from the ear drum to a flexible oval window which is situated at the end of a spiral, snail shaped organ called the cochlea, which is full of fluid. Within the cochlea the movements of the fluid are picked up by thousands of tiny hair cells which in turn transmit impulses along the auditory nerve to the brain and this creates the sensation we interpret as sound.

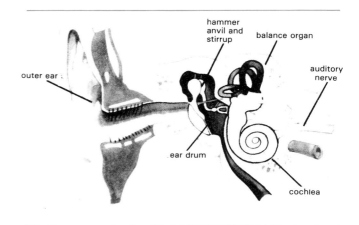

Although the ear is sensitive to an amazingly wide range of sound pressures, the tiny hair cells in the cochlea can only take so much energy. Under normal conditions they should last for a lifetime although of course they are subject to deterioration due to ageing. However, the structure of the ear evolved in a non industrial environment and so excessive exposure to dangerous levels of occupational noise wears out the tiny hair cells before their time.

TYPES OF HEARING LOSS

There are basically two kinds of hearing loss. The first is called conductive hearing loss and is associated with problems in the outer or middle ear. The earhole may be filled with wax, an infection in the middle ear might fill it with liquid and make it swell, or middle ear disease may have led to permanent damage. Alternatively, damage to the drum or the bones of the middle ear may have been caused by an explosion or a bang on the head.

The second kind of hearing loss is damage to the hair cells and nerves of the inner ear which convert vibrations, transmitted from the ear drum via the ossicles and turn them into nerve messages for the brain. This kind of hearing loss is referred to as sensorineural hearing loss. It can be caused by disease and infection but nearly all noise induced deafness is of this kind.

THE EFFECTS OF NOISE

The effect of occupational noise on the hearing of workers has been recognised from the very beginning of industrial development. In 1866, in Britain, occupational deafness amongst Glasgow boilermakers was studied by a Dr Barr. The Chief Inspector of Factories, quoting from Dr Barr's study, stated in 1908 *"it is generally known that men employed in certain trades are liable to have their sense of hearing seriously impaired, if not entirely destroyed in course of time, as a result of long continued exposure to loud noises"*.

NOISE AND TEMPORARY HEARING LOSS

For noise that is above 80dB(A) and is continuous, the sound energy transmitted to the hair cells of the inner ear is so great that they adapt by raising their threshold of response, *ie* they shift their field of sensitivity upwards and no longer respond to very soft sounds. This phenomenon is known as temporary threshold shift (TTS) and its extent depends on the intensity of noise, its duration, and to some extent on its frequency composition. Temporary hearing loss is most noticeable when starting on a noisy job.

People working in conditions noisy enough to induce temporary hearing loss can expect a permanent loss to the same degree after about ten years exposure to these conditions.

Recovery from temporary hearing loss usually takes a few hours or at most a couple of days if the noise exposure has been severe. On the other hand, where those exposed to noise are never away from work for more than two days temporary hearing loss, in effect, becomes permanent hearing loss.

PERMANENT HEARING LOSS: OCCUPATIONAL DEAFNESS

Loud continuous noise rarely hurts the ear drum of the little bones of the middle ear; what it damages are the sensitive hair cells in the inner ear. These cells are actually killed by continuous loud noise. This damage is irreversible and the cells cannot be replaced.

TINNITUS

Noise not only damages hearing sensitivity but can also give rise to tinnitus, a disturbing 'ringing in the ear'. This usually persists all the time and is especially worrisome at night when it can prevent sleep. Recent research explains tinnitus as the exaggerated reverberation of the hair cells' response to sound; it is actually the echo of our own hearing mechanism. In people with normal hearing it will get drowned out, but as deafness sets in the echo becomes tormenting.

RECRUITMENT

Furthermore, hearing loss caused by noise exposure is often accompanied by an accelerated growth of loudness, called recruitment. Noises get louder suddenly. The person with noise-damaged hearing has to ask people to speak up – then when they do, has to tell them not to shout. Recruitment also acts to distort common sounds.

The results of all these changes is that even a slight impairment of hearing may result in a significant and irreversible reduction in the quality of life. Hearing loss cuts its victim off from other people: social interaction becomes more and more of a strain; family life becomes difficult. It means having to turn up the television or having to drop out of a conversation in the pub. Hearing aids offer little help to the occupationally deaf. All these aids do is magnify sounds – they cannot redeem the distortion. If trying to follow a conversation or a speaker at a meeting, the hearing aid simply brings all the background sounds crashing in making discrimination even more difficult.

It is true that auditory rehabilitation is advancing, and that hearing aids are getting smaller and more sophisticated. But a course of rehabilitation is costly and available only to the few. It is not offered on the National Health Service.

The best cure for occupational deafness is prevention – the control of noise at source.

OTHER EFFECTS

Besides causing temporary or permanent hearing loss, noise can also be a safety hazard. Most obviously, noise interferes with verbal communication leading to errors and failures to respond to warning sounds and shouts. This is, of course, made worse where individuals have 'got used' to noise as a result of temporary or permanent hearing loss. Such deafness can not only affect workplace safety but may affect the safety of the individual outside the workplace.

High noise levels are also thought to act on the body as a stress producing agent. It is suggested that this occurs as a result of the triggering of bodily reactions which were laid down in evolution as 'fight or flight' responses. These stress mechanisms are thought to give rise to changes in body chemistry designed to prepare the body to deal with crisis situations. The evidence is very strong that over a long period of time, such stress can contribute to circulatory problems, digestive problems, psychological disturbances and symptoms such as nervousness or sleeplessness.

Besides being a safety hazard and increasing stress, high noise levels also affect work performance, particularly delicate tasks requiring concentration. This in turn can further contribute to stress and to errors which, in certain circumstances, may have safety implications.

MEASURING NOISE

Noise can be measured by a range of instruments. The chief instrument is the electronic sound meter, consisting of a microphone which translates fluctuations in sound into fluctuating electric current. This current is then amplified and rectified and fed into a voltmeter calibrated either in dB or dB(A). The current produced is thus used as a measurement of sound intensity and measurements are averaged over a standard time period – either one second or one-tenth of a second.

Noise level meters easily 'drift' and must be calibrated regularly. This is done using a pure tone emitted at a standard intensity by a small device attached to the meter. Failure to calibrate the instruments may lead to dangerously inaccurate measurements being taken. If safety representatives wish to take measurements themselves, they need to read the instructions carefully to ensure that they do not make mistakes, such as using the meter with flat batteries or recording not the external noise but the internal electrical noise of an overloaded instrument.

To examine the frequency characteristics of noise, octave band analysers can also be used. These consist of an ordinary sound meter fitted with a series of electronic filters so that readings can be obtained for sound levels at different frequencies. This information can either be plotted by hand, or be fed into a computer so that results can be displayed visually. These are portable instruments and provide instant and total analysis of every major noise and room acoustic characteristic, including broad band levels, octave bands, reverberation and vibration and results can be displayed visually.

CONTINUOUS EQUIVALENT SOUND LEVEL

Because sound levels tend to fluctuate over time, a

method has been devised to produce an average value by approximating the fluctuations according to their level of duration. These values are expressed as continuous equivalent sound levels and are usually represented in units of dB(A) Leq. Essentially, instruments capable of measuring Leq store the information they receive about sound levels and express values that correspond to the sound history they have measured over a given time period. An attractive feature of this is that it corresponds fairly closely to the total dose of energy which has been transmitted to the ear during any period. For this reason standards of exposure to noise are most usefully expressed in terms of Leq.

The HSE "Code of Practice for Reducing the Exposure of Employed Persons to Noise" contains a clear explanation of how to calculate the '8 hour Leq' for any particular pattern of noise exposure.

NOISE CONTROL AND STANDARDS

Despite the fact that the hazards of noise have been recognised for over 100 years, the developments of standards for protection of workers from occupational deafness has been slow.

In 1972 the report of the Robens Committee on Safety and Health at Work made a specific recommendation for legislation to control the amount of noise to which an employer can expose his employees. In the same year the Department of Employment published the "Code of Practice for Reducing the Exposure of Employed Persons to Noise". This Code, which was voluntary, recommended a standard of maximum exposure in the absence of hearing protection of 90dB(A) for an 8 hour day or 40 hour week.

The main provisions of the 1972 Code were:

- continuous exposure to a reasonably steady noise should not exceed 90dB(A) for eight hours in any one day (Para 4.3.1);

- if exposure is for a period other than eight hours, or if the sound level is fluctuating, the equivalent continuous sound level (Leq) should not exceed 90dB(A);

- in circumstances where it may be difficult to measure and control exposure to non-continuous sound, any exposure at a sound level of 90dB(A) or more should be regarded as exceeding the accepted limit and requiring the use of ear protectors; and

- noise should never exceed a maximum level of 135dB(A), 150 dB(A) for impulsive noise, in the absence of hearing protection.

Other old legal standards included of the "1974 Woodworking Machines Regulations". These said that exposure to more than an Leq of 90dB(A) should be prevented firstly by 'reasonably practicable' noise control and secondly by the provision of ear protectors.

New regulations

In 1981 the HSE issued a draft Protection of Hearing Regulations and a draft Code of Practice. Key features of these proposals were:

- noise exposure was to be reduced below 90dB(A) Leq;

- ear protectors were to be used only when other methods are not reasonably practicable; and

- employers had to prepare a detailed programme of action against noise where levels exceed 90dB(A) Leq.

EEC Directive on Protection of Workers from Noise

On December 5, 1985, the EEC agreed the contents of a proposed Directive on Protection of Workers from Noise.

In response, the HSC has published proposals for new regulations. These would require all employers to carry out a noise assessment where levels are likely to exceed 85dB(A), the provision of hearing protection for all workers exposed in the range 85-90dB(A) and noise reduction so far as is reasonably practicable where exposure exceeds 90dB(A).

TUC policy

The TUC wants to see:

- a legal limit of 85dB(A) to be achieved by noise control (not ear protection) wherever possible;

- a target of 80dB(A) for all new machinery and processes; and

- lower limits for specific kinds of work *eg* work requiring special concentration.

METHODS OF NOISE CONTROL

Noise control is essentially about getting rid of noise by preventing its emission in the first place, or reducing the damaging effects of what remains.

Successful noise control is impossible without a noise survey which measures and identifies the sources of the noise by measuring both sound pressure (in decibels) and its frequencies (in Hertz).

Once the noise problem is identified, action is needed to get rid of it, but this may be difficult either because those at risk do not recognise the problem or employers and management think that noise control is either impossible or too costly.

Some typical arguments that might be encountered are shown overleaf.

THE FOUR STEPS TO NOISE CONTROL

Figure 8.1 summarises what can be done. It is usually more satisfactory to try step one first, then two, three and four, but the final solution to any noise problem may be a mixture of all four.

The four steps to noise control.

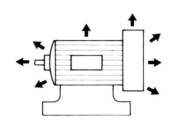

Step 1: *Re-design noise source or use other process.*

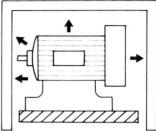

Step 2: *Maintain and modify existing source.*

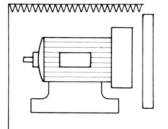

Step 3: *Block the noise transmission path.*

Step 4: *Enclose the workers. Reduce noise dose. Limit numbers of workers exposed.*

The HSE produce a very useful publication "100 Practical Applications of Noise Reduction Methods". This, along with the TUC's handbook *Noise at Work*, provides guidance on noise control methods. *If you have got noise problems you will need access to these two documents.*

PERSONAL PROTECTION

Although the main aim of any noise control programme must be the control of workplace noise levels, the use of personal hearing protection may nevertheless be necessary either as a temporary measure or as a last resort. Where personal hearing protection is used it is important to understand some of the problems and pitfalls that may be encountered with this sort of equipment. This chapter describes some features of the design and use of hearing protectors. It also deals with the subject of audiometry or measurement of hearing loss.

"I'm already deaf so you can't help me"

Not true. Noise affects other parts of the body and increases the risk of accidents. If deaf workers have not yet got "ringing in the ears" (tinnitus), then more exposure to noise could bring it on, if partially deaf workers have got little hearing left then it's all the more precious and worth preserving. Also what about making the job safe for someone else? Finally, just as trade unionists do not allow some workers to accept lower wages than the rest, neither is it acceptable for some workers to accept worse conditions than others. The noise from the machine operated by deaf workers may still harm the hearing of their colleagues.

"I've worked here for years and I'm not deaf"

Firstly, *this may not be true.* It's hard for people to know when they are going deaf because it happens so slowly and they adjust to it by learning to lip read and by turning the TV up etc. And if it is true, which it will be for some people, then that's because not all people are the same biologically. For example if a group of people are exposed to the same amount of asbestos they will not all suffer from asbestosis, lung cancer and mesothelima. The same principle applies to exposure to most toxic substances or harmful agents, including noise. Only some of those exposed will suffer at high noise levels commonly encountered in industry. But equally it is impossible to say who will be the victims. A certain number of people may have been lucky, but not all will escape the effects of noise. At 110dB(A) it is known that 10 per cent will go 70 per cent deaf after 10 years working and a much larger proportion will suffer from the other effects of noise.

"We already get ear muffs! The problem is that some of us don't wear them"

Ear muffs or plugs do not solve noise problems. They just mean that workers have to adapt to the hazard by wearing uncomfortable protective equipment which can also increase the risk of ear infections and also of accidents from loss of balance and of communication. Even if they are worn for most of the time they do not offer complete protection from risk of hearing loss because:

- they are not always designed to keep out the noise frequencies to which workers are exposed;

- they are not properly maintained; or

- it is impossible to wear them for 99.99 per cent of an eight hour shift.

At noise levels of 110dB(A) the ears only have to be left unprotected for more than five minutes a day to receive enough noise to break the limit in the 1977 Code. Over a longer period of time muffs can be very costly and they do not do anything to reduce noise outside the factory. Both the 1972 Code and

the approach advocated by the TUC, emphasise that a noise reduction programme must be introduced first, with ear defenders being introduced as a temporary measure whilst the programme is completed.

"You can't stop the noise from our machines – they'll always be noisy"

Not true. There have been techniques available for several years that can reduce noise levels from all kinds of noise sources to below 80 or 85dB(A).

The figure on page 75 summarises the four main steps to noise control. The rest of this chapter provides more detailed examples of how these steps have been applied in practice, so that even those who are doubtful about noise control can see that noise is not inevitable.

"It's too expensive to remove the noise – ear muffs are cheaper"

This is usually the last resort of those who are doubtful about noise control, but have they considered the following points?

- Noise control can bring some bonus savings from the better control of temperature, dust and fumes achieved with enclosures.

- Acoustical treatment can also save a great deal of expensive heat, and part of the noise control scheme may be eligible for energy grants.

- Productivity and industrial relations have been shown to improve dramatically in quieter surroundings, *eg* the error rate in one factory fell to one tenth of its previous level.

- Treatment for headaches and sickness absence have also declined following noise control.

- New, or improved machines or factory layout also lead to improved productivity which is independent of the workers personal efforts.

- Improving maintenance schedules is usually cost effective through reduced down-time etc.

- Many machines will be due for replacement anyway and will have already paid for themselves.

- Noise control is usually a one-off item of capital expenditure that can be depreciated over seven to ten years. A successful ear muff programme is a very labour intensive item of current expenditure that occurs and increases every year, making it more expensive in all but the short term.

- Noise control can be very cheap in many cases *eg* acoustical treatment of lorry cabs is possible for less than £100, and there are new quieter pneumatic drills which cost £60 less than the noisy models.

Personal protectors

There are basically four types of personal ear protector:

- disposable ear plugs;
- reusable ear plugs;
- canal caps supported by head band; and
- ear muffs.

All these forms of personal protection present problems:

- The hazard still exists, and so the working environment is unsafe. What if the protectors are lost, or broken?

- At high noise levels, removing the protectors for a short period of time can lead to the noise limit for the day being exceeded. In a jet engine room at 117dB(A), taking the protectors off for just one minute would give a dose equivalent to the recommended level of 90dB(A) for 8 hours.

- Ear protectors can interfere with verbal communication and can thus represent the same sort of accident hazard that noise itself does.

- Ear protectors are a device by which management shifts responsibility for safe working onto employees.

- In addition to masking speech, ear protection can also muffle other warning sounds and disguise their source. In some industries this can easily be fatal.

If ear muffs are to be used as a temporary measure then steps must be taken to identify and clearly indicate the 'danger' areas where they should be worn. This must be the first step in a programme to eliminate noisy areas. A hearing 'conservation' programme which places overall emphasis on disciplining the workforce to wear hearing protectors, rather than eliminating or controlling noise at source is probably badly planned and inefficient. In some cases it has been agreed between unions and employers that the wearing of hearing protection is a necessary condition of the job, then theoretically there is a duty under Section 7 and 8 of the Health and Safety at Work Act for employees to use this equipment. However because of the potential implications for collective bargaining and civil liability, care should be taken to ensure that making hearing protectors a condition of employment is just one part of an overall programme.

MEASURING HEARING LOSS: AUDIOMETRY

One aspect of noise control is the identification of those whose hearing has been adversely affected by exposure to noise. This may be done to establish, for compensation purposes, the degree of hearing loss experienced by individuals exposed to noise. It may be done to check on the effectiveness of preventive measures such as use of personal hearing protection. It may even be used by employers to screen out 'vulnerable' workers and move them on to non noisy jobs. In itself it is not a preventive strategy and is only relevant if accompanied by appropriate action to reduce noise levels or noise exposure.

Assessment of hearing capability is carried out by a technique called audiometry. This is the use of certain instruments and methods to determine the capacity of the ear to detect sounds of varying amplitude over a range of frequencies. It can be used to measure hearing capability or if used periodically it can be used to detect deterioration of hearing in the individual caused by either the natural processes of diseases or ageing and/or exposure to harmful environmental noise levels – notably occupational. Audiometry is most commonly used in industry to detect deafness during pre-employment medical examinations or to reveal loss of hearing capacity amongst those exposed to hazardous levels of noise. It involves asking the subject to listen to a range of pulsed pure tones over a chosen range of frequencies and recording hearing response on a chart called an audiogram. Assessment of the audiogram then enables conclusions to be drawn about the subject's hearing status.

Employers sometimes claim that they can use hearing tests to identify workers who are *sensitive* to noise damage. This claim should be rejected. All that audiometry reveals is how much your hearing has been damaged already, *not* how sensitive you are to damage.

Other problems with audiometry include the following:

- it concentrates on the individual worker not on the noisy workplace;

- it costs money which might better be spent on noise measurement and control; and

- it is used by some employers as part of a strategy to avoid damages claims.

However, if unions get access to the results, and if the tests are properly conducted by trained personnel, audiometry can be used to:

- raise awareness of the need for noise control;

- identify workers who could claim damages; and

- provide evidence for the need for better standards and for inclusion of more occupations in the DHSS Disablement Benefit scheme.

ACTION CHECKLIST

Step 1

Find out about noise. Make sure that you and other safety representatives have completed a TUC ten day safety reps' course. Buy (or persuade your employer or union branch to buy) a copy of the TUC handbook *Noise At Work* (£1.50 from Publications Department, TUC, Congress House, Great

Russell Street, London WC1 3LS). Read it carefully and discuss it with other safety reps.

Step 2

Prepare the union organisation at work. Make noise a regular item at safety reps meetings. Have you discussed noise with the stewards' committee or branch? Remember that, first of all, they are the ones who must be convinced about the need for action on noise.

Step 3

Devise a noise control strategy for your workplace. Work your way through the following action steps.

1. Identify your noise problem by doing your own survey of workers affected. Circulate a questionnaire.

2. If this reveals signs of deafness, persuade members to have their hearing tested at the local hospital.

3. Ask your employer or local HSE inspector, to carry out a noise survey of all suspect areas. Make sure noise intensity (dB(A)) and frequency (Hz) are both measured. This is important for noise control and selection of the right type of ear muffs if noise control is not possible.

4. Seek an agreement from your employer on a noise control level – the TUC recommends 85dB(A) for 8 hours. Also get agreement on a maximum noise level for new plant and machinery.

5. Get your employer to agree to a planned noise reduction programme. Agree priorities for action with your members once you have studied the noise survey. Remember to think about the noise level, the numbers exposed and the ease or difficulty of noise reduction to help you work out what you're going to tackle first.

6. Make sure your employer gets expert advice on noise control from HSE or reputable consultants. Make sure consultants consult with safety representatives. Most noise can be reduced through redesign, modification, maintenance or enclosure.

7. Get your employer to provide full information on the noise levels of all new plant and machinery.

8. Where ear muffs are necessary, get agreement on:

    - the marking of all hearing protection areas;

    - arrangements for selection and fitting of ear muffs, including provision of a trial range of equipment and consultation with safety representatives;

    - arrangements for inspection, maintenance, cleaning, storage and replacement of ear muffs;

    - information and training for workers on noise hazards; and

    - a target date for phasing out ear muffs where possible.

9. Make sure a senior member of management is made responsible for the noise reduction programme. Make sure it is monitored by the safety committee. Arrange regular resurveying of noisy areas to check on control measures.

10. If audiometry (measuring hearing loss) is suggested, look carefully at what is being proposed. Audiometry doesn't stop you going deaf – it merely indicates how deaf you've become. It may prejudice future civil claims for compensation or lead to job discrimination against workers with existing hearing loss.

11. Keep members up-to-date about progress with bulletins and meetings.

12. Make sure deafened members claim compensation from both the DHSS if they are in certain occupations (Occupational Deafness is a Prescribed Disease – see DHSS leaflet NI 207) and from their employer if their work, of whatever type, has caused their hearing loss as a result of the employer failing to take proper protective measures. Seek legal assistance from your union. Some recent settlements have been as high as £7,000.

FURTHER INFORMATION ON NOISE

TUC Publications

- **Noise – Get the level Down!** Poster
- **Say "No" to Noise:** a handy brief for on-the-spot reference in the workplace.
- **Noise at Work:** the booklet sets out a basic noise strategy including controlling noise at source.

HSE publications

Posters and leaflets

- **100 Practical applications of noise reduction methods**
- **Beware of noise**: pocket card – foundries; IAC L2
- **Beware of noise:** pocket card – cotton and allied textiles; IAC L9
- **It's your hearing: protect it!:** noise alert for construction workers; IAC L17
- **Noise from portable breakers** (construction); IAC L21

Guidance Notes

- **Chain saws;** GN: PM31.
- **Noise from pneumatic systems;** GN: PM56.

Code of Practice

- **Code of Practice for reducing the exposure of employed persons to noise;** (ACOP).
- 100 practical applications of noise reduction methods; booklet.

IAC Guidance

- **Noise in Construction:** *guidance on noise control and hearing conservation measures;* Construction Industry Advisory Committee, 1986.

9: Ionising radiations

Ionising radiations occur in nature and can be produced artificially but they cannot be detected by the human senses. There is considerable public concern about radiation. Yet ionising radiations of natural origin pervade the environment – and all people experience a certain amount of radiation exposure both from external natural sources such as cosmic radiation and internally as a result of inhalation and ingestion of naturally occurring radioactivity. Artificial radioactivity has been used for several decades in fields such as medicine and other sciences and in industry. It also arises in large quantities in nuclear reactors used to generate electricity and in nuclear weapons fallout.

Radiation is inherently harmful to living tissue and thus to human beings and people must be protected from excessive or unnecessary exposure to it. On average our greatest exposure is to radiation of natural origin and in most cases little can be done (or needs to be done) about this, although in some cases, exposure to natural sources such as radon gas in houses or underground mines can be relatively high. It is possible however to control exposure to radiation of artificial origin and the law requires that doses of radiation to workers and the public be minimised in a rational way and that certain limits should be observed.

Although the whole subject of radiation risk appears technically complex, it can nevertheless be considered in much the same way as risks presented by other harmful factors connected with work activity; for example, toxic substances or physical or microbiological hazards. When viewed in this way it is possible to identify a broad range of key questions such as: What harm can radiation cause? What doses do workers actually receive? What risks do they run? How much dose is too much? How can it be decided if doses have been reduced to the lowest practical level? What about protection of the public? And, most important of all, who is responsible for making decisions about these kind of issues?

WHAT ARE IONISING RADIATIONS?

The term 'radiation' embraces electromagnetic waves such as light, radio waves and X-rays, and the particles emitted by radioactive materials as they disintegrate or decay to reach a stable state. These particles and the more energetic of electromagnetic waves produce electrically charged particles – called 'ions' – in the materials which they strike. This process of ionisation can cause changes in cells of living tissue, which, if severe enough and not counteracted by the body's defence mechanisms, can lead to ill health effects such as mutations or cancer. Radiations, such as those produced by ultra-violet lamps, lasers and radio transmitters though hazardous, do not have sufficient energy to cause ionisation, and are only hazardous under certain circumstances.

The ionising radiations most commonly encountered are:

- **Alpha (α) particles** (the nuclei of atoms of the element helium): these are easily stopped and do not penetrate the skin. Radioactive materials that emit alpha particles can only be hazardous if swallowed or breathed into the body, or if they enter the body through a wound. Once in the body however, such materials can increase the radiation dose of tissues in which they are absorbed.

- **Beta (β) particles (electrons):** these have greater penetrating power than alpha particles but are generally stopped by relatively thin layers of glass or metal. Beta emitters can also be hazardous if taken into the body.

- **Gamma (γ) radiation and X-rays,** (electromagnetic radiations similar to light and radio waves but with higher energy): these can penetrate relatively great thicknesses of matter before they are absorbed but can be screened by sufficient thickness of lead, concrete or water. They can be produced by decay of certain radioactive materials or by X-ray equipment.

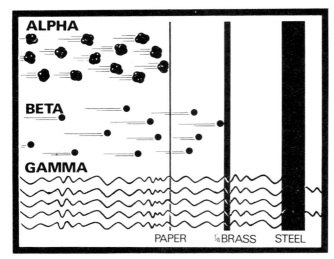

The diagram shows the relative penetrating power of alpha, beta and gamma radiations. (Source: *UKAEA*)

HALF-LIFE

An important feature of all radioactive materials is that their activity decays with time. Each material is characterised by what is called a 'half-life', that is the time taken for half the radioactivity to decay. In two half-lives the radioactivity is reduced to a quarter of its original level, and in ten half-lives to about one thousandth. Half-lives of various radioactive materials vary from fractions of a second to millions of years.

In general the most radioactive materials, emitting intense penetrating radiation and requiring heavy shielding, decay to negligible levels relatively rapidly. Long-lived materials tend to emit very little radiation energy – (generally in the form of radiations with low penetrating power) but such materials are hazardous if taken into the body – for example by eating contaminated food or water or breathing contaminated air.

RADIATION DOSE

Absorbed doses of radiation are expressed in terms of a unit called the gray (Gy)*, which is a measure of the amount of energy absorbed in any sort of matter. From a biological point of view, not only is the amount of radiation important, but also its type: equal absorbed doses of different types of radiation do not necessarily have equal biological effects because of the way they yield up their energy as they pass through tissue. In radiation protection work, a second unit, which takes these differing effects into account is used. This is the sievert (Sv)*.

*The gray replaces the unit used formerly, the rad, which was 100 times smaller. The sievert replaces the rem, which was also 100 times smaller.

One sievert of alpha radiation delivered, for example, to the thyroid is reckoned to create the same risk of inducing a cancer as one sievert of beta or gamma radiation. However some tissues are more sensitive to radiation damage than others so the magnitude of the risk is different for different organs within the body.

The overall risk of exposing the whole body to radiation is assessed by adding together the individual risks of harm to each organ which is affected. If the dose received by each organ is multiplied by an appropriate weighting factor to take account of its sensitivity to radiation, the sum of the products is a quantity called the effective dose equivalent – commonly abbreviated to 'dose'. This is also measured in sieverts. The sievert is a very large unit, and dose equivalents are more commonly expressed in terms of submultiples of the sievert:

- the microsievert (μSv) which is one-millionth of of a sievert; and

- the millisievert mSv/which is one-thousandth of a sievert.

Doses of tens of sieverts to small regions of the body are used in radiotherapy to destroy cancerous growths. At the other extreme, a typical chest X-ray gives about one-fiftieth of a millisievert.

1 millisievert (1 mSv) is roughly:

- about twice the annual dose to the most exposed members of the public from discharges by the nuclear industry;

- half the average annual dose from natural radiation in the UK;

- 50 times the dose received during a single chest X-ray.

1 microsievert (1 μSv) is roughly:

- one-twentieth of the average dose from a single chest X-ray;

- one-tenth of the annual dose from radioactive fallout in the UK in the 1980's;

- two-thirds of the average dose to the UK population due to discharges from existing nuclear installations.

TYPICAL DOSES TO WORKERS

Typical doses to workers

About 300,000 workers in the UK are routinely exposed to radiation in the course of their work. These include workers in science, industry and medicine as well as workers in the nuclear industry and workers exposed to enhanced levels of natural radiation such as tin miners. By law, employers have a duty to ensure that doses to workers are "*as low as reasonably achievable"* (ALARA). Where doses exceed 15 mSv in any year, the employer has to carry out a formal investigation to see whether all reasonably practicable measures are being taken. In addition, the maximum dose that any worker may receive is limited to 50 millisieverts (mSv) per year.

In the TUC's opinion this limit is far too high – but few workers ever receive doses close to this limit and the majority only receive a relatively small fraction of it. The average dose to medical workers for instance is about 0.7 mSv in a year and to workers in the nuclear industry about 2.2 mSv and to industrial radiographers about 1.2 mSv. In recent years the general trend in these averages has been downwards. Nevertheless in the light of new information about radiation risks, the National Radiological Protection Board (NRPB) has recently recommended a new maximum average dose target of 15 mSv per annum.

Figure 9.1: Average annual radiation exposure of people at work in the UK.

	millisieverts (mSv)
non-coal miners (*eg* tin miners)	8.9
Amersham International (Radioisotopes)	3.8
Tritium workers	3.4
MoD workers	2.4
Nuclear industry workers	2.2
Aircraft crew	1.6
Industrial radiographers	1.2
Coal miners	1.2
Medical workers	0.7
Other industrial workers	0.3
Research workers in Universities and Polytechnics	0.1
Dental workers	0.1

SOURCE: NRPB, based on NRPB survey of occupational radiation exposure 1984-85.

Doses from natural background and other sources

To put occupational radiation exposure into perspective, it needs to be remembered that the average dose from the natural background sources in the UK, (including cosmic radiation and radiation from naturally occurring radioactive materials swallowed or breathed into the body), is about two millisieverts (one five-hundredth of a sievert) per year. In some areas of the UK, where the rocks and soil contain higher than average concentrations of radioactive minerals, background levels are up to three or more times the average value, and in some houses, where the concentration of the naturally occurring radioactive gas radon is particularly high, doses can be up to fifty times the average value. It is important, therefore, that additional occupational exposures are minimised.

Medical practices, mostly diagnostic X-rays, contribute a dose of about a quarter of a millisievert per year to the average UK citizen. The activities of the nuclear power industry in the UK result in an average dose to members of the public of two microsieverts per year, (*ie* about 0.002 μSv). Debris from atmospheric testing of nuclear weapons during the 1950s and 1960s currently contributes an average of about ten microsieverts per year and a similar dose results from air travel and miscellaneous sources of radiation such as luminous watches and TV sets. The average dose in the UK from contamination from the Chernobyl disaster was equivalent to just over 3 per cent of the total average dose from all sources for the year May 1986 to April 1987. It will be a markedly declining proportion in subsequent years.

The collective dose* to the whole UK population from these kinds of artificial sources of radiation (other than exposure as patients) is considered by the NRPB to be about 1700 man Sv per year. On the basis of present risk estimates (see page 83), this is taken to imply a possible total of 20 deaths a year from cancer and a similar number of serious hereditary defects in all subsequent generations. But this has to be compared with the risks associated with the collective dose from natural background radiation in a year and the implied number of deaths which is about 60 times greater.

RADIATION EFFECTS

If the whole body is exposed to very high doses of radiation, damage to tissue is so great that the body is unable to recover and death is almost certain. Instantaneous absorbed doses of 10Sv or more lead to severe radiation sickness and are almost invariably lethal. If such doses are limited to specific parts of the body, there is a possibility of recovery. Exposure however of the testes to this kind of dose is likely to lead to sterility or possibly gross hereditary damage to the individual's descendants.

Below the relatively high dose levels which can cause this kind of acute radiation damage, radiation exposure produces no readily visible symptoms, but it raises the chances of those exposed developing certain kinds of ill effects such as cancer which may not appear until sometime later. This is because, when radiation energy is absorbed in living tissue, it can cause very small changes in the genetic material (DNA) which carries the coded information necessary for the successful functioning of the cells, of which every part of the body is composed. Many such changes occur during the life of effects such as:

- abnormalities or disease in children born of mothers exposed to radiation during pregnancy;

- cancer of various kinds; or

---

*eg if a population of one thousand people each receive a dose of one millisievert, the collective dose to that population is 1 man sievert (1000 people × .001 Sv = 1 man sievert).

Figure 9.2: Radiation exposure of the UK population: contributions to the average annual dose.

The overall effective dose equivalent from radiation of natural and artificial origin is about 2150 μSv a year, on average, for members of the population of the United Kingdom. The percentage contribution of each source to the overall value is shown here. Natural radiation contributes almost 90 % and dominates all other sources. Doses from it vary considerably, but neither this nor its size justifies additional doses from the other sources. A central tenet of radiological protection is that every source must be considered on its merits.
Source: NRPB.

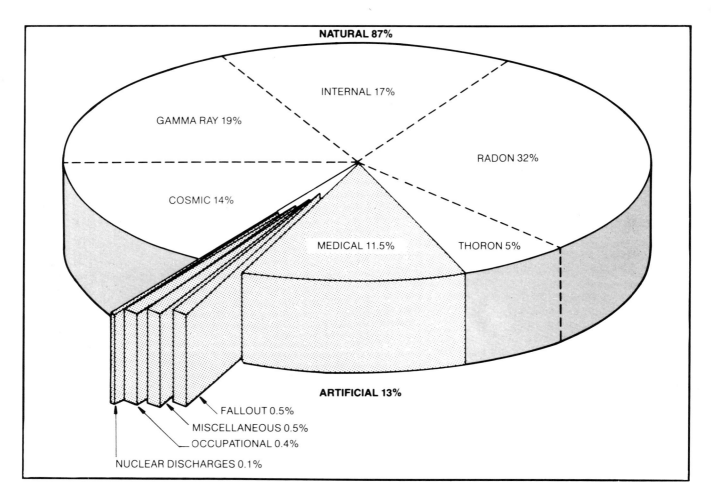

possibly hereditary defects in later generations as a result of eggs or sperm being damaged in potential parents.

Thus radiation can affect both the individual receiving the dose (somatic effects) and subsequent generations (hereditary effects).

RISK FACTORS

The precise mechanisms by which cancer is induced by exposure to radiation are not fully understood. However, an excess incidence of cancers has been observed in groups of people who have been exposed to high doses of radiation in the past. Not all people exposed to radiation contract cancer and not all

cancers arise as a result of irradiation since malignant diseases are very common and can have many causes (about one-in-four people die of cancer). But what is known is that every person exposed to doses of radiation has an increased probability of contracting cancer and that this probability depends largely on the quantity of dose received.

By studying the excess incidence of cancers in exposed groups of individuals, and comparing this with the incidence of cancers in similar non irradiated groups, it is possible to calculate the risk of cancer per unit of dose absorbed. This is called a risk factor. It usually relates only to cancers that are fatal because this is easier to calculate and to compare with other fatal risks in life. (It is thought however, that the risk of inducing non fatal cancer from a given exposure is about three times that of a fatal cancer). Besides helping to judge the effectiveness of standards of protection for radiation workers, risk estimates are also important in deciding how many excess cancers might be expected from an accidental release of radioactivity and in setting emergency action levels and maximum tolerable levels of radioactive contamination in the environment or in foodstuffs.

Research shows that cells which are rapidly dividing (like stem cells in the red bone marrow or cells in the developing foetus) are more vulnerable to radiation damage. This is because the chances of disruption are greater when they are preparing for division than when they are in a more stable state. This shows up in the difference between the chances of a given radiation dose producing each of the three different kinds of effect above. The chance of foetal damage is highest and that is why pregnant women have to be protected from radiation sources. The next highest risk is that of people exposed to radiation developing cancer. The lowest risk is thought to be that of genetic defects, although this effect has only been observed in animal experiments and no evidence has actually been seen in humans. In very rough terms, the maximum risk to the foetus (at a particularly sensitive stage of its development) is thought to be about 50 times the genetic risk. A range of values for risk factors for fatal radiation induced cancer have been suggested by various international scientific bodies as follows:

Reviewing body	Cancer deaths
	(per 10,000 persons per sievert)
BEIR (1972)	115-621
UNSCEAR (1977)	75-175
ICRP 26 (1977)	125
BEIR III (1980)	158-501

These risk factor calculations are based on studies of populations such as the survivors of the atomic bombings in Japan, patients who have been exposed to radiation for therapeutic or for diagnostic purposes, people exposed to intense weapons fallout, uranium miners, and workers in the radium luminizing industry. Information from such sources is reviewed regularly by the United Nations Scientific Committee on the Effects of Atomic Radiation (UNSCEAR). In its 1977 Report UNSCEAR estimated that the risk factor for radiation induced leukaemia to be about 1 in 500 per sievert. This means that if a person receives a dose equivalent to 1 sievert to the red bone marrow, there is a 1 in 500 chance that they will die of leukaemia as a result (but death would not occur for about a decade after the dose was received).

Recent re-evaluation of some of the above data however indicates that risk estimates for fatal radiation induced cancer may have to be revised upwards by a factor of 2 to 3.

RISKS AT LOW DOSES

Traditionally it has been assumed that the risk of health damage decreases in proportion to decreasing dose (half the dose, half the risk). Studies however, have only been carried out on persons exposed to relatively high doses delivered in short periods. This is not the normal pattern since most people are usually exposed to relatively low doses delivered over long periods. For beta and gamma radiation, some experts suggest that risk factors at lower doses may be over-estimated.

On the other hand, other researchers contend that, overall, the true risk at low doses is disproportionately higher than is predicted by the linear model. The majority of radiation biologists believe that the linear model should be used, agreeing that at present there is no evidence to assume that there is any threshold below which neither cancer nor hereditary defects can be caused by radiation. *Every exposure is therefore presumed to produce some additional risk, however small.*

It is this assumption of a linear dose response relationship (independent of dose rate and with no threshold) that underpins the approach to protecting people from radiation advocated by the International Commission on Radiological Protection (ICRP). It is also used to calculate the likelihood of cancers and hereditary defects in populations as well as individuals. It makes no difference in communal terms whether in a community of 40,000 each receives an effective dose equivalent of 2 mSv or in a community of 20,000 people each receives 4 mSv, the collective dose in each community is 80 man Sv and in each case (on current ICRP risk estimates) there is likely to be one cancer death.

LONG-TERM MONITORING

In order to continue to study and refine concepts about risk estimates, the National Radiological Protection Board (NRPB) has established a National Registry for Radiation Workers so that the causes of death and the incidence of malignant diseases among people who are occupationally exposed to radiation under supervised conditions, can be assessed statistically over time. This will enable any differences between the incidence of cancer amongst radiation workers and other groups to be identified and thus will provide a check on present risk factors. A difficulty in this approach is that because about 25 per cent of deaths in the United Kingdom are due to cancer and cancers induced by radiation are indistinguishable from those that have other causes, any small excesses of cancer that arise as a result of radiation will be hard to detect. In addition, in employed populations, where the overall level of health of workers tends to be above average, it is difficult to make accurate comparisons of disease and death rates with similar data for the population as a whole where the general health profile is poorer.

RADIOLOGICAL PROTECTION PRINCIPLES

The measures used to control radiation and minimise associated risks are elaborate and extensive and are based on recommendations of the ICRP. Although the TUC has been critical of the role of the ICRP (because it is largely self selecting and contains no trade union representatives), its recommendations form the basis for legislation and practice in most countries. They include three general principles as follows:

a) every practice resulting in an exposure to ionising radiation shall be justified by the benefit it produces;
b) all exposures shall be kept as low as reasonably achievable; and
c) doses shall not exceed certain limits.

Applying these principles in practice means using engineering controls and design features (such as shielding, containment, distance from radiation sources, warning lights etc) and working procedures to reduce exposure of workers and the public.

ICRP recommends that those whose occupations expose them to radiation such as X-ray technicians and nuclear industry workers, should not receive a dose greater than 50 mSv per year. For the public the individual dose should not exceed 1 mSv per year although 5 mSv may be reached in some years provided that the lifetime average does not exceed 1 mSv per year. NRPB have recently advised that in future, radiological activities should aim to control possible exposure of workers to less than 15 mSv per annum (averaged over a lifetime) and exposure of the public to below a level of 0.5 mSv per annum from a single installation.

Mere adherence to these limits however is not considered adequate. Because of the possibility of harm resulting even from the very lowest doses of radiation, the ICRP have placed particular emphasis of the idea of keeping doses 'as low as reasonably achievable' (ALARA). This is because given that no radiation dose is entirely free from risk, doses should be reduced whenever and wherever that can be done by reasonable means. Eventually however, a point is reached where further reductions become unreasonable in terms of social and economic costs.

The result of the ALARA principle over the last two decades has been that the average annual dose to radiation workers is now less than one tenth of the limit of 50 mSv. As an aid to help decide when doses are ALARA, cost benefit techniques have been developed to calculate the point at which extra resources to bring about any further reduction in doses balance the social value of that reduction.

These techniques however, do not replace the day to day use of professional judgement and common sense in implementing control measures.

The result of this approach in the United Kingdom is that, on present ICRP risk estimates, the average risk of a radiation worker contracting a fatal cancer over a working lifetime is currently thought to be about one in a thousand (lifetime dose 100 mSv). This is roughly one third of the lifetime risk of fatal accidents faced by workers in hazardous industries such as construction but roughly equivalent to the risk of fatality faced by workers in industries such as food, drink and tobacco and textiles.

On the other hand, a three times revision in ICRP risk estimates, as advised by NRPB, would imply an average lifetime risk of fatal disease of about 1 in 300 and this would put such workers near the top of the occupational risk league. (It needs to be noted however that occupational accident and radiation disease risks are not strictly comparable since the former are constant and cease on retirement while the latter are cumulative and persist when exposure ceases. On the other hand, occupational risks in most industries are an average figure for the whole workforce, many of whom may not be exposed to the risk (*eg* office workers), whereas occupational radiation risks are calculated for radiation workers only).

LEGISLATION

The three key ICRP principles above, which have been reinforced by obligations arising from Britain's membership of the European Community, have been embodied in Acts of Parliament and subsidiary instruments. Responsibility for radiological protection at places of work falls to the Health and Safety Commission (HSC) supported by the Health and Safety Executive (HSE) and its Inspectorates.

In January 1986 the Ionising Radiations Regulations, 1985 came into effect replacing earlier radiological protection legislation. These regulations have wide application throughout industry, transport and public services and also universities, colleges, hospitals and research institutes – in fact any work activity in which ionising radiations or radioactive substances are usually encountered.

The Regulations are enforceable by the HSE and are supported by an Approved Code of Practice which indicates the preferred ways of implementing the various requirements of the regulations. They are quite lengthy and cover issues such as dose limitation (ALARA), dose limits, designation of controlled and supervised areas, designation of classified persons, requirements for dose monitoring and assessment, arrangements for the control of radioactive substances, and monitoring of ionising radiation. They also require the carrying out of hazard assessments and the investigation and notification of over-exposure. Other sections place duties on manufacturers of articles for use on work with ionising radiation and equipment used for medical exposure.

The Regulations require radiation protection advisers (RPAs) to be appointed whenever expert advice is needed and their appointment has to be notified to the HSE. They also require the appointment of appropriate radiation protection supervisors and the formulation and enforcement of effective local rules. The employer has to make an assessment of possible hazards before commencing work and to prepare contingency plans to deal with foreseeable emergencies that might arise. This is closely linked with the requirement in the Regulations to identify working areas, which from the point of view of either radiation dose rate or potential levels of contamination, have to be designated as controlled areas or supervised areas.

Under the Safety Representatives and Safety Committees Regulations, trade union safety representatives also have extensive involvement, for example in consultations about radiological protection regimes and in reviewing doses, investigating incidents and recommending further improvements.

Practical guidance on complying with the regulations is contained in the Approved Code of Practice, and Guidance Notes which have been developed by (or in conjunction with) HSE covering areas such as X-ray optics, use of radiation in site radiography, medical, dental and veterinary practice and offshore activities. Additional training on radiation and the application of the Ionising Radiations Regulations, Codes and Guidance should be provided by employers for all Safety Representatives under Regulation 7 of the SRSC Regulations.

TUC POLICY

As with any other harmful factor which is capable of disturbing the subtle workings of the cell with potentially disastrous results, it is prudent to assume that there is no absolutely 'safe' level of exposure to ionising radiations. This means that in any activity which involves radiation exposure, doses should be reduced as far as reasonably possible in order to reduce risk to health to the lowest practicable level. This obviously involves making careful judgements based on the best possible scientific understanding of the dose/risk relationship. Because there is acknowledged uncertainty about such risk estimates, particularly at low doses, the TUC favours a very cautious approach when making radiological protection decisions.

The present regime for radiological protection in the UK Ionising Radiations (IR) Regulations includes the following requirements:

a) employers have to ensure doses are 'as low as is reasonably achievable' (ALARA);

b) employers have to carry out ALARA investigations when any worker's dose exceeds a 'tripwire' of 15 mSv per annum;

c) where a worker's dose exceeds 30 mSv in a calendar quarter, their employer has to notify HSE; and

d) no radiation worker's dose should exceed 50 mSv per annum.

This dose limit is designed to set an outer boundary beyond which no worker should be exposed. Below this limit the primary control mechanism is ALARA reinforced by the 3/10th investigation "tripwire".

In the TUC's view the present maximum permissible range of annual (and thus lifetime) exposure is too wide. Although the ALARA principle has achieved some success in reducing doses, its application is discretionary and may vary in different circumstances. The TUC therefore has proposed improvements in the regime as follows:

a) employers should have to carry out ALARA investigations where doses exceed 7.5 mSv per annum;

b) employers should have to notify HSE of cases where doses exceed 15 mSv in a calendar quarter;

c) no radiation worker should be exposed above a limit of 25 mSv per annum (calculated as a rolling average); and

d) over a radiation worker's career their average annual dose should not exceed 10 mSv. *This would represent a five times reduction on what is permissible at present.*

The reduction of the present annual limit from 50 mSv to 25 mSv combined with a lower annual average limit would still allow some year on year flexibility for some areas of radiation work where occasional excursions could not be avoided. If however, a worker in such an area were to exceed 25 mSv in any one year, it would eat into their permissible dose in future years – so the five times better maximum level of protection would not be infringed.

The overall effect of the TUC's proposals would be to intensify pressure for further reductions in annual and lifetime doses for radiation workers. This is because employers would need to aim to restrict all annual exposures to less than 5 mSv if they were to be sure of avoiding ALARA investigations. At present about 94 per cent of doses received annually by the 140,000 workers in the UK who are routinely monitored for radiation exposure are in the 0-5 mSv range. About 5 per cent are in the 5-15 mSv range. About 1 per cent are in the 15-50 mSv range and less than .01 per cent receive annual doses exceeding the present annual dose limit of 50 mSv.

FURTHER INFORMATION ON RADIATION

- **Living with radiation**: Chilton NRPB, (from HMSO).
- **The effects and control of radiation**: UKAEA 1986.
- **Radiation and Life**: EJ Hall: Oxford, Pergamon Press 1984.
- **Radiation and Health**: edited by Robin Russell Jones and Sir Richard Southwood; John Wiley and Sons.

Legislation

- **The Ionising Radiations Regulations 1985**
- **The Ionising Radiations Regulations 1985 –** Approved Code of Practice: the protection of persons against ionising radiation arising from any work activity; available from HMSO.
- **Approved Code of Practice – Part 3:** Exposure to Radon.

Official advice

- **Guidance notes for the protection of persons against ionising radiations arising from veterinary use;** NRPB.
- **Guidance notes for the protection of persons against ionising radiations arising from medical and dental use;** NRPB.
- **Interim Advice on the Implications of Recent Revisions of Risk Estimates and the ICRP 1987 Como Statement:** NRPB-GS9.

10: Biological hazards

Workers in a wide range of occupations may be exposed to an enormous range of biological hazards. This term, in its widest sense, encompasses anything of a biological nature which has the potential to cause harm to human beings. It includes such things as viruses and bacteria which can cause infection and disease, dangerous plants and animals (for example parasites or insects), or harmful by-products of living things. Workers at risk thus include those who deal or come into contact with the whole range of the biological kingdom.

In some cases there are infectious organisms which are innately part of the job exposure (such as those found in health care work in hospitals and the community) or are incidentally part of job exposure such as those found in sewer work or agriculture. There are now also micro-organisms which have been deliberately genetically altered for use in industrial processes. Some workers are exposed to plants which can cause health problems, for example plants like Giant Hogweed which can cause skin rashes, or spores from mushrooms or mouldy hay which can pose acute respiratory hazards for mushroom workers or farm workers. There are also a wide variety of jobs which involve exposure to substances of biological origin such as wood dusts, juices from plants or dust generated in the handling of food stuffs. In many cases exposure to complex organic substances from sources such as these can produce allergic responses in sensitive individuals, such as occupational asthma. The approach to control of such hazards is very similar to the control of chemical hazards (see *Chapter 5: Chemicals and toxic substances*).

Many diseases caused by exposure to biological agents at work are prescribed diseases under the National Insurance (Industrial Injuries) Act 1965. They also have to be reported to the Health and Safety Executive by employers under the Reporting of Injuries, Diseases and Dangerous Occurrences Regulations 1985.

This chapter outlines some of the more common biological hazards faced by people in different jobs.

It aims to illustrate different approaches to prevention and control and to emphasise that often things of biological origin may be just as dangerous as other sources of risk faced by people at work, such as fire, explosion, unguarded machinery, vehicles or manufactured chemicals.

LEPTOSPIROSIS

This is the name given to a group of diseases caused by infection with a number of different types of bacteria called leptospires. The most well-known form is a condition called Weil's Disease found for example in sewermen and water workers, and which is caused by the variety Leptospira icterohaemorrhagiae which is excreted in the urine of rats. This is the most serious form of leptospirosis and in some cases may even result in death. Other varieties of leptospires which cause this disease include leptospira canicola (found in dogs' urine) and leptospira hebdomadis or hardjo (found in the urine of cattle, sheep and pigs). Leptospirosis is considered to be the most widespread zoonosis (disease transmitted by animals) in the world. This is because the reservoir of infection in terms of its host animal population is so large. In the UK for example it is estimated that between 20 to 40 per cent of cattle herds are infected with leptospirosis hardjo.

Leptospires enter the human body through cuts and abrasions in skin, through the mouth and eyes and through the nose where, for example, they may be breathed in on minute droplets of urine in the air. The number of cases of Weil's Disease reported every year in the UK has increased slightly in recent years. In the five years 1978-83 there were 177 notified cases compared with 150 cases of hardjo and 31 cases of canicola. Hardjo infections however are considered at present to be under diagnosed because often its symptoms, which include fever and jaundice, are only mild and are often confused

Examples of jobs with risks from biological hazards

Biological hazard	Disease or effect
Agricultural workers	
Dangerous animals	Physical injury
Spores in mouldy hay	Farmer's lung
Handling horses	Glanders
Exposure to urine from cows, pigs and sheep	Leptospirosis (Weil's Disease)
Grain dust	Asthma
Dairy workers	Brucellosis
Pig breeders	Meningitis from Streptococcus suis
Handling birds	Ornithosis
Health Service Staff	
Exposure to pathogens *eg*	Tuberculosis, Viral Hepatitis (an infection of the liver by a virus)
Sewer and water workers	
Leptospira from contaminated water	Leptospirosis
Vets	
From animals	Physical injuries, Zoonoses of all kinds
Millers and bakers	
Flour and grain dust	Asthma
Abattoir workers, butchers	
Leptospira	Leptospirosis
Brucella	Brucellosis
Streptococcus suis	Meningitis
Brush and glue workers	
Handling imported camel and goat hair	Anthrax
Miners	
Hookworm (rare in UK)	Ankylostomiasis
Laboratory workers	
Exposure to pathogens	Tuberculosis, AIDS, Viral Hepatitis
Detergent manufacture workers	
Proteolytic Enzymes	Asthma

by doctors with 'flu or glandular fever. This variety of the disease however can still be very unpleasant and can involve slow recovery to full health with a lengthy period of lassitude. If diagnosed early it is easy to treat using antibiotics.

In addition to waterworkers and sewermen, other workers at risk from leptospiral infections include dairy workers on farms, vets, dog handlers and also abattoir workers – since leptospires can survive for several days in slaughtered animals.

Weil's Disease is the most fully developed and most virulent form of leptospirosis. In fatal cases deep jaundice develops, with delirium and heart failure. In less severe cases, recovery commences after two weeks and is usually complete in a further three weeks. The possibility of death varies with age and is greatest in those over 50. Most cases however recover completely. Other forms of leptospirosis such as hardjo or canicola take a milder form. The onset is sudden with shivering or rigors and severe, often intractable headaches. The disease is usually self-limiting and, recovery is usually complete. Diagnosis of leptospirosis is made by isolating leptospires from the blood or urine of patients ten days to six weeks from the onset of the disease and is confirmed by the presence of antibodies in blood serum.

Prevention

Because of the widespread distribution of leptospira in the host animal population and the way these organisms are distributed in the environment, preventive measures are difficult. One long-term approach is to promote widespread vaccination of cattle as is done in New Zealand (but at present this is only a recommendation by the Ministry of Agriculture in Britain). So far, safe human vaccines have not been developed, so preventive measures centre on limiting exposure to the organism. Amongst dairy workers, for example, this means using protective clothing, ensuring high standards of hygiene, limiting contact with urine (here eye level 'herring bone' milking parlours may make things worse) and covering cuts and abrasions. The organism can also survive in water courses, so swimming in contaminated rivers and pools should also be avoided. Where the disease is contracted, early diagnosis is very important and workers at risk of leptospiral infections should be issued with warning cards which they should take with them to their doctors if they suspect they are suffering from symptoms. An example of such a card is *given below.*

NOTES FOR THE GENERAL PRACTITIONER
The holder of this card is engaged in work which may bring him into contact with rodent or cattle urine or with materials contaminated by these animals.

As you are aware, persons working in these conditions may occasionally develop Leptospirosis (either due to L icterohaemorrhagiae or L hebdomadis) and this card has been prepared to warn you of the possibility of the infection. Early diagnosis and treatment are vital in Weil's Disease as jaundice is often absent in the early stages. Leptospirosis hebdomadis may cause an influenza-like illness of varying severity which may be modified by antibiotic treatment.

It would be very helpful if you could report any attack of Leptospirosis to the Civil Service Medical Adviser's Office, Tilbury House, Petty France, London, SW1H 9EU.

A space has been provided on the back of this card for recording the patient's immunisations against other organisms.

Medical Adviser to the Civil Service

Further information on Leptospirosis

- **Zoonoses:** Chapter 16; J. Van de Hoeden; Elsevier Amsterdam 1964.

- **Update on Leptospirosis:** British Medical Journal, Vol 20 May 1985.

- **The changing pattern of Leptospirosis in Great Britain:** Environmental Health Vol 92 No 11.

- **Leptospirosis in Cattle:** ADAS leaflet, Ministry of Agriculture 1985.

HEPATITIS B

Hepatitis B is the name given to a viral inflammation of the liver. Because the disease is transmitted mainly by contact with human blood (but also occasionally by other routes) it has long been recognised as a hazard affecting staff working in the Health Service. But it can also be a risk to other groups of workers where there may be contact with blood or excreta – for example school teachers, prison officers or staff in residential institutions. The symptoms of the disease are vague to start with and may include fatigue, abdominal discomfort, skin rashes, nausea and vomiting. These may be followed later by the classic symptoms of hepatitis including brown urine, pale stools, and jaundice (the skin and whites of eyes turning yellow). However, many infected people have no symptoms at all. Diagnosis is confirmed by a blood test.

Fortunately about 95 per cent of people who contract hepatitis B recover from it completely. Recovering can take up to six months. A small percentage of people however cannot produce antibodies to fight the disease which can then become chronic. Chronic hepatitis may lead to liver damage, and in some cases, even death. Chronic hepatitis is also linked with liver cancer. Approximately 10 per cent of hepatitis B sufferers will become carriers of the virus. This means that they remain permanently infectious to other people and should take precautions to avoid passing the virus to others (see 'prevention' below).

Health Service staff are vulnerable to infection. Staff at greatest risk include nurses, mental hospital staff and physicians – for example renal and drug rehabilitation unit staff, those in blood transfusion centres and clinics for sexually transmitted diseases, midwives and theatre nurses are all likely to come into contact with the hepatitis B virus. Between 1975 and 1979 there were 287 cases reported in the NHS. Between 1980 and 1984 this rose to 364 with an increasing frequency amongst laboratory staff, nurses and surgeons.

One of the most common modes of contamination with hepatitis B virus is the 'sharps' injury – the accidental penetration of the skin by needles, glass instruments or slides that have been used in treating hepatitis B patients. Infection can also occur when the virus enters the body through minor cuts and abrasions if contact is made with infective blood, blood products, or sometimes other bodily secretions. One of the problems here is that the infection can be passed on from individuals who show no signs of having the disease.

Prevention

The first line of approach to controlling hepatitis B risks involves the adoption of work practices designed to prevent contact with sources of infection. When dealing with blood or other body fluids, strict procedures have to be applied to control the possibility of infection – for example by wearing protective gloves and aprons; eye and mouth protection where there is a risk of splashing hands after handling body fluids; immediately clearing up and disinfecting after spillages; and safe disposal or thorough disinfection of equipment, clothing and linen contaminated with body fluids. All cuts, grazes and breaks in the skin should be covered with waterproof dressings.

Where blood and other samples suspected to be contaminated with hepatitis B antibodies or antigens are handled in laboratories, strict guidelines must be observed. These have been agreed with representatives of Health Service trade unions through the Health and Safety Commission's Health Services Industry Advisory Committee. Strict procedures should also be followed by operating theatre staff. Proper procedures must be adopted for the safe disposal of infected wastes and all 'sharps'. All skin cuts and punctures should be allowed to bleed then washed with soap and warm water and reported.

Where contamination has occurred, it is possible to administer immunoglobulin which, if given within 24 hours of infection, will limit the course of disease. All those with contaminated 'sharps injuries' for example should seek this treatment. Long-term protection is given by hepatitis B vaccines, which should be offered to all staff at high risk of contracting hepatitis at work. This vaccine is considered to be 95 per cent effective in preventing development of the disease. Administration of the vaccine for high risk groups will depend on local conditions and policy.

Further information on Viral Hepatitis:

- **Safety in Health Services laboratories: Hepatitis B:** Health Services Industry Advisory Committee; Health and Safety Executive, 1984.

- **Guidance for health care personnel dealing with patients infected with Hepatitis B virus:** (DHSS 1984).

- **Industrial injuries, prescribed industrial diseases:** (DHSS 1983).

- **The Code of Practice for the Prevention of Infection in Clinical Laboratories and Post Mortem Rooms:** DHSS 1978; (The Howie Code).

- **Immunisation against infectious diseases:** (DHSS memorandum, April 1984).

- **Hepatitis B and NHS Staff:** DHSS advice; 31 December 1982.

- **The safe disposal of clinical waste:** Health and Safety Commission, 1982.

- **Categorisation of pathogens according to hazard and categories of containment:** Health and Safety Commission.

AIDS

The letters AIDS stand for Acquired Immune Deficiency Syndrome. This is a very serious condition caused by a virus that attacks the body's natural defence system against infection and disease. The virus responsible is known as HIV (previously called LAV/HTLV III). At present there is still no cure for AIDS and the disease is fatal. However not everyone who has been infected by the virus has developed AIDS – but they can still pass the virus on to others.

The AIDS virus is transmitted in various ways: by sexual intercourse with an infected person; from an infected mother to her baby; and by innoculation with blood or body fluids from a person infected with the virus. This latter route for transmission of the infection means that AIDS can be a source of risk to workers such as health care workers and others who come into contact with blood and body fluids from AIDS patients or carriers who may thus be at risk of inoculation through accidental contamination of cuts or abrasions – for example through 'sharps' injuries occurring with contaminated slides or needles.

The AIDS virus is not considered to be transmitted naturally by the airborne route and earlier fears that AIDS might develop following exposure to airborn droplets from coughing, sneezing or spitting have not been borne out. Neither is there any evidence that the AIDS virus is transmitted by non-sexual contact with an infected person or by sharing eating or drinking utensils or using the same toilet or washing facilities. This latter point is important to emphasise when seeking to allay fears about AIDS and possible discrimination in employment against high risk groups such as homosexual men and those with a history of drug abuse.

Prevention

Guidelines on controlling AIDS risks were published by the Health and Safety Commission's Advisory Committee on Dangerous Pathogens in 1984. They have now been revised to take account of the latest world wide information on the disease. What follows is a brief explanation of how these guidelines apply to Health Service staff.

Generally speaking precautions adopted in the Health Service to protect staff from other sources of infection are appropriate to prevent infection with the AIDS virus. These are laid down in local rules which are intended to guide staff to achieve safe work practices. They should lay emphasis on the following countermeasures designed to prevent occupational exposure to the AIDS virus.

a) prevention of puncture wounds, cuts and abrasions in the presence of blood and body fluids, and the protection of existing wounds and skin lesions;

b) application of simple protective measures designed to avoid contamination of the person or clothing and good basic hygiene practices including regular hand washing;

c) control of surface contamination with blood and body fluids by containment and disinfection; and

d) safe disposal of contaminated waste including 'sharps'.

Whether or not a patient is known to have the AIDS virus, all health care workers coming into contact with blood and body fluids should cover exposed cuts and abrasions, (especially on the hands and fingers), with waterproof dressings and take care to prevent puncture wounds, cuts and abrasions from used needles, other 'sharps' and glassware. If such accidents do occur, they should be treated immediately by encouraging bleeding and liberally washing with soap and water. Any puncture wound or contamination of broken skin, mouth or eyes should be reported and recorded.

Uniforms and overalls are forms of protective clothing and offer a degree of protection against contamination. But when dealing with AIDS patients there will be instances when there is a need to wear additional protection such as rubber gloves and/or an apron, *eg* when coming into contact with blood, body fluids or contaminated articles.

Spillages contaminated by blood and body fluids should not be tackled without suitable protection and the work should be done strictly in accordance with local rules. The hands and any other exposed parts of the body should be washed after contact with contaminated material and on completion of duties, especially at meal times.

All clinical waste from AIDS sufferers must be properly bagged and identified in accordance with local rules and all contaminated 'sharps' must be disposed of in a properly constructed 'sharps' container and not carelessly put down where they may find their way into plastic waste sacks and laundry bags which they can easily penetrate and then be the cause of an accident.

Finally, there is no evidence that there is actual risk from giving mouth to mouth resuscitation to AIDS sufferers. However, anyone giving respiratory resuscitation should, where possible, as a precaution use any special equipment provided for this *eg* a resuscitator or a plastic airway with a non-return valve.

Further information on AIDS

- **AIDS in employment:** TUC/CBI joint statement (prepared with ACAS).

- **Trade unionists and AIDS:** report of TUC seminar on AIDS.

- **Fact Sheet on AIDS:** Health Service Advisory Committee, 1986.

- **Revised Guidelines on AIDS:** Advisory Committee on Dangerous Pathogens; Health and Safety Commission, 1986.

LEGIONNAIRES DISEASE

Legionnaires Disease is often confused with humidifier fever which is an influenza-like condition caused by an allergic response to micro-organisms (and their by-products) circulating in poorly maintained air conditioning systems. Legionnaires Disease is a potentially much more serious condition and is caused by a bacterium Legionella pneumophila which is commonly found in soil but which can establish itself in water systems in plants and buildings. Growth of the bacterium is favoured by temperatures between 20°C and 45°C, particularly in the presence of scale or algae. In addition, certain materials have been known to harbour the organism such as shower heads and rubber gaskets used in hot water systems. Infection may occur when fine water droplets containing the bacterium are breathed in. Incubation usually takes two to ten days. Most outbreaks have involved exposure to spray from cooling towers or shower heads.

Legionnaires Disease is not necessarily a disease of occupation. Most people (about 95 per cent) are immune to infection. Most cases have occurred in hotels and hospitals. People in poor health are more likely to be affected. Typical symptoms of the disease are fever, persistent cough, muscle aches, chills, headaches and diarrhoea. The lungs are often affected and other organs such as the kidneys, liver, stomach and nervous system may be involved. The disease has a death rate of between one-in-four to one-in-ten of all those affected. The disease is confirmed by blood tests.

The 1984 Report of the Chief Medical Officer DHSS reported 151 cases of Legionnaires Disease of which 15 had been fatal. In the following year there was a major outbreak at the Stafford District General Hospital involving 101 cases with 28 deaths. The resulting inquiry produced new recommendations to prevent the disease in NHS establishments. The true incidence of the disease is likely to be much higher than the 180-200 cases that are notified annually.

Prevention

Measures to control Legionnaires Disease have been recommended by the DHSS since 1980. These cover disinfection and chlorination and thorough draining and regular inspection of all cooling towers and evaporative condensers. This is recommended at least twice-yearly and cleaning should involve use of anti-scaling compounds and algicides to reduce opportunities for colonies of the bacterium to build up. This advice also applies to reservoirs and pipework of humidifiers which should be regularly disinfected, drained, thoroughly inspected and cleaned. Water in cold water systems should be kept as far as possible below 20°C since at this temperature the growth of the bacterium is restricted. At the other end of the scale hot water should be stored at a temperature of not less than 60°C and distributed at not less than 50°C. Where such water passes through shower heads and similar fittings these should be regularly disinfected and there should also be regular microbiological monitoring of water to check for the presence of the Legionella organism.

Wherever systems which use recirculated water are in use, regular inspection and assessment of risk should be undertaken, and operational engineering staff should be provided with detailed guidance on the operation and safe maintenance of such systems. Systems should also be regularly reviewed to see whether possible risks such as zones and conditions in which bacteria can multiply can be eliminated through changes in practice and design.

Further information on Legionnaires Disease

- **Legionnaires Disease and Hospital Water Systems:** DHSS Health Notice HN (80) 39; Health Service Management; 1980.

- **Legionnaires Disease:** DHSS Health Notice HN (HAZARD) (86) 1; Health Service Management.

- **Cooling Towers and Evaporative Condensers:** Interim Guidance No 2.

- **Drainage systems for air conditioning plants:** DHSS Health Notice HN (HAZARD) (85) 6; Health Service Management; Legionnaires Disease; Interim Engineering Guidance Note.

- **Cooling Towers and Evaporative Condensers:** DHSS Health Notice HN (86) 16; Health Service Management; Legionnaires Disease; Engineering Guidance Note 3.

- **First Report of the Committee of Enquiry into the Outcome of Legionnaires Disease in Stafford in April 1985;** HMSO; Cmnd 9772, 1986.

ORGANIC DUST DISEASES

Hundreds of thousands of workers in sectors such as agriculture, pharmaceuticals, furniture making and food manufacturing are exposed to dusts of animal and vegetable origin. Examples of materials involved include antibiotics, cereals, flour, milk and egg powder, spores of fungi, and yeasts. In some cases exposure to organic dusts such as wood dust can lead to toxic effects or can cause cancer. The biggest problem however arises from the provocation of allergic reactions in susceptible individuals. Allergic reaction take two forms – asthma or extrinsic allergic alveolitis.

Extrinsic allergic alveolitis (or hypersensitivity pneumonia) is a common name given to lung disease caused by breathing in particles of organic dusts which penetrate into the lungs causing an allergic reaction and leading to tissue damage (fibrosis) and impairment of lung function. These diseases are characterised by an acute phase with constitutional symptoms and a chronic phase. Some of the more well known forms are mushroom workers' lung; farmer's lung; and bird fancier's lung *(see below)*. In the acute form, symptoms, including cough, chills, sweating, fever, and dyspnoea, begin a few hours after exposure to the allergen; lung function is restricted and there is a reduced gas transfer. Symptoms of the acute stage are usually short lived in the absence of further exposure. In the chronic form of the disease however, symptoms may develop insidiously over a long time period and irreversible chronic pulmonary fibrosis may develop. Multiple acute attacks may also progress to pulmonary fibrosis. Many causes of extrinsic allergic alveolitis relate to job exposure but only a few of the many recognised types occur in the United Kingdom.

Farmer's Lung: this can follow exposure of persons who have previously become sensitised to the dust generated on moving certain spoiled vegetable produce, particularly hay and corn. When hay and corn are harvested in a damp condition and stored either in bales or loose, the growth of micro-organisms may cause heating. The micro-organisms responsible for 'Farmer's Lung' are among those which grow well in overheated produce and their spores may, therefore, be expected to be present in mouldy hay or corn which has overheated in this way. Spoiled hay is, however, only one of the potential sources. The spores are common in litter and in various stored fodders, including silage. Hardly any sample of stored grass or grain is likely to be entirely free of organisms which cause the disease. When such produce is disturbed, for example, in grinding corn or feeding cattle, the dust containing the spores may be breathed in. Such an exposure may sensitise people doing this work and after this, exposure to even quite low concentrations of the spores will produce symptoms.

Mushroom Worker's Lung: this is caused by exposure to fungi which grow in compost used to spawn mushrooms. The precise fungal agent has not been isolated however. Reports of degree of recovery vary considerably.

Maltworker's lung: this is caused by inhaled organic dust containing spores of the fungus Aspergillus clavatus which are released into the air in large concentrations during the turning of barley in open floor maltings. Severity of symptoms varies.

Bird Fancier's lung: this is well recognised in pigeon breeders and budgerigar fanciers. The causative agent comes from the birds' serum protein and the disease results from exposure to dust from bird droppings and feather dust. Symptoms are similar to those found in Farmer's Lung. To a lesser extent symptoms have been noted in poultry workers.

Bagasossis: this is caused by exposure to spores in the handling of fibrous cellulose material from the inner stalk of sugar cane which has been crushed and the juice extracted. This can be prevented by treatment with a biocide.

Other causes: other causes of extrinsic allergic alveolitis have been reported including certain hardwood dusts, mouldy wood products, cork dust, cheese moulds, coffee bean dust, moulds on preserved meat products, fish meal, and dry rot dust.

Asthma caused by organic agents

Occupational asthma is characterised by widespread partial obstruction of the airways and may occur in susceptible individuals as a result of exposure to dusts, fumes or vapours. It can vary in severity. Sometimes symptoms can be reversed. Organic dusts are a major cause including grains, flour, plants, gum, insects, animal products, and woods. An allergic reaction does not occur on first exposure but only after an interval which may vary from weeks to years. Once sensitisation has occurred, symptoms of chest tightness and breathing difficulties are provoked by re-exposure to the causative agent. Symptoms can vary in intensity for a whole variety of reasons. Atopic subjects (those who are prone to allergic reactions – about a third of the population) may be at particular risk.

Prevention

The first line of approach in preventing organic dust diseases must be to change to alternative processes or materials or to eliminate exposure by enclosure. Where this is not possible, exposure should be controlled either by exhaust ventilation or use of respiratory protection (see *Chapter 6: Dust* and *Chapter 2: Personal protection*). In the case of asthma it is sometimes suggested that atopic subjects should be excluded from work involving exposure to allergens – but this leads to discrimination whilst the hazard remains. All potential exposure to organic dust – particularly mouldy materials – should be identified before work starts and appropriate precautions adopted. If symptoms do occur, it is important that these are reported to a doctor while effective treatment is still possible.

Organic agents that may cause Occupational Asthma

Agent	Occupation(s) affected
Wheat, grain and flour	Millers, bakers, farmers and grain handlers
Hops	Brewers
Coffee beans	Coffee handlers
Castor beans	Gardeners, bean baggers, millers
Gums	Printers
Tobacco dust	Tobacco workers
Wool	Wool workers
Beetles, locusts, cockroaches	Laboratory workers
Crickets, grain weevils	Millers, farmworkers
Rats and mice	Grain storage, laboratory workers
Prawn and oysters	Shell fish processing
Fungi	Bakers, farmworkers
Cedarwood, boxwood, redwood, resin, African Zebrawood	Carpenters, woodworkers, and finishers

FURTHER INFORMATION ON ORGANIC DUST DISEASES

- **Occupational Lung Disorders:** Occupational Asthma (including Byssinosis); Raymond Parkes; Butterworths; Disorders caused by Organic Agents; Chapter 11.

- **Occupational asthma:** DHSS Leaflet NI 237.

- **Farmer's Lung:** AS Leaflet; HSE

- **Notes on the Diagnosis of Occupational Disease:** DHSS; HMSO.

11: Skin hazards

Injury to workers' skin from burns, cuts, abrasions and work-induced skin cancer and dermatitis is responsible for the loss of nearly one million working days every year. The total financial cost to the sufferers and the community can only be guessed at, but it certainly runs into tens of millions of pounds every year. The many causes of injury include:

- mechanical damage due to injury, friction or pressure;
- corrosive substances eg acids and alkalis;
- solvents;
- oils and petroleum products;
- resins; and
- physical agents eg heat, cold, sunlight, radiation.

The main parts of the skin most often affected are the face, neck, hands and forearms because being the most exposed, these are the parts of the body which are most easily contaminated. Other areas can also be affected, particularly if they are in contact with tight, contaminated clothing.

THE SKIN

In order to understand how skin disorders are caused it is helpful to think about the structure and function of the skin. It is the largest single organ of the body — it is estimated the total skin area of an average man is 100 square feet — and far from being a mere covering for our flesh and bones, it is a living part of us. It is a complex self-repairing protective coat which breathes and disposes of waste from the body; it also regulates the temperature of the body. The skin can provide a natural protection, as long as it is not damaged by cuts or subjected to irritation or injury.

Many substances can, when in contact with the skin, cause irritation. The resulting condition

known as dermatitis may be just a reddening of the skin with a mild itching, a rash, a swelling or in some cases open weeping sores. Substances which cause dermatitis can be gases (vapours), liquids or solids. In addition to the substances previously mentioned workers dealing with plating, adhesives, solvents, enzymes, detergents, photographic developers, bleachers or paints, to name but a few substances and processes can have skin problems if the proper precautions are not taken. Solvents which are used for degreasing and other cleaning operations will remove the skin's natural oils leaving it unprotected.

Some chemicals not only irritate the skin but also cause an allergic rash. This is called 'sensitisation' and sensitised workers can develop a severe reaction if subsequently exposed to even a tiny amount of the chemical involved.

MECHANICAL DAMAGE

This includes cuts and grazes caused by sharp edges, splinters or fragments. Friction or pressure on parts of the skin can also cause blisters, 'friction burns' and patches of hard skin. Besides being painful, any breaks in the skin can allow infections and chemicals to get in. These hazards can be avoided by improved work systems, the use of guards and protective equipment. For more details about gloves, see the later section in this chapter.

CORROSIVE SUBSTANCES

Some chemicals such as strong acids and alkalis cause chemical burns when in contact with skin that are very similar to those caused by heat. Both destroy skin tissue. Corrosive chemicals cause damage until removed or neutralised or the corrosive reaction is complete. Some chemicals, in addition to being highly corrosive, are also poisonous when absorbed through the skin. An example of this is phenol. Corrosive-resistant protective clothing and ventilation are needed to prevent chemical burns.

The first treatment for every chemical burn is to flood the affected area as quickly as possible with water; even a few seconds delay can be very serious. Contaminated clothes should be taken off immediately. It is extremely important that emergency showers are available near to where they might be required, for example chemical manufacture. Eye burns are very serious and no time should be lost in washing with large quantities of water; preferably this should be done by a properly designed eyewash fountain using large amounts of low-pressure water. With eye burns, care is needed not to cause mechanical damage to the eye by a forceful jet of water. To prevent infection of the wound, loss of body fluid and shock, medical attention should be sought for treatment of all but the most trivial of burns. Corrosive chemicals need not necessarily be liquids — they can also be gases or solids.

PHYSICAL AGENTS

Burns can also be caused by extreme heat, cold (frostbite) and radiation, including sunlight. People working in hot conditions may suffer from heat rashes caused by blocked skin pores and friction. Over-exposure to radiations such as the natural radiation in sunlight, can cause skin cancer. Protective equipment should be provided, to prevent skin contact with hot surfaces or radiations, for example ultra violet light.

SOLVENTS

Solvents are used to clean things by dissolving grease and oils. They will also dissolve the protective coating of oil in the skin when in direct contact. Unfortunately, the more efficient the solvent, the more harmful it is to your skin. Many substances act as solvents — water, soaps, detergents, metal degreasers, cleaning fluids, thinners, to name but a few. Direct contact between skin and solvent should be avoided by using impermeable protective clothing and good ventilation to get rid of solvent vapours. Strong solvents are the most damaging to the skin, so the weakest solvent that will still do the job should be used. Solvents like 'trike', meths or toluene should never be used to clean dirt or oil off your skin. After cleaning with a mild soap, conditioning cream will replace natural oil in the skin and prevent chapping.

OILS AND PETROLEUM PRODUCTS

Many of these also act as solvents or have solvents added to them. The most serious effect on the skin is cancer, but dermatitis and acne are also caused by skin contact with these. More information about mineral oils is given in *Example 1* in this chapter.

RESINS

Resins, both natural and synthetic, are among many hundreds of chemicals that cause skin irritation or sensitisation. Epoxy resins can irritate the skin and can cause an allergic reaction in some workers. These problems and precautions that should be taken, are common to many chemicals and are covered in *Example 2* in this chapter.

PREVENTION

Preventing skin damage entails controlling exposure to any of the above harmful agents either by selecting a less harmful substance or changing working methods, by isolating the operators by use of protective clothing or by ensuring high standards of personal hygiene preventive strategies normally involve a combination of all these approaches.

SKIN CLEANSING

It is often said that more damage is done to workers' hands by removing contaminants *after* work than anything else. This is true in many cases where strong solvents are used to clean up. Only mild soaps and special cleansers should be used. Cleansing is a balancing act — try to remove the contamination without removing all the natural oil in the skin. After cleansing clean towels or hot air driers should be provided and conditioning creams help to replace natural oil in the skin. After all, apart from the risk of skin disorders, who wants raw, discoloured hands with ingrained dirt and mucky nails?

GLOVES

For complete protection for skin, prevention is better than cure and guards, enclosures and mechanical handling devices may be necessary for safe working with damaging substances. Personal protection should be regarded as a second line of defence, but where necessary, it should be the correct type.

Gloves are the most common form of protection against skin diseases. There must be at least 20 different types of glove manufactured for use in work activities. Among the main types are heat resistant leather, chrome leather and asbestos-substitute for intense heat work. For work where there is a risk of severe abrasions and cuts, chrome leather reinforced with chain mail mesh are necessary; whilst for work involving acids, alkalis and other corrosives, oils and solvents, gloves made from PVC, natural rubber, Neoprene or Nitrile should be used. Expert advice should be obtained on the right type of glove for the job, including when to replace disposable gloves and methods of repair and use of non-disposables where necessary. When working with toxic substances that can be absorbed through the skin particular attention should be paid to permeability and 'break through' times for protective gloves.

BARRIER CREAMS

There has always been some doubt expressed about the degree of protection given by barrier creams. Some people swear by them, others contend that they are ineffective — indeed harmful if they are used to give a false sense of security or if they are used as a cheap alternative to gloves and other more expensive forms of protection. The truth is, as often the case tends to be, somewhere between these two extreme views. Barrier creams can be used as a cheap alternative to full skin protection by unscrupulous or indifferent managements, but nevertheless, where exposure of the skin to a harmful substance is unavoidable, the use of a proper type of barrier cream is an advantage to skin health.

There are so many complex creams manufactured that expert advice is necessary to choose the right type for the particular job. The companies who manufacture barrier creams supply between them, dozens of different types; some of them supply a skin care service to give advice and meet specialist needs.

EXAMPLES

Two examples of common skin hazards are outlined in this chapter — mineral oils and epoxy resins. Both illustrate general preventive principles which can be applied to the prevention of skin-disease caused through work.

EXAMPLE 1: MINERAL OILS

It is estimated that some ten million workers in industry come into contact with some form of mineral oil every day of their working lives. In doing so they run the risk of developing skin health problems if certain basic safety and hygiene precautions are not taken. The most common of these problems are acne and dermatitis. There is also a risk — although of a lesser degree — of scrotal cancer and also to respiratory health from inhalation of oil mists and vapours.

The term 'mineral oil' is used to describe all oil extracted from the earth and comes in many forms — petrol, white spirit, paraffin, diesel oil, lubricating oil, paraffin wax, asphalt and bitumen are all oil based products. All mineral oils present some sort of danger to health. Wherever oil is used therefore, potential risks should be assessed and precautions adopted.

Types of oil

Apart from fuel oils, the commonest use of oil in industry is for cooling and lubricating the cutting edges of tools and to prevent welding between the metal and the tool tip from the heat generated. Oils are used in a variety of operations such as turning, grinding, milling and honing, and for the working of many different metals. The oil is poured on to the cutting edge at the rate necessary for effective cooling, which may be as high as thirty gallons a minute. Each machine may have its own supply of oil or a line of machines may have a common supply.

Cutting oils are used either neat or as an emulsion in a watery medium — the former being used for certain specialised operations. These oils are basically mineral oils of the lubricating type which may be blended with some vegetable or animal oil. Additives may be used with these oils to make them more suitable for particular purposes. Some of these substances may present problems too. Additives include extreme pressure additives, anti oxidants to improve the efficiency of coolant, emulsifiers, wetting agents, water softeners and hardeners, and other agents designed to prevent the growth of bacteria in oil. Oil additives also include mercury, lead, and, as anti-rust agents, chrome and sodium nitrate. Opposite is a table listing types of additives and their chemical make-up that are in common use within the UK.

Soluble oils are essentially mixtures of oils and emulsifying agents such as petroleum soaps. When the oil is added to water, the emulsifiers ensure the dispersion of fine droplets of oil in the water. To make the emulsion stable, a coupling agent is used. Soluble oils are made by diluting the oil with water to the desired degree which may vary from about 1:3 to 1:100. With constant use increasing quantities of breakdown substances formed in the high temperature zone between the cutting tool and the workpiece tend to build up in cutting oils. Some of these substances are considered to have cancer inducing properties.

Additive	Example
Corrosion inhibitors	Lead napthenate, sodium sulphonate
Anti-foam agents Emulsifiers Antioxidants	Polyorgano siloxanes, fatty oils, fatty acids, 2.6 ditertiary butyl paracresol, phenyl naphthylamine
Detergents	Metal sulphonates, metal phenates
Viscosity index improver Anti-wear agents	Tricresylphosphate
Extreme pressure agents	Sulphurised fatty oils
Bacteriocides	Phenols

Source: Encyclopaedia of Occupational Health and Safety Third Edition, ILO Geneva

The concentration of carcinogenic (cancer inducing) substances present in mineral oils can be reduced by a process called solvent refining — literally washing oils in petrol, benzene, or other solvents. This is also taken to refer to the refining procedure in which oils are washed with sulphuric acid, liquid sulphur dioxide etc. Although this reduces the concentration of carcinogens, it is still unwise to assume that solvent washed oils are entirely safe. Breakdown products will still build up in lubricating oils over a period of time; additives may be present that are harmful or can cause sensitisation, and thus the danger of dermatitis is always present.

In addition to cutting oils, many other types of oil are commonly used in industry. For example, paraffin oil is used extensively in industry for metal cleaning and degreasing and it is also used in large quantities as jet fuel. Naphthas are widely used as solvents, diesel oils as fuel for internal combustion engines and furnace 13 oils for steam-raising and heating. Lubricating oils vary from thin spindle oils to the very viscous cylinder oil used for steam engines, and mineral oils are used for quenching, as electrical oils in transformers, and a variety of other special uses. Greases are commonly manufactured from lubricating oils solidified by soap.

Skin hazards

The mineral oils such as paraffin, naphtha, diesel and other lubricating light oils are more likely to provoke dermatitis and oil acne rather than skin cancer. Such dermatitis usually appears as an irritation which can vary from slight reddening with mild itching to more serious rashes or small eruptions with intense itching. In severe cases, there may be open or weeping sores possibly accompanied by swelling. It usually affects the hands and arms, but, if neglected can spread to other parts of the body.

Cutting oils, however, present a greater risk, particularly neat oils and unrefined oils. The latter are often used for cheapness, but are less safe than solvent washed oils. Whatever type of oil is used, the degree of risk is increased by greater contact of the oil with the skin. For example, operators of certain types of machines are liable to have hands and arms continually exposed to cutting oils. The outer layer of the skin is softened, broken down, and the way opened for infections.

Other parts of the body may be contaminated by splashes or contact with machines, particularly the lower half of the body which can be affected by oil-soaked overalls. When a male operator bends over, straddles or rubs against machines, his scrotum can be at risk from contamination. The keeping of oily 'wipers' in trouser pockets is a common way in which the lower parts of the body can be exposed to oil, as is failure to wash oily hands before going to the lavatory.

Although cancer of the scrotum is an uncommon disease, it is invariably cured by prompt treatment. The first stage — a rough patch of skin or wart on the scrotum (the bag containing the testicles) — requires immediate medical attention. Once contracted, the course of this disease is not affected by personal cleanliness. Indeed, amongst most sufferers personal cleanliness is generally high.

The fatality rate amongst those who contract cancer of the scrotum is undoubtedly high because, due to ignorance and modesty, many fail to report the matter to their doctors early enough. *Rough patches, boils, warts and lumps on the scrotum call for prompt medical attention — delay can be dangerous!* If every worker who developed a wart or sore on his scrotum reported this at once to his doctor, there would be only a small risk of serious consequence, since the rate of cure is over 90 per cent in early diagnosed cases.

Women too can develop genital cancer from contact with mineral oils. Precautions apply to men and women working with these oils.

Other hazards

Working in oily conditions frequently means being exposed to oil mist in the atmosphere. This can be produced in a number of ways: from a machining process itself; from the fumes given off at the cutting point (which contain breakdown products of the oil itself); from air compressors; and from lubrication systems which deliberately produce a spray of coolant directed onto the workpiece. The breathing of oil mists and fumes not only gives rise to coughs, sore throat, and other respiratory problems, it also increases the risk of cancer of the lung. Control of oil mist either entails preventing the formation of mists or controlling its release into the atmosphere — for example by using Local Exhaust Ventilation. Advice on controlling atmospheric contamination is contained in *Chapter 6.*

Prevention

The first approach to the problem of exposure to oils must be one of prevention of physical contact with the substance and its additives. This means ensuring that machinery is provided with adequate splash guards which effectively prevent oil being thrown off onto the operator. These guards, to be efficient, should provide for total enclosure with effective sealing to prevent leakage from the guarded area.

Even though every effort should be made to ensure oil using processes are splash free, in many cases this is difficult to achieve. Therefore, protective clothing must be used, particularly to prevent contamination of the lower parts of the body via oil soaked overalls etc. Frequently, protective equipment is clumsy and uncomfortable to wear. However, where oil contamination is a problem which cannot be combated by other means, protective clothing is unfortunately the only answer.

Regular solvent dry cleaning of overalls and rags is also an essential step towards lessening the hazards of oil. In contrast to ordinary washing, this cleaning can remove most of the oil from a contaminated garment. Weekly issue of dry cleaned overalls is recommended for all persons exposed to oil.

Adequate washing facilities must be provided together with a suitable range of waterless hand cleaners. Showers too may be necessary in some circumstances. On no account should hands be washed in oil or suds. The use of barrier creams on hands and forearms is a useful preventive measure. Care should be taken, however, to make sure that the correct type is provided in relation to the oil in use. Hand conditioning creams should also be available for use after washing. Finally, periodic medical examinations have proved useful in the past in detecting problems at an early stage. Nevertheless, if any health problem is suspected, advice from a doctor should be sought *immediately*.

Remember there are four golden rules for safe working with oil:

- make use of protective facilities, clothing, splash guards, impermeable aprons, barrier creams;

- change into working clothing; make sure that overalls are cleaned regularly; dry cleaning is desirable as wet washing only removes 50 per cent of oil contamination;

- pay careful attention to personal cleanliness; wash your hands before going to the toilet, as well as afterwards; wash your genital areas regularly; and

- obtain immediate first-aid treatment for all skin injuries and seek early advice for any skin rashes or itching areas.

EXAMPLE 2: EPOXY RESINS

The major problem in handling these materials comes from the curing agents used to harden epoxies. So they may be moulded or machined, it is necessary to use different hardeners for different epoxies. Some of these hardeners are harmful in themselves and it is from these that most skin related problems seem to arise.

Epoxy resins have to be divided into two categories, Cured and Uncured. Most cured resins have little or no toxic effect unless curing is incomplete, when there may be some hazard. With uncured resins there is much more potential danger to anyone handling them. The degree of toxicity of uncured epoxy resins varies, and is partly dependent on the extent of uncreated curing agents. In the case of both cured and uncured expoxy resins, they are dangerous when heated to decomposition, as they emit highly toxic fumes.

Safety precautions

The following safety precautions should be carried out when working with epoxy resins.

Whenever undertaken indoors, the mixing of epoxy resins should be carried out only in properly ventilated areas, fitted, where possible, with extraction fans, or in fume cupboards. Use of prepared mixtures should likewise be confined to areas provided with efficient exhaust ventilation. Whenever the fully cured or hardened material is to be machined (sawn, filed, etc), the work area should be fitted with an exhaust system or effectively ventilated by some other method.

Handling techniques

Handling techniques should ensure that no uncured resin or other epoxy material comes in contact with the eyes or skin. To this end, the wearing of goggles is strongly advised and it may be practicable to mount a transparent shield between the operator and the workpiece. Eye or face shields are particularly necessary where a possibility exists of droplet contamination of the eyes. Precautions should be taken when handling powder filters to avoid inhalation. The work area must be adequately ventilated. The wearing of dust respirators approved by the Health and Safety Executive is advised.

Cleanliness in working is of the utmost importance. Benches should be covered with replaceable paper for removal and destruction when contaminated. Containers should be kept, as far as practicable, in a clearly marked-off area of the work space. Spillage and the contamination of tools and equipment, or the outsides of containers, should be avoided. If spillage or contamination does occur, the affected area must be cleaned up immediately.

Protective equipment

Workers should be provided with equipment to minimise personal contact with uncured resins and hardeners. Protective clothing and neoprene gloves suitable for the materials being handled should be worn by those working with such materials. The insides of gloves must be kept clean. Damaged gloves must be replaced. Care is needed to keep cuffs free from contamination and, when necessary, protection should be provided for the sleeves and upper arms. When powder fillers or glass-fibres are in use, clothing should be designed to prevent any risk of these materials lodging between clothing and the skin. Overalls are essential for all operators engaged in continuous processes involving the use of epoxy resin materials, and in some instances, heavy-duty plastic or rubber aprons may be required for added protection. Contaminated clothing should be replaced and thoroughly cleaned before re-issue.

Skin cleaning

If, despite all these precautions, the skin does become contaminated, the affected area should be washed immediately with warm soapy water. Disposable paper towels or warm air driers should be used for drying. Specially compounded creams should be kept conveniently at hand for removing any epoxy material still adhering to the skin. Do not use powerful solvents. Routine cleansing of the skin should be carried out thoroughly at the end of each working period and sufficient time allowed for 'cleaning-up' before all break periods. For all these precautions to be implemented in full, it is of course necessary for management to provide the required working accommodation, equipment and materials indicated above. Washing facilities should include mild soaps, disposable towels, barrier creams and special resin-removing creams.

7: Are there adequate washing facilities?
- clean running hot and cold water?
- mild soap?
- disposable towels or hot-air driers?
- special proprietory cleansers where necessary?
- skin conditioning creams, for use after washing.

8: If barrier creams are provided, are they the right type to protect against the hazard?

9: If chemicals are used at work, do you know what they are, what effects they have on health (including skin damage) and what precautions should be taken?

10: Is medical advice available?

USEFUL PUBLICATIONS

HSE advisory leaflets

- **Skin cancer caused by pitch and tar:** MS(B)4.
- **Skin cancer caused by oil:** MS(B)5.
- **Dermatitis and work (occupational dermatitis):** MS(B) 6.
- **Dermatitis from flour, dough or sugar (cautionary notice):** SHW355.
- **Dermatitis from synthetic resins (cautionary notice):** SHW366.
- **Dermatitis (cautionary notice):** SHW367.
- **Effects of mineral oil on the skin (cautionary notice):** SHW397.
- **Occupational Skin Diseases - Health and Safety Precautions:** HSE Guidance, Note EH26.
- **Contact Dermatitis:** E Cronin; Churchill Livingstone, London (1980).

CHECKLIST: SKIN HAZARDS

Information on the incidence of skin complaints in your workplace can often help to identify causes. Ask your medical or personnel department for this information.

1: In what areas/processes are skin problems occurring?

2: Is it possible to use less hazardous materials or change methods or work where isolation is necessary?

3: Are guards, screens, mechanical handling devices etc. provided to remove irritants and dust?

4: Is ventilation provided to remove irritants and dust?

5: Is protective clothing provided and used?

6: Does the protective clothing protect against the skin hazards in your workplace eg acids, solvents, heat, sharp edges?

12: Hazards of physical work

Many jobs — particularly those involving manual work — do damage to the body. Exposure to vibration from tools or equipment can cause back damage, damage to joints, knees and elbows, shoulders and wrists as well as 'white finger'. Manual handling of loads can cause back damage, hernias, trapped nerves and other injuries. Repetitive manual work can cause tenosynovitis, tennis elbow or frozen shoulder. Too much standing or badly designed seating can lead to spinal damage, varicose veins or circulation problems. Working with arms outstretched or operating heavy foot controls can lead to muscle pain and tendon damage.

Exposures to sources of stress such as these at work are responsible for a heavy toll of suffering, much of which is endured in silence and never fully recorded or reported. Thousands of workers have to leave their jobs each year because they are crippled by disabilities caused by work-related strain injury; thousands stay on at work only to suffer further. Some 90,000 back injuries are reported to the Health and Safety Executive every year (the biggest cause of job related injury and responsible for more than 2 million lost working days a year). Tenosynovitis is the second most common prescribed industrial disease — in 1981/82, 2,282 successful claims for DHSS Benefit were made. Most of this suffering can be prevented however, through forethought, planning and observing recognised standards.

Aches, strains and pain result from damage to the structure of the body. The main elements in this structure are described in the table, top of page opposite.

Examples of groups of workers who are at risk from physical work include:

- miners, construction and agricultural workers, nurses, porters, home helps, and teachers — all of whom are at risk from back damage;

- forestry workers and fettlers who get white finger from exposure to vibration;

- VDU operators, light assembly workers, and bricklayers who get tenosynovitis; and

- office workers who get backache.

In order to combat injuries like these, the TUC has been pressing for improved standards in legislation and guidance. These include proposals for new regulations and guidance on manual handling published by the Health and Safety Commission and guidance on human factors in the operation of VDUs (see *Chapter 24*). The TUC has published its own guidelines on Manual Handling entitled *Lighten the Load* and is also continuing to press for improved compensation arrangements. The aim of this chapter is to help safety representatives identify sources of risk and eliminate them as far as possible by making the job fit the worker rather than the other way around. It deals with four common sources of injury associated with manual work:

a) bad posture;

b) manual handling;

c) repetitive work; and

d) vibration, and gives guidance on how to identify hazards and how to secure improvements to tackle them.

WORK POSTURE

Uncomfortable work-posture can cause a range of problems for example: varicose veins; piles; back-damage and aggravation of repetitive strain injuries (RSI) (see page 107). The main causes of such problems are badly-designed seating; having to stand for too long; reaching too far and inadequate lighting forcing people to get too close to their work. Because many people at work may try to get used to bad work posture, it can become a major source of problems.

Few jobs have been specifically designed to

Element	Function	Example of damage
Bones	Solid units which give your body its structure.	Breaks. Excess growth at the joints. Osteoarthritis.
Ligaments	Strong flexible webs which: • hold your bones together; • surround your body cavity; and • encase the jelly pads to form the discs between the bones of your spine.	Stretching and tearing, 'sprains', hernias, ruptures or ('slipped') discs.
Joints	Lubricated connections between your bones with mechanical arrangements which allow them to slide over each other easily.	Inflammation and degeneration — 'arthritis'. Looseness due to stretching of ligaments.
Muscles	Units of fibre which can contract to cause or limit movement.	Overstretched — 'pulled muscles', fatigue, wasting.
Tendons	Strong flexible cords which connect muscle to bone via smoothly lined ligament sheaths.	Inflammation of: • tendons — 'tendonitis'; • sheath – 'tenosynovitis'.
Blood vessels	Carry sugar and oxygen to your tissues and organs and take away waste via fine capillaries.	Varicose veins, bruises, restriction of flow through capillaries – 'white finger'.
Nerves	Carry signals from and to your brain.	Trapping and pressure causing pain, numbness, muscle wasting — 'carpal tunnel syndrome'.

ensure comfortable work-posture. Many workers are therefore at risk — particularly those whose jobs involve a lot of sitting or standing — for example office work, light assembly work, packing, check-out operators and counter staff.

If a job feels uncomfortable then it is probably doing harm. Safety representatives should make a detailed survey of all jobs in the workplace which involve standing or sitting and draw up proposals for improvements based on legal standards and official guidance.

Continuous standing should be avoided wherever possible. This view is supported by the relevant sections of the Factories Act and Offices, Shops and Railway Premises Act (OSRPA) (see page 103). Where jobs have to be done standing, workers should be able to work with their upper arms at their sides, without excessive bending or twisting of the back.

Attention should also be paid to working height. The diagram and table herewith shows how comfortable working height varies with the height of the worker doing the job. Both are adapted from a

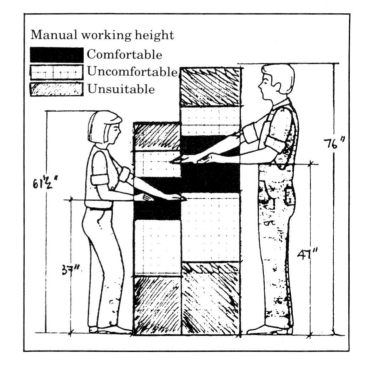

Height of worker	Unsafe below	Uncomfortable between	Comfortable between	Uncomfortable between	Unsafe above
5' 0"	15½"	15½"-31"	31"-43½"	43½"-39½"	49½"
5' 3"	16"	16"-32½"	32½"-46"	26"-54"	52"
5' 6"	17"	17"-34"	34"-48"	48"-54½"	54½"
5' 9"	17½"	17½"-35½"	35½"-50"	50"-57"	57"
6' 0"	18½"	18½"-37"	37"-52½"	52½"-59½"	59½"
6' 3"	19"	19"-38½"	38"-54½"	54½"-62"	62"

(Table and diagram adapted from Ordnance (AFS 1983:6) concerning work postures and working movements — Swedish Board of Occupational Safety and Health.)

recent Swedish legal standard on workplace design. The table can be used however as a rough guide to assess the job design.

Where work has to be done standing, footrests can help reduce the strain on the back and enable workers to change positions. Resilient floor covering or duckboards can help reduce the strain on joints. Seats or stools enable posture to be varied.

Attention should be paid to jobs which involve reaching. Such work should preferably be done between eight and twelve inches in front of your body, and should not be done beyond 16-20 inches.

Some jobs have to be done standing up — but obviously sitting is preferable to standing — provided of course no heavy lifting is required. Nevertheless work station design and layout are very important if problems are to be avoided. From this point of view the bench or desk and seat need to be considered as one unit. The seat should fit the worker and the work surface and work layout should fit the worker when seated. Here the same guidance on reaching applies as for standing.

When assessing the suitability of seating, a number of features should be born in mind — particularly for office seating.

Seat height should always be adjustable to between 13½″ and 20″ while the seat is in use. There should be a padded backrest — adjustable for height with an angle and 'fore and aft' position, mounted on rubber. The seat itself should be firmly padded and at least 16½″ wide with a turned down front edge to avoid pressure on the thighs. Porous upholstery is best because it enables sweat to evaporate. A swivel should be incorporated in the design to enable the body to be twisted safely and the seat should have a firm base with castors when used on carpets or glides on other surfaces. Here it should be remembered five legs are more stable than four. Removable armrests are a useful feature and there should be adequate clearance between the thighs and the underside of the worksurface, and between feet, shin and thighs and the rear of the work surface.

All these features should be discussed with workers and their safety representatives when new work arrangements and layouts are being proposed. Management should be pressed to make a commitment to proper design in their purchase policy for all new equipment. Here it is possible to point to legal standards (page 108) which are rather limited in scope and are to be found in Section 60 of the Factories Act and Sections 13 and 14 of the Offices, Shops and Railway Premises (OSRP) Act. Some useful official guidance on seating facilities for use at VDU's is to be found in the HSE booklet "Visual Display Units", whilst older more general guidance is to be found in the Department of Employment's booklet "Seats for Workers in Factories, Offices and Shops" published in 1970. This contains guidance and a large number of photographs on seating design in a number of industrial and commercial settings.

Further information on work posture

- **TUC Guidelines on VDUs.**

- **Seats for workers in factories, offices and shops:** Health and Safety at Work booklet No. 45; HMSO.

- **Visual display units:** *useful guidance on workstation design;* HSE, 1983; HMSO.

- **Ordnance (AFS 1983:6) concerning work postures and working movements:** Swedish Board of Occupational Safety and Health; Stockholm, Sweden; *a short, clear summary of how workplaces should be designed to avoid aches, strains and pain.*

MANUAL HANDLING

About a quarter of all accidents notified to the Health and Safety Executive (HSE) every year are connected with the manual handling of loads. Past evidence from Industrial Injury benefit claims suggest that there may be:

- nearly 100,000 back injuries in Britain every year;

- leading to the loss of some 2 million working days;

- costing in the order of £60 million each year in lost time alone;

- with further costs to the NHS and insurance funds.

But the true cost of manual handling accidents cannot be measured in financial terms.

Damage to the back or spinal column — which is the key to all body movement — can quite literally disable its victims, making any sort of bodily activity either impossible or extremely painful. Back injuries can rarely be seen. They are often slow to heal and once damage has been done they often recur.

Manual handling accidents also cause sprains and strains of other parts of the body and can lead to other sorts of accidents — for example, when carrying dangerous substances or losing control of heavy loads which may be in situations where others may also be at risk.

Neither are manual handling injuries at work limited to the traditionally heavy industries. Analysis of strain injuries carried out by the HSE in 1982 shows a wide distribution of such injuries throughout all sectors of the economy.

Reducing the number of manual handling injuries at work means a radical approach to the problem.

In the past, the main emphasis has been on encouraging safe manual handling techniques at the workplace. Whilst this is important, it will only ever provide part of the answer. A more effective solution must be found by trying to eliminate manual hazards to which workers are exposed or reducing the scale of manual handling activity.

Assessing manual handling problems

By using their rights and functions under the Safety Representatives Committees Regulations, safety representatives can help identify sources of risk, mobilise their own members and press employers to make improvements in systems of work. For example, when carrying out regular health and safety inspections at your workplace, safety representatives should make a detailed assessment as follows:

- look critically at all work operations that involve lifting, carrying, pushing or pulling;

- make a list of all such tasks;

- what sort of loads are involved? — bags, boxes, bales, sacks, drums of chemicals, workpieces? — note their size and shape and weight;

- ask members how often they have to handle manually heavy loads; also through what heights? over what distance? under what conditions? how often? with what assistance?

- circulate a short questionnaire to members;

- make an inventory of typical loads and manual handling tasks for each department;

- look at the accident book — how many accidents seem to be connected with manual handling?;

- look at sickness absence records – how much is associated with 'back trouble' or 'rheumatism'?;

- ask members if they have ever suffered with a back problem — to what extent was it caused or aggravated by manually handling loads at work?;

- how many members with limited manual handling capacity (through age, size, poor health, pregnancy, etc) are being required to manually handle heavy loads?;

- are members required to handle heavy loads outside the workplace, *eg* delivering goods? — if so, they may be particularly at risk;

- rank the problems identified in terms of priority and work out which to tackle first.

Having assessed the size of the problem, safety representatives should make a short written report and discuss this with fellow members or post a copy on the workplace notice board, for example giving details of the total weight of loads manually handled by each member on a daily or weekly basis.

Legal standards

The present law is too vague to protect most workers from manual handling hazards.

In theory, all workers doing manual handling work are protected by Section 2 of the Health and Safety at Work Act. This requires all employers to ensure, so far as is reasonably practicable, the health, safety and welfare at work of all their employees by providing safe systems of work and adequate information, training and supervision.

In addition, older provisions like Section 72 of the Factories Act offer some assistance. It says: *"A person shall not be employed to lift, carry or move any load so heavy as to be likely to cause injury to him."*

There is a similar clause in the Offices, Shops and Railway Premises Act.

In practice, however, these requirements offer only limited help to workers. The emphasis is only on the weight of a load and no idea is given of how you decide what is too heavy. The law sets no limits on the frequency with which lifting can be carried out. In a few instances — (pottery, textiles, jute, agriculture) — maximum weights have been set, for men, women, and young people, but they are so high that they only protect against the very worst cases.

In 1982 the Health and Safety Commission published proposals designed to alter this situation. In a consultative document on manual handling they proposed new regulations and guidelines on manual handling to take other factors into account rather than just the weight of loads to be manually handled.

The TUC has generally welcomed this document but has called for its proposals to be strengthened in a number of important respects. Further proposals for a new package consisting of regulations, a code of practice and guidance are being prepared. There is also to be a European Directive on manual handling.

HSC's draft Regulation 3 suggested: *"A person shall not be employed to handle manually any load likely to injure him because of:*

a) *its weight, shape, size or lack of rigidity; or*

b) *the frequency with which he handles loads; or*

c) *the conditions under which the load is to be handled."*

Draft Regulation 4 placed a firm duty upon employers to make their workplace safe for lifting and carrying. It stated: *"Every employer shall ensure that systems of work involving the manual handling of loads shall be, so far as is reasonably practicable, safe."*

The HSC's draft guidelines, which were intended to accompany the new regulations, focused on sources of manual handling risks and how to tackle them. They advised that employers should develop safe systems of manual handling by careful consideration of the problems that exist and all possible solutions. They also stressed the need for full consultation between employers and trade union representatives on manual handling issues.

Solving manual handling problems

Once manual handling risks in the workplace have been identified the employer should be urged to solve the problem.

There are three broad approaches to reducing the hazards of manual handling.

- **elimination** — change to mechanical handling;

- **modification** — change the way manual handling work is organised or reduce its scale; and

- **adaptation** – match the workers to the task, *ie*, by relying on selection and training.

The solution to manual handling problems at the workplace often involves a mixture of all three approaches. But it needs to be remembered that tackling manual handling problems is rarely a one-off exercise. It requires a sustained campaign with short, medium and long-term objectives.

The best answer is to get rid of manual handling altogether — particularly the high risk manual handling tasks. In many cases this might not be possible straightaway, but it should not be assumed that lifting and carrying loads is an inevitable feature of work systems. For example:

- can lifting and carrying be avoided — for example, by using trolleys or conveyor systems?

- can the layout of the job be altered to remove the need for items to be carried from one place to another?; and

- can a bit of thought and good design get rid of difficult or awkward handling operations?

There usually is a lot of scope for improving existing manual handling operations, but often the best chance of changing the system lies in introducing new machines, processes or systems of work.

Safety representatives have a right to information about new processes, including plans and proposed workplace layouts and by being involved at the design stage they have the chance to get rid of problems before a new machine, process or work system is installed.

Mechanical handling

Mechanical devices may solve some of the lifting problems, but it is important to make sure that a whole new set of hazards are not introduced. Safety representatives should be provided with catalogues produced by manufacturers or suppliers of handling aids and equipment.

Cranes and lifting tackle must be inspected regularly under the provisions of the Factories Act and records kept of periodic examination and maintenance. Other devices, such as conveyors, trucks and trolleys, should also be examined regularly to make sure they are in good working order. This includes fork lift trucks for which

separate HSE guidance about maintenance and training requirements is available. All mechanical handling devices should be covered by a planned maintenance scheme, and all moving parts should be properly guarded.

Safety representatives should also make sure that increasing the unit size of loads by using mechanical handling techniques does not present somebody else with a manual handling problem further down the line.

Matching the job to the worker

If manual handling cannot be eliminated then the main aim should be to cut the weight of loads and to see that they are handled less often. At the same time, jobs should be reviewed to check that the health and safety of workers are not threatened by the loads they are lifting, carrying or moving about. It is important to remember that work systems should be adapted to suit workers, and not the other way round. In the end, there may be a few tasks which cannot be altered and which involve difficult lifting problems. In these cases, the workers who are required to do them should be physically suited and specially trained.

The relevant factors to be considered in matching the job to the work included their personal characteristics, their degree of skill and experience, the nature of the task, working conditions and the rate of work.

Protecting those most at risk

When requiring manual handling work, employers have a general duty to consider factors which might put workers at risk of injury such as their age, strength, state of health and degree of bodily development.

The HSC's draft guidelines advise that when changes occur in a worker's health, either permanently (*eg* physical disablement) or temporarily (*eg* hernia or post-operative recovery), manual handling work should be suitably adapted or they should be allocated alternative work.

The guidelines also say that women should not be required to handle manually heavy loads during pregnancy or during the 12 weeks immediately following confinement. It is often suggested that women should not be employed in work which involves manual handling. The Sex Discrimination Act specifically exempts physical strength or stamina as genuine reason for justifiable sex discrimination in employment.

Research shows that, in general, women's capacity to lift loads is roughly 45 to 60 per cent that of men. But their range of abilities will mean that many women can deal safely with greater loads than many men. Thus whenever manual handling ability amongst either men or women, appears to be a limiting factor, make sure they are not banned from such work but see that the work system is modified to suit their abilities. It should also be remembered that young people who are still growing are also at risk, often because of lack of experience and a tendency to over-enthusiasm. So it is important to make sure they are properly trained and supervised when doing manual handling jobs (see *Chapter 27: Young workers*).

Safe maximum weights?

When preparing a case for improved manual handling standards, the first thing to remember is that there is no such thing as a 'safe maximum weight'. Although of major importance, weight is only one factor that needs to be considered in deciding how much force is required to move a given load (and therefore how much risk is involved) under specific conditions.

People vary greatly in their ability to handle loads safely. What may be safe for the majority in a given situation may still leave a minority at risk. Task conditions can make a big difference as well.

Another way of looking at the problem is to consider the overall manual handling 'dose' to which the individual is subjected. Handling moderate sized loads frequently can often pose as great a risk as handling heavier loads only occasionally. This is because the injurious effects of repeated handling on muscles, joints and ligaments tend to be gradual and cumulative. A recent Health and Safety Commission Report on manual handling of patients in the Health Services estimated that in some areas nurses who handled patients were moving the equivalent of one and a quarter tonnes per hour! So it is important to agree a maximum weight per shift as well as a maximum weight for individual manual handling tasks.

As a starting point however, average weights can be specified to give a very rough idea of what most people can lift under 'laboratory' conditions. Laboratory research carried out at Surrey University suggests that, for fairly compact loads in ideal circumstances:

- 90 per cent of healthy adults can safely lift loads of up to 16 kg (35 lbs);

- 80 per cent of healthy adults can lift with comparative safety loads up to 34 kg (75 lbs); with specialist training, 10 per cent of healthy adults can safely lift loads of more than 34 kg (75 lbs) and up to 55 kg (120 lbs).

Weight ranges and suggested action by employers are given opposite, which are relevant to handling tasks involving the regular manoeuvring of fairly compact loads by an individual, in a good environment.

It is important to remember these levels, which have been derived from research findings, are set for ideal conditions. *They should not be accepted as safe maximum weights.* They can be used however as a rough starting point from which to arrive at specific values for particular manual handling tasks

in the workplace. But to do this it is necessary to take account of the following factors:

- the task conditions, including the overall working environment;
- the nature of the load;
- its weight;
- the nature of the lift;
- the rate of the work; and
- personal characteristics of those doing the work.

In other words:

- what loads?;
- weighing how much?;
- handling in what way?;
- how often?;
- under what conditions?; and
- by whom?

The answers to these six questions will enable safety representatives to *work downwards* from the weight ranges in the table below to arrive at more realistic maximum weights for specific manual handling tasks in the workplace. Each of the factors should be ranked in order and allocated percentage reductions.

WEIGHT RANGES IN LIFTING: RECOMMENDED ACTION BY EMPLOYERS

Range	Action
All weights	• All employees should be made aware of good practice relevant to their manual handling activities. • Employees who may be especially at risk should be identified and their capacity for manual handling. • Reducing the scale of individual manual handling activities should be periodically considered.
Below 16 kg (35 lb)	• No additional action required.
From 16 kg (35 lb) to 34 kg (75 lb)	• Exclude people unable to lift safely such loads with mechanical aids.
From 34 kg (75 lb) to 55 kg (120 lb)	• Mechanical or team systems or handling aids should be introduced wherever reasonably practicable. • Special selection, training and supervision will be necessary for unaided lifting.
Above 55 kg (120 lb)	• Mechanical handling or team systems or handling aids should be introduced except only where the workpeople involved are assessed capable of the regular lifting of such loads. *Note:* There will be very few people in this category. Special selection, training and supervision will be necessary for unaided lifting.

Task conditions

In addition to agreeing action for specific manual handling tasks it is also important to pay attention to task conditions. Here are some of the conditions that should be met for safe manual handling:

- workers should be fully trained in handling techniques — manual handling tasks should be properly supervised;

- operations should be conducted at a convenient height, preferably between waist and shoulder level — however, wherever possible, loads over 10 kg (22 lbs) should not be stored above this height;

- repetitive handling jobs should be avoided by reorganising work arrangements — if this

cannot be done, rest breaks should be provided;

- boring tasks should be prevented by introducing changes in the work pattern;

- loads should not be such that the carrier does not have a clear view ahead;

- where loads are particularly heavy, arrangements should be made for handling by two or more persons. When this is the case, special arrangements, instruction and supervision are needed to ensure teamwork and good communications — handling aids such as ropes and slings may be needed;

- if loads present special hazards, eg chemicals, livestock, hot materials etc, particular care is needed. Everyone involved should be aware of

---

MANUAL HANDLING CHECKLIST

Make a manual handling assessment at your workplace

1. What sort of loads are moved by whom, and how often?

2. Through what height?

3. Over what distance?

4. Under what conditions?

5. With what assistance?

6. What weights are involved?

7. Look at accident and sickness records for signs of 'back trouble' and 'rheumatism'.

8. Identify workers who may be at special risk.

9. Circulate a questionnaire to members.

10. Make a short written report to your shop stewards' committee, union branch or safety committee. Post a copy on the notice board giving details of loads manually handled by your members. Make a plan of action. Counter the opposition and mobilise support.

11. Press your employer to agree a forward programme of action and to examine ways of eliminating manual handling altogether by mechanical handling or modifying systems of work to reduce the scale of manual handling – preferably at the design stage – but pay attention to mechanical hazards. Ask for information from manufacturers and suppliers of mechanical handling aids.

12. See that your employer matches the job to the workers. Make sure they protect those most at risk, including workers disabled by ill health, pregnant women, young workers etc. But guard against job discrimination or dismissal.

13. Agree appropriate weight ranges with your employer for particular manual handling tasks. Make a list of all

relevant factors which justify reduction of the weight values set out in the above table including:
- nature of load;
- its weight;
- working conditions;
- nature of lift;
- frequency of handling; and
- skill, experience and any relevant personal factors.

14. Also agree a maximum weight per shift.

15. Where loads above agreed limits have to be handled, examine arrangements for:
- personnel selection;
- training workers in manual handling techniques (especially for itinerant workers) and 'authorisation' of trainers;
- supervision of manual handling tasks;
- rest periods or job rotation;
- personnel protection; and
- manning arrangements and provision for assistance with difficult loads.

16. Also ensure:
- heavy loads are stored at the correct height;
- the weight, contents and centre of gravity of heavy loads (including those above agreed action levels) are marked;
- all work areas are well laid out and adequately lit;
- that all means of access and exits are clear and free from obstruction;
- floors and walkways are clean and free from water or oil; insist on non-slip surfaces where necessary;
- the use of ladders as a means of manoeuvring heavy loads from one level to another is discouraged;
- make sure members understand the need for safe manual handling techniques; examine the need for retraining; and
- re-survey your workplace regularly to pinpoint manual handling hazards and review accident and ill health records for signs of manual handling injury.

the potential hazards and should be trained in emergency procedures;

- where specific risks arise from a load, suitable personal protection should be made available, *eg* gloves, aprons, goggles etc;

- loads should be easy to grip (for example, be provided with handles) and working surfaces, *eg* floors, table tops, trailers etc, should be smooth, dry and slip free;

- all work areas should be adequately lit; and

- loads should be clearly marked to give the approximate weight, and where appropriate, the contents and centre of gravity.

Safety representatives will need to look at these and other features in agreeing the best possible manual handling arrangements with their employers. It is most important to identify all the sources or risk that will justify reducing the ideal weight ranges and recommended actions set out in the table on weight ranges.

Further information on manual handling

- **Lighten the load:** *TUC brief on manual handling at work;* TUC, July 1983.

- **The lifting of patients in the Health Services:** HSC Health Services Advisory Committee; HMSO, 1984.

- **The handling of reels of paper and board:** HSC Paper and Board Industry Advisory Committee; HMSO, 1984.

- **Bale handling:** HSE Joint Standing Committee for the Wool Textile Industry; HMSO, 1985.

- **Manual handling:** a review paper; JDG Troup and FC Edwards; Health and Safety Executive, 1985.

- **Force limits in manual work:** Materials Handling Research Unit; University of Surrey.

- **Work Practices guide for manual lifting:** National Institute for Occupational Safety and Health (NIOSH). NIOSH Publication No. 81-122. 1981.

- **Health and Safety (Manual handling) Regulations 198X:** a consultative document issued by the HSC; the HSC is planning a further consultative document; HMSO.

REPETITIVE WORK

Repetitive work involving use of hands, arms, or legs can cause repetitive strain injuries (RSIs). These are injuries to the joints, muscles, nerves and tendons, caused by physical overload from repeated use of hands, limbs etc, repeated pressure being applied and the maintenance of a rigid posture. Repetitive strain injuries can result in pain, fatigue,

and crippling disability. They are much more widespread than is generally recognised and are frequently misdiagnosed. Potentially every worker who does a job which involves a repetitive movement is at risk. The following table lists some of the main RSIs, their symptoms, and typical causes.

Part of the problem in identifying whether the symptoms outlined above are those of RSI is that the same symptoms occur in muscle and tendon diseases which are not caused by repetition strain. But although eliminating repetition strain will not get rid of all muscle and tendon diseases, it will help eliminate those caused through work and make other musculo-skeletal problems easier to live with.

Most cases of RSI are difficult to treat. If however, they are caught in the early stages, when symptoms only appear towards the end of a shift, it may be possible to take action to prevent further damage — for example by getting rid of risk factors in the job, reducing the work rate, moving to other work, (or alternating with non repetitive tasks) or increasing the number of breaks from repetitive work.

In bad cases, surgery to treat carpal tunnel syndrome or tenosynovitis is sometimes recommended, but the results are frequently poor and do not allow the worker to return to repetitive work. When symptoms become acute, the only answer is to secure time off work until they have abated or to arrange transfer to alternative work — without loss of pay.

Other than the employer's general duties under the HSW Act, there are no legal requirements such as Codes or regulations designed to prevent RSIs. HSE have published a guidance note MS10 "Beat conditions — tenosynovitis" but this is out of date and ignores many causes of RSIs.

The key to preventing RSIs is making sure that manual jobs are fitted to the worker (and not the other way round) and that as far as possible certain hazardous features are designed out of manual work tasks. These include:

- forceful use of muscles in a repetitive way — *eg* using a hand screwdriver all day;

- using muscles at great speed for prolonged periods — *eg* keyboard operation; or

- working at the limit of the range of movement or reach.

Modifying job design to overcome these problems can be approached in a number of ways:

- reducing work rate;
- reducing repetition;
- bending controls and tools rather than the wrist;
- redesigning hand grips or controls;
- allowing arms to be kept low and elbows close to the body; and
- avoiding static work.

INJURY	SYMPTOMS	TYPICAL CAUSES
Bursitis: inflammation of the soft pad of tissue between skin and bone, or bone and tendon. Can occur at the knee, elbow, shoulder. Called 'beat knee', 'beat elbow' or 'frozen shoulder' at these locations.	Pain and swelling at the site of the injury.	Kneeling, pressure at the elbow, repetitive shoulder movements.
Carpal tunnel syndrome: pressure on the nerves which pass up the wrist.	Tingling, pain and numbness in the thumb and fingers, especially at night.	Repetitive work with a bent wrist. Use of vibrating tools. Sometimes follows tenosynovitis (see below).
Cellulitis: infection of the palm of the hand following repeated bruising, called 'beat hand'.	Pain and swelling of the palm.	Use of hand tools, like hammers and shovels, coupled with abrasion from dust and dirt.
Epicondylitis: inflammation of the area where bone and tendon are joined. Called 'tennis elbow' when it occurs at the elbow.	Pain and swelling at the site of the injury.	Repetitive work, often from strenuous jobs like joinery, plastering, bricklaying.
Ganglion: a cyst at a joint or in a tendon-sheath. Usually on the back of the hand or wrist.	Hard, small, round swelling, usually painless.	Repetitive hand movement.
Osteo-arthritis: damage to the joints resulting in scarring at the joint and the growth of excess bone.	Stiffness and aching in the spine and neck, and other joints.	Long-term overloading of the spine and other joints.
Tendonitis: inflammation of the area where muscle and tendon are joined.	Pain, swelling, tenderness and redness of hand, wrist, and/or forearm. Difficulty in using the hand.	Repetitive movements.
Tenosynovitis: inflammation of the tendons and/or tendon sheaths.	Aching, tenderness, swelling, extreme pain, difficulty in using the hand.	Repetitive movements, often non-strenuous. Can be brought on by sudden increase in work load or by introduction of new processes.
Tension neck or shoulder: inflammation of the neck and shoulder muscles and tendons.	Localised pain in the neck or shoulders.	Having to maintain a rigid posture.
Trigger finger: inflammation of tendons and/or tendon sheaths of the fingers.	Inability to move fingers smoothly, with or without pain.	Repetitive movements. Having to grip too long, too tightly, or too frequently.

Very often the rate at which manual tasks have to be performed is related to job pressure such as clearing backlogs of work, understaffing or badly designed bonus schemes — so the first approach is to make sure the pace of work does not put health at risk. The second line of approach is to reduce repetition through changing tools or equipment — for example mechanised materials handling, mechanised as opposed to manual fastening, redesigning stacking and storage systems — in other words designing out repetitive and stressful manual operations. This may be relatively easy for simple manual tasks but for more complex tasks where dexterity is involved it may be more difficult.

Here a third step which can be taken is to see whether tools and tasks can be redesigned to avoid bending the wrist, or hand grips can be redesigned so as to avoid sharp edges and small surface areas on grips. Improved controls or triggers can be provided which can be operated by more than one finger or tools or equipment can be redesigned to allow two-handed operation.

In addition to the design of tools and equipment, a fourth and very important factor which must be considered is the design of the work station itself — avoiding work layouts which involve raising the arms or shoulders.

Finally, all static work tasks which require muscles to be held in a fixed position should be avoided since often these can be more damaging than using moving muscles. For example the workpiece can be clamped or the body can be supported or braced against solid supports. Finally, reaching and stretching from a fixed position can be eliminated through good design.

The solution to RSI hazards often involves applying a combination of all the above approaches. In order to do this, safety representatives should identify a priority list of manual work tasks for redesign and improvements for example by doing a simple member questionnaire to indentify symptoms of RSI, observing jobs or looking at sickness records and drawing up a list of improvements to put to management. RSI hazards should always be examined when new work practices and layouts are being planned so that any problems can be controlled at the design stage. Here information from manufacturers of plant and tools should be studied to identify types which reduce RSI problems.

Finally if members do develop RSI they should be advised about compensation and their rights to benefit. A limited range of RSIs have been prescribed as industrial injuries under the Industrial Injuries Scheme (see *Chapter 30: Workplace health and safety services* for further details).

Further information on repetitive strain injury

- **Strains and sprains — a workers' guide to job design:** United Auto Workers; Detroit, Michigan, 1982; *a useful guide, including many good illustrations; good on repetitive strain injuries.*

- **Beat conditions, tenosynovitis:** HSE Guidance MS10; HMSO.

VIBRATION

Vibration hazards at work usually present themselves in two forms — whole body vibration (where the body is shaken by a machine or vehicle such as a lorry or a tractor) or hand/arm vibration where the vibration effect is localised to a particular part of the body — for example when using vibrating tools such as pneumatic hammers or chisels, chain saws, or electric grinders.

Whole body vibration

In the case of whole body vibration, the risk of damage depends on the frequency of vibration, its intensity (amplitude) and the length of exposure to it. Very low frequency vibration (less than one vibration per second) can cause motion sickness. Low frequency vibration (between one and 80 vibrations per second) may cause a range of symptoms: including weakness, fatigue, disturbed sleep, hernias, injuries to internal organs, blurred vision, and varicose veins in the anus (piles). Many of these problems are made worse by other sources of work strain such as bad posture, and muscle strain.

Vibration is measured by using equipment similar to noise meters. A special sensor is clamped to the point at which vibration needs to be measured and this is connected to a meter on which readings are given in metres per second (m/s) at different frequencies. Some metres combine intensities across a whole range of frequencies to give an overall reading. This reading in m/s can then be compared with prescribed limits.

There are no regulations in Britain describing limits for exposure to whole body vibration and no advice has been issued by HSE. Guidance has been issued however by the International Standards Organisation (ISO). This provides a framework for

ISO LIMIT — VERY LOW FREQUENCY VIBRATION (0.1-0.63 HZ)

	Exposure time	8 hrs	2 hrs	39 mins	1-4 min
Vibration	Severe discomfort	0.25	0.5	1.0	—
limit m/s	Reduced comfort	—	—	—	—

Source: ISO Standard 2631-1978 (addendum 1980)

ISO LIMIT — LOW FREQUENCY VIBRATION (1-80HZ)

	Exposure time	24 hrs	8 hrs	4 hrs	1 hr	16 mins
	Exposure limit	0.28	0.63	1.1	2.4	4.2
Vibration limit m/s	Limit to prevent fatigue	0.14	0.31	0.53	1.2	2.1
	Limit to preserve comfort	0.044	0.098	0.17	0.37	0.67

Source: ISO Standard 2631-1978

assessing whole body vibration hazards and covers very low frequency vibration (0-1 vibrations per second), and low frequency vibration (1-80 vibrations per second). The longer the exposure time, the lower the limit.

There are three broad approaches to reducing exposure to whole body vibration. These are:

- preventing vibration happening in the first place;
- isolating workers from it; or
- reducing the time for which workers are exposed.

Examples of preventing vibration are improving the design of vehicle suspension systems, improving the surface of road ways for fork lift trucks, improving engine design and mounting and preventative maintenance of plant and machinery. Examples of isolating workers from vibration can be seen in suspended cabs which are used on some commercial vehicles or trailers and the use of vibration isolating seats on both on and off road vehicles where these are provided either as standard fittings or optional extras provided by specialist seat manufacturers.

If these approaches do not work then altering work patterns may be the only solution in order to reduce exposure time. Since the only effective solution to whole body vibration hazards is to design out exposure from vehicles or plant, it is very important that such hazards are identified by safety representatives during consultation about new investment at the workplace. Comprehensive vibration data should be available from manufacturers and suppliers.

Hand and arm vibration

Wherever vibrating tools are used in agriculture or industry, cases of white finger (dead finger or Reynaud's phenomenon) are reported. This condition results from persistent microscopic damage to nerves and blood capillaries in the hands and fingers as a result of long term exposure to vibration. Under certain conditions — for example, exposure to cold — the blood supply to the fingers is cut off resulting in tingling and numbness. As can be seen from the following table these symptoms can get worse with time.

There is no effective treatment for white finger. If exposure to vibration stops however, symptoms may improve. Often vibration aggravates damage done by manual handling and repetitive work — for example carpal tunnel syndrome. Some of the different factors which influence the amount of damage done to the hands and arms by vibration include length of exposure; tightness of grip on tools, materials being worked, frequency of breaks, temperature, and the weight of the tools.

Vibration white finger was known about for many years, for example amongst stone cutters and riveters. It was only in 1981, as a result of TUC pressure that the Government's Industrial Injuries Advisory Council recommended that vibration white finger should be made a prescribed industrial disease. Some of the jobs in which it has been recognised as a problem include: using pneumatic drills, fettling, wheel dressing, chain sawing, swaging, riveting, using chipping hammers, concrete vibrating and shoe pounding.

Because of the potential damage to nerves, blood vessels, bones, joints, ligaments and tendons, it is important to assess the extent and nature of the vibration in order to understand how much damage will be done by a given exposure. Measurement of hand-arm vibration therefore is essential and the same techniques are used as for whole body vibration. For hand arm vibration however, it is essential to record the vibration intensity at different frequencies. This process is called octave band analysis and corresponds to a similar technique used in noise surveys (see *Chapter 8: Noise*). It is important to see that vibration measurement is carried out by an expert and HSE are often able to advise on organisations who can undertake such work.

STAGE	CONDITION	WORK AND SOCIAL INTERFERENCE
O	No blanching of digits.	No complaints.
OT	Intermittent tingling.	No interference with activities.
ON	Intermittent numbness.	No interference with activities.
1	Blanching of one or more fingertips with or without tingling and numbness.	No interference with activities.
2	Blanching of one or more fingers with numbness. Usually confined to winter.	Slight interference with home and social activities. No interference at work.
3	Extensive blanching. Frequent episodes summer as well as winter.	Definite interference at work and home and with social activities. Restriction of hobbies.
4	Extensive blanching. Most fingers; frequent episodes summer and winter.	Occupation changed to avoid further vibration exposures because of severity of signs and symptoms.

At present there are still no regulations or guidelines to limit exposure to hand/arm vibration. This is partly the result of continuing arguments about the extent of VWF and lack of data from which to predict the exact amount of damage likely to be done by a vibrating object. British Standard BD43 however provides a framework for making a rough assessment of vibration hazards. This hazard has two limits – a lower limit which can be reached for up to no longer than 400 minutes per shift – vibration which exceeds this limit is acceptable provided the period of exposure is reduced below 400 minutes – and an upper limit which can be reached for up to 150 minutes per shift and which can never be exceeded. The Standard excepts however, that sticking to these limits will not necessarily prevent VWF from developing.

Controlling vibration hazards

Controlling vibration hazards means first and foremost trying to remove the need for vibrating tools and machinery — for example improved mould making techniques in foundries can often reduce the need to fettle castings. Another example is the use of air arc gouging as a vibration free way of removing metal — or robots can be used where vibration is unavoidable.

The next step is to use vibration reduced tools. Some modern pneumatic tools have been specially designed to produce less vibration than their predecessors. Some of these have vibration isolating handles — for example as on modern chainsaws.

None of these approaches however will work unless tools and equipment are adequately maintained. This may involve for example, the correct dressing of grinding wheels, regular renewal of vibration isolators, regular tuning of engines, frequent sharpening of cutters or regular general maintenance. Sometimes things can be improved by supporting tools or workpieces or removing exposure to cold — for example by warming the tool or workpiece or warming the workplace.

Finally, if none of these approaches is practicable, then the only solution is to reduce time on the job by job rotation, by reducing output or by having more regular breaks.

More information on vibration

- **Vibration injuries of the hand and arms:** M J Griffin; HSE Research Paper No. 9; HMSO, 1980; *detailed review of the hazards and the standards; does not cover control measures.*

- **Chain-saws:** HSE Guidance PM 31; HMSO.

13: Machinery guarding

A large number of the most serious accidents people suffer at work involve machinery of one kind or another. Hundreds of lives are lost and tens of thousands of workers are injured or maimed every year because of faulty machine guarding, despite there being strong legal standards of safety for the protection of people coming in contact with dangerous parts of machines.

Accidents occur on machinery for several reasons:

- the guarding on the machine is badly designed, causing workers to raise the guard so they can do the job;

- the machine and guards are not maintained properly;

- guards are not provided;

- no attempt is made to ensure guards are used;

- the system of payment by bonus rates has taken no account of safety factors, and encourages workers to cut corners;

- workers are inadequately trained; and

- inadequate systems for maintenance and breakdown work.

Carelessness is often used as a reason for machinery accidents. However blaming workers for accidents can divert attention from the real problem. Machines have to be guarded effectively, removing the hazard at source. There are many ways that a worker may be injured by machinery. The British Standards Institute (BSI) has published BS Number 5304, setting out the principles of safe machinery guarding. This standard is referred to in the rest of this section.

HOW WORKERS GET INJURED

A person may be injured at machinery as a result of:

- coming into contact with moving parts or materials – being hit or getting caught;

- getting trapped between moving parts or material and any fixed structure; or

- being hit by material or machine parts which have been thrown out of the machine.

DANGEROUS PARTS OF MACHINERY

These can be arranged in the following groups:

Rotary motions

a) *Shafts*
Includes couplings, spindles, chucks, leadscrews, mandrels and bars.

b) *Projections and apertures*
Some rotating parts are even more dangerous because of projections or apertures. For example: fan blades, spoked pulleys, chain wheels, gear wheels, flywheels, mixer and beater arms, spiked cylinders, carding surfaces, cages in centerfuges, projecting keys, set screws, cotter pins on shafts.

c) *Abrasive or cutting tools*
These parts come into contact with material in order to alter its shape, size or finish. For example: abrasive wheels, all kinds of cutting tools, circular saws, milling cutters.

d) *In-running nips between:*

- parts rotating in opposite directions;

- rotating and moving parts; and

- rotating and fixed parts.

Reciprocating or sliding motions

The moving part is usually supported in guides. The danger point occurs when the moving part approaches or passes another fixed or moving part.

Rotating/sliding motions

Some mechanisms contain a combination of sliding and turning movement. For example: certain cam gear designs, the nip points between the connecting rods or links and rotating wheels, the mechanism on some flat-bed printing machines, textile machines.

Oscillating motions

Some arrangements of machinery parts may present oscillating movements such as in a pendulum. Other trapping points may occur because of scissor movements.

Contact with material

At some machinery injury can be caused by contact with the material being processed. For example: a rotating stockbar in a lathe, or risk of being struck by sheet metal being formed in a press brake. More commonly, accidents involving material being processed are not caused by the material alone but the material drawing a person into contact with dangerous parts of the machinery.

Ejection of machine parts

Injury can be caused by the ejection of parts of machinery. For example: the flying shuttle of a loom, a loose cutter on a vertical spindle moulding machine, broken tooling on a press, the bursting of an abrasive wheel.

Ejection of material

Several machine processes create a risk of material being thrown out with enough force to cause injury. For example, flying swarf, ejection of a workpiece, molten metal splash from a diecasting machine, sparks from a welding process.

LEGAL STANDARDS

Health and Safety at Work Act

Sections 2, 3, and 4 of the HSW Act put a duty on employers to safeguard the health and safety of employees and others.

Sections 2(2)(a) and 2(2)(c) provide a duty to provide and maintain safe plant and safe systems of work. There is also a duty to inform, instruct, train and supervise.

Section 6 of the HSW Act places a duty on manufacturers, designers and suppliers to provide machinery that is safe and to provide necessary information.

Factories Act 1961

Sections 12-21 of the Factories Act 1961, together with various regulations, list the requirements. Standards are also given in section 82 of the Mines and Quarries Act 1954; section 17 of the Offices, Shops and Railway Premises Act 1963 and the Agricultural (safety, health and welfare provisions) Act 1956. Many of the standards laid down in these Acts are similar to those in the

Factories Act and it is this Act that is examined in more detail below.

Section 12 states that every moving part of a prime mover (an engine or appliance giving mechanical energy), and every part of electric generators, motors and rotary converters should be securely fenced.

Section 13 deals with 'transmission machinery' which includes shafts, wheels, couplings and driving belts. This section states that all dangerous parts should be securely fenced unless a device is fitted which will automatically prevent the operator from coming into contact with the dangerous part. This qualification allows interlock devices of guards of the photo-electric kind to be used, if they are as safe as fencing would be.

Section 14 states that every dangerous part of machinery shall be securely fenced. This section is the most important section of the Factories Act where the guarding of machinery is concerned. Although the terms used may seem very general, they are capable of very strict application. *If the part of machinery is dangerous it must be guarded*, even if it means the machine can't be used.

Section 15 states that only if machines need to be examined, oiled, or adjusted while in motion, may they be approached without guards in place. Then only by certificated machinery attendants who must be skilled, over 18, properly dressed and accompanied by another person who will know what to do in an emergency.

Section 16 deals with the construction and maintenance of fencing. It states that fencing must be of substantial construction, maintained in efficient working order, and kept in position when the parts required to be fenced are in motion.

Section 17 is concerned with the manufacturers of machines for sale or hire in this country. They must see that gears which do not need adjustment in motion, and set screws, bolts or keys on transmission shafts or wheels, are guarded. But that is all. It is the employer who must see that the machinery is guarded to meet the standards of other sections of the Factories Acts.

Section 18 stipulates that every uncovered fixed vessel, structure, sump or pit containing anything dangerous which people might fall into must be either securely covered or fenced to at least three feet above the ground. It goes on to give details of the type and size of the fencing.

Section 19 says that there must be a gap of at least 18 inches between the outward travel of self-acting machines and fixed structures where the movement would obstruct a passageway. It also says that no workers should be in that gap. Proper instructions must be given to the person in charge of the machine to ensure that nobody is working in the 'trapping' area.

Section 20 prohibits young people under 18 from cleaning machinery while it is in motion.

Section 21 deals with the training and supervision of young people under 18, who work with dangerous machines. It states they should receive adequate training and supervision while working at the machines. A number of machines are listed in the Factories Act as 'dangerous'.

Other regulations

Regulations have also been made to allow certain dangerous types of machines to be used, *eg* abrasive wheels and woodworking machines. On the other hand the Power Press Regulations 1965 impose very strict standards of guarding, inspection and training. As a result of these regulations accidents at power presses decreased significantly. Safety representatives should apply this type of 'safe workplace' strategy to all dangerous machines in factories, offices, schools, and hospitals.

METHODS OF GUARDING

The main types of guards are:

- *fixed guards* – these should prevent contact of any part of the body with the dangerous part, no matter what the angle of operation is.

- *interlocking guards* – these should ensure the opening is automatically closed before the machine can be operated, and will remain closed till the operation is completed.

- *automatic guards* – these are usually of the photo-electric type for power presses.

- *trip guards* – these should ensure that, if the position of operation is such that the operator is liable to be injured, the guard will automatically stop the machine.

Examples of trip devices are:

- *mechanised trip devices* – if part of the body touches the barrier the device operates;

- *pressure sensitive mats* – if the operator stands on the mat the dangerous part should stop; and

- *photo-electric trip devices* – if a part of the body interrupts a light curtain the machine stops.

MACHINERY MAINTENANCE

Sections 2(1), and 2(2)(a) of the Health and Safety at Work Act and the *HSC Checklist* cover the maintenance of machines. Regular maintenance and inspection of machines and their safeguards are essential, in order to discover potential problems and put them right. Safeguards should not be installed and then left without preventive maintenance by a competent person.

TRAINING

Section 2(2)(c) and the *HSC Checklist* cover the training of management, supervisors and members who work on machines. Too often it is assumed that people know all there is to know about machinery safety. Accident records show otherwise and good training policy can overcome this. BS 5305 states that even where machinery is adequately safeguarded managers, supervisors and work people should be properly trained in the safe operation of their machinery and to report guard defects so that remedial action can be taken. The training and supervision of young persons is particularly important.

Designers of machinery and guards should be trained in:

- methods of integrating safeguards into machinery at the design stage;

- ergonomic consideration; and

- factors contributing to failure to safety.

Plant engineers should be trained in:

- principles of safeguarding machinery;

- maintenance of safeguards; and

- precautions during maintenance work, including safety systems of work, and where necessary, permit work and lock-off systems – for example, padlock, captive key, interlock key exchange.

Maintenance staff should be trained in:

- principles of safeguarding machinery;

- electrical and mechanical safety; and

- safe systems of work, including permit-to-work and lock-off systems during maintenance operations.

SAFE SYSTEMS

Management are required to provide safe systems of work under the HSW Act Section 2. Maintenance workers need to enter danger areas on occasions. Here they may be out of sight and exposed to danger if the plant is switched on.

To meet trade union standards and legal obligations management should initiate a 'permit-to-work' system, requiring formal action on the part of those doing the work, those responsible for it, and those authorised to sign such permits.

OPERATOR'S CHECKLIST

Check every time that:

- you know how to stop the machine before you start it;
- all fixed guards are fitted correctly and all mechanical guards are working properly;
- all materials to be used are clear of working parts of the machine;
- the area around the machine is clean, tidy and free from obstruction;
- your supervisor is told at once if you think a machine is not working properly; and
- you are wearing appropriate protective clothing and equipment, such as safety glasses or safety shoes.

Never:

- use a machine unless you are authorised and trained to do so;
- attempt to clean a machine in motion – switch it off and unplug it;
- use a machine or appliance which has a danger sign or tag attached. Danger signs should be removed only by an authorised person who is satisfied that the machine or process is safe;
- wear dangling chains, loose clothing, gloves, rings or long hair which could get caught up in moving parts; or
- distract people who are using machines.

FURTHER INFORMATION

British Standard BS 5304 *Safety of Machinery* is a useful guide. It illustrates machinery hazards and methods of safeguarding them. Your supplier or machine manufacturer should also be able to advise you. There are several HSE publications on machinery safety including the following:

- **Circular saws; AS11.**
- **Safety with chain saws; AS20.**
- **Power take-off and power take-off shafts; AS24.**
- **Obligations on importers of machinery, plant and substances in Great Britain; IND(G) 1(L).**
- **Power presses and press brakes: minimum safety tests for guards and other safety devices: (set of five cards); IND(G) 7(C)-11(C).**
- **Guarding of portable pipe-threading machines; 1984; GN: PM1.**
- **Guards for planing machines; 1976; GN: PM2.**
- **Dough dividers; 1976; GN: PM6.**

- **Tripping devices for radial and heavy vertical drilling machines; 1977; GN: PM10.**
- **Safety in the use of woodworking machines; 1981; GN: PM21.**
- **Photo-electric safety systems; 1981; GN: PM23.**
- **Safety of bandsaws in the food industry; GN: PM33.**
- **Safety in the use of reversing dough brakes; 1983; GN: PM35.**
- **Application of photo-electric safety systems to machinery; 1984; GN: PM41.**
- **Expanded polystyrene moulding machines; 1986; GN: PM62.**
- **Scrap baling machines; GN:PM66.**
- **Safety in the use of abrasive wheels; HS(G)17.**
- **Guarding of cutters of horizontal milling machines; HS(G)24.**
- **Catering safety: food preparation machinery; HS(G)35.**
- **Pie and tart machines; HS(G)31.**
- **A guide to the Woodworking Machines Regulations 1974; HS(R)9.**

14: Cranes and lifting gear

Cranes are by their very nature, dangerous to work with, and dangerous to work near. The main dangers stem from poor maintenance, mishandling of equipment and lack of care by those working with or near cranes and lifting machines.

LEGAL REQUIREMENTS

The safety measures required in the operation of cranes and lifting gear are laid down in section 27 of the Factories Act, 1961, the Construction (Lifting Operations) Regulations and Shipbuilding Regulations. The definition of a lifting machine is given as a crane, winch, teagle, pulley block, gin wheel, transporter or runway.

There are a number of legal requirements in the Factories Act which can be briefly summarised as:

- all parts must be of good construction, free from defects and properly maintained;

- before a crane is used for the first time it must be thoroughly examined and tested by a competent person and a certificate obtained which specifies the safe working load;

- this safe working load (usually shown as SWL) must be clearly marked on the crane, and no crane should be loaded beyond this limit;

- no person is allowed to work on the wheeltracks within 20 feet of a crane – similarly no one is allowed to work under a crane where they might be struck, unless effective steps are taken to warn them;

- every part of the crane must be thoroughly examined every 14 months; and

- a register must be kept giving particulars of the tests, dates of examinations, defects found and steps taken to remedy them.

The Construction (Lifting Operations) Regulations 1961, state that cranes should, besides being examined every 14 months, *"be inspected at least once a week by the driver"*. So as far as the Construction Regulations are concerned the crane driver is, in many cases, expected to be able to carry out working inspections. These inspections are different from the 'thorough examinations' which are normally carried out by suitably qualified outside specialists, such as engineers and insurance company surveyors.

TYPES OF CRANE

The three most common types of cranes in use are the electric overhead travelling (EOT) crane, the mobile crane and the tower crane. There are various types of mobile crane such as the self-propelled, lorry-mounted, crawler-type, and rail-type. Many accidents take place on, or near, the EOT crane, particularly to workers engaged on maintenance work. Some hazards to look out for are:

- people working on the wheeltrack may be struck by a crane on the same, or adjacent, track;

- people working on a moving EOT crane may be trapped in places of limited clearance;

- people carrying out their duties above floor level may be struck by an EOT crane or by the load carried;

- tools or equipment may fall from an EOT crane and cause injury to people working below;

- people working on an EOT crane may fall to floor level; and

- workers may come in contact with live electric conductors.

CRANE DRIVERS AND TRAINING

With the various types of mobile cranes, the most important safety factor is the skill of the crane driver. As the mobile crane becomes more complex, drivers must have a greater degree of skill than in the past. Drivers are now expected not only to drive the crane safely but to carry out such tasks as erecting the jib and attending to the hoist and derrick ropes. They also have to fit the correct balance weight, correct load radius indicator and set the automatic safe load indicator. All this requires special training, because an untrained crane driver is an unsafe crane driver. Training courses will vary, but should include some of the following points:

- *controls* – drivers must be fully familiar with the controls of the crane;

- *signals* – drivers must know the code used in the workplace, and must understand that signals should be accepted only from the slinger responsible for the lift, except in cases of emergency when a signal to stop is given;

- *overloading* – drivers must be aware of the weight of a load, and be sure that the safe load indicator (where provided) is working properly;

- *misuse* – drivers must be aware of misusing the crane, and avoid shock loads, fast slewing, and lifting loads they cannot see without a signaller. The overwind limit switch should not be used for controlling normal hoisting motions – this device is a safeguard, and is not intended to be used as part of the operating mechanism; and

- *ground* – drivers must be able to make a sound assessment of the ground on which they are operating, so that they will know when there is a risk of overturning because of the slope or subsidence.

The importance of training crane drivers, applies equally to tower crane drivers though many accidents with tower cranes come from faulty installation.

LIFTING TACKLE

Due regard must be paid to the importance of chains, ropes and other lifting tackle such as slings, rings, hooks and swivels. The Factories Act states that these items must be of good construction, sound material and adequate strength, and that the lifting gear must be tested and examined by a competent person, who should issue a suitable certificate. Other details spelt out in section 26 of the Factories Act are:

- tables of safe working loads must be posted in the tackle store and in prominent positions in the works – these tables need not cover any gear which has the safe working load marked on it;

- no chain, rope or lifting tackle may be used for any load exceeding the safe working load;

- chains, ropes and lifting tackle must be thoroughly examined by a competent person every six months;

- wrought iron gear must be periodically annealed, or effectively heat treated by some other method; and

- a register must be kept giving particulars, for each item of gear, of the test certificate, dates of thorough examinations, defects found and steps taken to remedy them, the dates of annealing or other heat treatment (where appropriate).

FOUR KEY POINTS

There are many other requirements for lifting gear in various regulations, but there are four important things to look out for:

- all lifting gear should be obtained from reliable manufacturers;

- lifting gear must have been tested and thoroughly examined by a competent person before being used;

- if the safe working load is not marked on the gear, this information must be given in tables to which the slinger can easily refer; and

- the use of home-made or improvised gear is dangerous and illegal, unless it has been tested and thoroughly examined by a competent person.

CHECKLIST

1. The training and health of crane drivers are of crucial importance.
2. What training has the crane driver at your workplace had?
3. Is the person's eyesight good enough for the job; has their sight been tested and when?
4. Is the safe working load (SWL) of the crane clearly indicated, both for slinger and crane driver?
5. Are there adequate, safe ways of entering and leaving for the crane driver?
6. Systematic examinations of cranes and equipment are important – they should be thoroughly examined every 14 months, with more frequent inspections.
7. Who is responsible for seeing that lifting tackle is properly stored and tested? Where are the results of the tests kept?
8. Mobile cranes should not be operated on unstable ground or near excavations – unless they are safely shored up.
9. Slinger and banksmen should be experienced, competent persons. What training do these workers receive, and who trains them?

CHECKING UP REGULARLY

Safety representatives may themselves be crane
drivers or slingers, but, if not there are a number of
valuable things that can be done to anticipate and
prevent accidents. For example, checking to see
that maintenance is carried out regularly; that tests
are undertaken by responsible members of
management; that a good standard of housekeeping
is kept, and that crane drivers get proper training.
Any lowering of standards should be reported
immediately to the supervisor, and if no satisfaction
is obtained, to the Safety Committee.

USEFUL PUBLICATIONS

General

- **Code of Practice for safe use of cranes**
  (mobile cranes, tower cranes and derrick
  cranes): British Standards Institution; CP 3010;
  1972.

- **Safety handbook for mobile cranes:** ROSPA.

- **Erection and dismantling of tower cranes;**
  1976; GN: PM3.

- **Lifts — thorough examination and testing;**
  1982; GN: PM7.

- **Passenger-carrying paternosters;** 1977;
  GN: PM8.

- **Access to tower cranes;** 1979; GN: PM9.

- **Cable-laid slings and grommets;** 1981; GN:
  PM20.

- **Safety at rack and pinion hoists;** 1981; GN:
  PM24.

- **Safety at lifting launchings:** GN: PM26;
  HMSO.

- **Construction hoists;** 1981; GN: PM27.

- **Suspended access equipment;** 1983; GN:
  PM30.

- **Safety in the use of escalators;** 1983; GN:
  PM34.

- **Escalators: periodic thorough
  examination;** 1984; GN: PM45.

- **Wedge and socket anchorage for wire
  ropes:** GN: PM46; HMSO.

- **Lifting gear standards;** 1985; GN: PM54.

- **Safe working with overhead travelling
  cranes:** GN: PM55.

- **Inclined hoists used in building and
  construction work;** 1987; GN: PM63.

15: Hazards from hand tools

Hand tools are man's oldest working instruments. They are so familiar that very little thought of danger enters a worker's head when using them. However, accidents through the use of hand tools run into tens of thousands a year. In factories alone the figure is over 20,000 a year.

The type of hand tools we are considering here are such things as hammers, chisels, drifts, spanners, screwdrivers, knives, files and scrapers and hand tools used on lathes. While it is important that these tools are used properly it is extremely difficult to work safely with faulty or worn equipment. It is important, therefore, that all tools that are not in good condition should be returned to the stores or supplier, and the defects pointed out. This is often a nuisance and requires a bit of effort, but a bit of effort may save someone's eyes or fingers.

SAFETY PRECAUTIONS

Safe working with hand tools is like many other activities – it is a mixture of common sense, safe procedures and intelligent observation. There are four golden rules for working with hand tools:

- use the correct tool for each type of job;
- use only tools which are in good condition;
- stow all tools safely, particularly at heights; and
- wear eye protectors when provided.

The following detailed safety procedures should also be observed.

HAMMERS

The head should be securely attached to the shaft. The head should be in good condition, and the face free from chipped edges and not rounded from wear. The shaft should be in good condition and, if it is split, broken or loose, the hammer should not be used.

SPANNERS AND WRENCHES

Do not use set spanners or wrenches with splayed jaws, or box spanners which show signs of splitting. Use a fixed spanner – either rigid jawed or ring – of the correct size wherever possible in preference to an adjustable spanner. Do not use a tube to obtain extra leverage, or hammer the end of a spanner. Do not use a spanner as a hammer. See that the hand will clear any obstructions when the nut turns. Always use the right size of spanner for the job. Never pack the gap between the spanner and the nut with shims or washers. Never use a spanner as a wedge.

CHISELS AND DRIFTS

Never use a chisel with a mushroomed head. At the first sign of mushrooming, the chisel head should be correctly dressed on a grinding wheel. Use the chisel to cut in a direction away from the body. Cutting edges of chisels must always be kept sharp so that the original shape and angle of the cutting edges is maintained. The resharpened chisels should be suitably hardened and tempered.

SCREWDRIVERS

Frequent cause of accidents is holding the workpiece in the palm of the hand while tightening up screws, a slip can result in a serious injury through the screwdriver penetrating the hand or wrist. The piece being worked upon should not be held in one hand and the screwdriver used in the other – work should be secured in a vice or held on other firm support.

See that the handle is secure. Never use a screwdriver as a chisel or strike it with a hammer. Do not use a screwdriver with a split handle, even if it is bound with string or tape. Scrap the tool or fit a new handle. Use the correct size of screwdriver for the job.

For electrical work, screwdrivers with insulated handles should be used, but these should not be taken as giving absolute protection against electric shock.

FILES

Never use a file with an exposed tang, it is more sensible to have a handle fitted. Do not use a file as a lever or toggle-bar, hardening has made it brittle and it will easily snap. If filing in a lathe do not place your hand or file near the chuck, it is safer and more efficient to learn to do filing left-handed. Always check that the handle of the file is secure. In many cases, using a file on lathework is a lazy way of doing the job, and this can often be done more safely and efficiently by a tool mounted in the tool post.

KNIVES

When used for cutting greasy materials, the handle should be designed to offer a firm grip and a shield should be fitted between the handle and the blade. It may also be necessary to wear a stout apron to protect the abdomen in case the knife should slip. So far as possible, the cut should always be made away from the body.

TRAINING AND SUPERVISION

Adequate training and supervision is needed:

- to ensure that hand tools are used correctly;
- that the correct ones are used for specific work;
- that they are maintained in a fully serviceable condition;
- that they are properly guarded and stowed safely when not being used; and
- that they are scrapped and replaced when worn.

ERGONOMIC DESIGN OF HAND TOOLS

From an ergonomic point of view a number of basic requirements for the design of an efficient hand tool have been specified:

- it should effectively perform its intended function;
- it should be properly proportioned to the dimensions of the user;
- it should be appropriate to the strength and endurance of the user;
- it should minimise user fatigue; and
- it should provide sensory feedback.

CHECKLIST

1. Wooden handles of hand tools should be:
    - made of best quality straight grained material;
    - of suitable shape and size; and
    - smooth, without splinters or sharp edges.

2. Where there is any risk of an explosive atmosphere being ignited by sparks, the hand tools used should be of a non-sparking type.

3. Hammers and sledges, cold chisels, cutters, punches and other similar shock tools should be made of special material, hard enough to withstand blows but not so hard as to chip or break.

4. The head of shock tools should be dressed or ground to a suitable radius on the edge as soon as they begin to mushroom or crack, they should be tempered, dressed or repaired only by competent people.

5. Hand tools should be:
    - issued through a tool room, in which they are stored safely on racks or shelves, in cabinets or tool boxes; and
    - inspected periodically by competent people – if inspection reveals faulty equipment, repaired or replaced before re-issue.

16: Protection of eyes

Of all the risks workers have to face, injury to the eye is often the most unpleasant and each such incident is potentially serious. This is because there is no certainty that a 'minor' eye injury will not turn into a major impairment of vision or even loss of sight. Latest available figures show that there are over 10,000 accidents to the eyes occurring each year at work which cause people to be absent for more than three days.

The risks to which the eyes may be exposed and for which protection may well be necessary include:

- impact of flying particles;
- splashing of liquids;
- dust;
- irritation by gases and vapours;
- molten metal splash; and
- exposure to non-ionising radiations – infra-red, ultra-violet and visible light and lasers.

EYE INJURIES

The presence of a foreign body is the most common form of minor eye injury. Most small particles tend to be washed out by tears but some will be retained in the eye, particularly within the margin of the upper eyelid or may become embedded in the surface of the cornea where they cause irritation followed by reddening of the surface and, if not removed, they may produce an ulcer or infection.

Major injuries to the eye occur when the eyeball is perforated, burnt by heat or chemicals or disrupted by a blow. Severe blows can cause fractures of the bones around the eye, which may produce subsequent distortion of the lids or malposition of the eye leading to double vision. Occasionally, the whole eyeball may be torn out of its socket with injury to the muscles and the optic nerve. There is also the possibility of retinal detachment or internal bleeding.

One of the possible consequences of eye injury is the development of cataract. For example, traumatic cataract can develop fairly rapidly within weeks as a result of a penetrating injury which damages the lens of the eye. Heat cataract on the other hand can take a period of years to develop and may occur even after the worker has left the industry which caused it. Heat cataract usually affects workers in industries such as steelmaking, furnace, and foundry work, glassmaking and ceramics, but they may be caused by any exposure to heat and glare, rays from molten metal or red hot materials – this is a Prescribed Industrial Disease No A2. Radiation Cataract can affect workers exposed to other forms of radiation, *eg* ionising radiations such as gamma rays, X-rays, or neutrons.

HIGH RISK INDUSTRIES

There are numerous occupations in which accidents to the eye are a special risk. In agriculture there are many minor injuries from smoke, fertilisers, sawdust, chaff and insects, the more serious injuries occurring from work with hedges and in forestry, where perforating wounds are not uncommon.

In industry, foundry work, engineering, building construction and work in the chemical industry are the chief causes of eye accidents, of which one-half may be caused by particles or splashes.

Special dangers arise from the dry grinding of metal, the turning of non-ferrous metals or of cast iron and from the use of hand tools or portable electric power tools or pneumatic tools for the cleaning and fettling of metal castings, cutting rivets or bolts, chipping or scaling boilers and breaking stones and concrete. Much risk occurs from the use of chipping tools such as hammers and chisels. Hazards also arise from the manipulation of sodium hydroxide, the handling of calcium oxide, pipework or supply lines containing dangerous liquids or gases and the opening of drums or containers of dangerous liquids in which pressure has been caused by dents. Operations at hardening plants, where there is a risk of cyanide or metal nitrite splashing, and work in tinplating and tar and pitch plants are also especially hazardous. The use of compressed air for clearing dust is a major source of danger.

Ultra-violet light produced by welding and cutting or oxyacetylene burning produces acute inflammation of the eyes (arc eye), particularly in bystanders who may fail to wear personal protective equipment. Here it is worth pointing out that the use of contact lenses, whether they are made of plastic or glass, does not present any additional hazard to the cornea and indeed they may well reduce to some extent the penetration of ultra-violet light. It is, of course, possible that, if the wearer of contact lenses were to sustain a flash burn, the lenses might give rise to additional irritation. (If the eyes started to become painful after exposure to flash, a sensible precaution would be for the wearer to remove the lenses and not to replace them until the irritation had subsided).

Chemical burns are not unusual in industry and of these, burns from alkalis are the most serious, because they penetrate more easily than acids. Ammonia is a particular risk owing to its widespread use. Work in the iron and steel industry and foundries leads to a risk of severe burns from molten metal. Some fumes may cause eye irritation at low concentrations in air *eg* styrene and butanol.

PROTECTION OF EYES REGULATIONS

The Protection of Eyes Regulations 1974 specify 32 processes in which it is necessary for employers to provide suitable and approved eye protection for their employees. These Regulations apply to premises subject to the Factories Act 1961 but in fact similar requirements apply to other premises and work activities because of the general duties on employers under the Health and Safety at Work Act 1974.

The Regulations require that eye protection must be issued on a personal basis for most of the processes except where an individual is only 'occasionally employed'. The eye protectors must be suitable for the individual in relation to the degree of protection necessary and they must also be made to a specification approved by HM Chief Inspector of Factories. At the present time, eye protectors complying with one or a combination of three British Standards are approved, these are:

- **Industrial Eye Protection:** BS 2092;

- **Equipment for eye, face and neck protection against non-ionising radiation**

Schedules 1 and 11 of Protection of Eyes Regulations
Approved eye protectors are required for:

- shot-blasting of buildings;
- use of high-pressure water jets;
- use of cartridge tools;
- use of hammers, chisels or punches;
- chipping of paints, slag or rust;
- use of metal cutting saws or abrasive discs;
- pouring or skimming of molten metal;
- operations at molten salt baths;
- work in the presence of acids, alkalis and dangerous corrosive materials;
- injection of liquids into building structures;
- breaking up, cutting or dressing of metal castings, glass, plastics, plaster, slag, stone, etc;
- removal of swarf by compressed air;
- furnace and foundry work;
- wire rope manufacture;
- cutting of wire or strapping under tension; and
- glass manufacture.

Fixed shields or approved shields are required for:

- work with electric arcs or plasma arcs.

Processes where eye protector or approved shields or approved fixed shields are required:

- gas welding;
- hot-fettling of castings;
- flame cutting;
- lasers;
- turning or dressing of abrasive wheels;
- work with power hammers, drop hammers and horizontal forging machines;
- dry-grinding of materials held by hand;
- fettling of metal castings;
- any machinery process where fragments may be thrown off; and
- electric arc welding.

Protection required for persons in the presence of but not directly engaged in:

- chipping of metal or knocking out, cutting or shearing of rivets, bolts, plugs, nuts, lugs, pins, collars and similar articles by means of hand or portable power tools;
- processes where there are exposed electric or plasma arcs;
- work with drop-hammers, power-hammers or forging machines;
- fettling of castings; and
- lasers.

arising during welding and similar operations: BS 1542; and

- **Filters for use during welding and similar industrial operations:** BS 679.

In addition, a separate specification for laser eye protection has been approved. For some processes fixed-shields may be provided as an alternative.

BRITISH STANDARDS

BS 2092:1967

This Standard sets out the requirements for eye protection (spectacles, goggles and face-shields) for use where danger arises from contact with objects and flying particles, molten metal, liquid splash, dust and gases.

In relation to protection against mechanical hazards where there is only a need to protect against occasional small impacts, the 'General Purpose' grade of spectacle may be used. This type of protection may use lenses made of toughened glass or plastic making it more robust than a normal pair of spectacles. It will not be suitable where exposure to fast-moving particles is likely such as, during grinding operations, nor where other risks may be present. Both lenses and frames of 'General Purpose' spectacles will be marked BS 2092.

Where exposure to more serious mechanical hazards is likely such as when grinding, drilling, hammering, using lathes, etc, eye protectors manufactured to impact Grade 1 or 2 are essential. The grade to use depends on the job but Grade 1 gives the best protection and should be used if in doubt. In fact, Grade 1 provides 7 times the protection of Grade 2 which gives 14 times the protection of General Purpose protectors. These impact grade protectors are marked BS 2092.1 or BS 2092.2 on the lens(es). The frames are also marked but these will not necessarily be to the same grade as the lens – so it is important, if a complete protector is needed, for it to be to the higher impact category and for both lenses and frame to be appropriately marked.

Goggles or visors can be obtained to both levels of impact protection but spectacles are not available to Grade 1. All protectors claiming Grade 1 or Grade 2 impact performance will have lateral protection but again not necessarily to the same standard as the lens itself.

Eye protectors for use against molten metal splash, dust and gases/vapours are subject to additional tests and they will be marked with additional letters as follows:

- for protection against molten metal splash – BS 2092.M;
- for protection against liquid splash and droplets

– BS 2092.C;

- for protection against dust – BS 2092.D; and
- for protection against gases, vapours etc – BS 2092.G.

Only goggles and face-shields are considered suitable for each of these duties and it may be possible to get eye protectors complying with almost any combination.

BS 1542 and BS 679

BS 1542 gives a specification for goggles, face-shields, hand-shields etc. for use during welding and similar industrial operations where harmful radiations, visible light, infra-red and ultra-violet may be generated. The equipment needs to comply with the same mechanical strength test as for 'General Purpose' eye protectors in BS 2092. The filters which actually reduce the amount of light entering the eyes are specified in BS 679.

PRESCRIPTION SAFETY SPECTACLES

There is a considerable demand by workers for the provision of prescription safety spectacles as eye protectors, and many employers already provide optically ground safety lenses for spectacle wearers although the Protection of Eyes Regulations 1974 do not, in most cases, specifically require them to do so. Care needs to be taken to ensure that such lenses are suitable for the type of work being undertaken and the level of risk involved. They are only generally available to General Purpose standard and are therefore only suitable in restricted work situations. In machine-shops, for example, they might only be suitable for drilling, light milling or up to six-inch lathework and even then there generally needs to be side shields, properly fitted.

Where greater levels of protection are required, then box-type goggles or face-shields will be necessary, worn over the spectacles. Where eye protection is worn over untoughened spectacles, it is necessary to ensure that there is an adequate gap between the outer surface of the spectacle lens and the inner surface of the goggle or face-shield lens to avoid the possibility of the spectacle lens shattering when the outer lens is struck. Six millimetres (¼ inch) will almost certainly be sufficient.

EMPLOYEES' RESPONSIBILITIES

Every employee provided with eye protection equipment must use it when engaged in any of the processes outlined in the Regulations. There is also the general duty on an employee to co-operate with his employer in the carrying out of any duties imposed upon him. Failure to comply with these duties may render an offender liable to prosecution.

There are a few cases where the wearing of eye protectors may be made unnecessary by the use of fixed shields. In general, however, an employee cannot legitimately argue that he/she cannot wear a particular kind of eye protector for some reason (headaches, vision problems etc). The aim should not be to dispense with eye protection but to find a type which is suitable. It is generally desirable for a choice of protective equipment to be made available as questions of comfort and wearability can be very much influenced by personal tastes.

The Regulations require that workers take reasonable care of protectors and do not misuse them and if the protectors are lost, become defective or are destroyed, they should report the matter immediately to their employer, who is normally under an obligation to replace them. No charge can be levied by the employer for the issue, upkeep or replacement of eye protection equipment that is required to be provided in accordance with the Regulations but this is not necessarily the case where protectors have been issued in accordance with the general duties of the Health and Safety at Work Act 1974.

CHOOSING THE RIGHT EYE PROTECTOR

A wide range of eye protectors are available: spectacles (with or without side shields), goggles (box type and cup type), and face-shields. To choose the best type for a particular job and person involves considering the following questions:

What are the hazards? (occasional slight knocks, low level impact, high level impact, molten metal splash, chemical splash, dust, fume, radiation, etc). The answer will determine the grade of eye protection necessary. Sometimes, all-round coverage of the eyes will be required – for example where they may be exposure to injurious fumes and only complete enclosure of the eyes will be acceptable using a goggle. Closeness of fit to the face also needs to be considered and this tends to vary considerably from person to person. It may not be possible to obtain a good fit on all users from a single equipment manufacturer. In the case of molten metal and chemical splash, full face-shields are also allowed. In many cases these are preferable due to the 'misting' problems associated with goggles. Where protection of the lungs is also necessary both respiratory and eye protection can be provided by using an air-fed helmet. Where full all round protection is not necessary, spectacles with or without side shields may be considered.

If eye protection is to be worn over glasses, eye protectors should be suitable for this – again ensuring adequate gap over untoughened spectacles where these are also used. If other head protective equipment is required *eg* safety helmets, the various items will need to be compatible with each other. Sometimes this is difficult to achieve and may

involve trying out a range of equipment from different manufacturers to obtain satisfactory results.

SUPPLIERS OF EYE PROTECTION EQUIPMENT

There are a number of firms which specialise in the manufacture and supply of eye protection equipment and they issue trade literature which outlines the different types of spectacles, goggles and shields that are available. Some carry out 'eye care' programmes which are tailor-made to each work situation and cover matters such as records systems, visual screening, opticians' services and education programmes.

Up to date information may be obtained from the Safety Equipment Distributors' Association, Gateway House, 50 High Street, Birmingham B4 7SY, 021-643 6271; or the Industrial Protective Equipment Manufacturers' Association, 69 Cannon Street, London EC4N 5AB, 01-248 4444.

CHECKLIST

1. Identify the main sources of risk including all processes covered by the Protection of Eyes Regulations *eg* all work and processes involving:

   - flying particles;
   - splashing of hazardous liquids;
   - dust;
   - irritant gases and vapours;
   - molten metal;
   - ionising radiations; and
   - intense heat and light.

2. What precautions have been taken to minimise risks at source?
3. Is the Management carrying out the requirements of the Protection of Eyes Regulations?
4. What system of eye protection is in force at the workplace?
5. Is there a choice of eye protection?
6. Who is responsible for the selection and purchase of the eye protection equipment?
7. What arrangements are there for information, training, supervision, storage and checking?
8. Do the safety representatives have a voice in these matters and how effective is it?

USEFUL PUBLICATIONS

Advisory leaflets
- **Protection of Eyes:** Advisory Leaflet SHW 31.

Guidance
- **Eyes:** HSE Guidance Note MS 11.

IAC guidance
- **Molten Metal:** FIAC leaflet on Eye Protection.
- **Fettling:** FIAC leaflet on Eye Protection.

17: Protective clothing and equipment

To do their work safely and in comfort, many workers need some form of protective clothing or equipment. This could take the form of overalls or rubber gloves, hard hats, respirators or eye protection. All protective clothing and equipment is designed to create a barrier between the worker and hazards in the workplace. But even the best designed clothing and equipment is still only a last line of defence and will not eliminate hazards, so controlling them at source is always preferable for safety. Nevertheless, there will be times when protective clothing and equipment must be used.

To be effective, clothing and equipment must be the right type for the job; it must fit properly and be regularly maintained. Sometimes using protective equipment can cause new problems. For example, masks can make seeing and talking difficult; hearing protectors prevent users hearing warning sirens; and workers wearing heavy equipment cannot move fast. If more than one type of protection must be worn, they should be designed to be worn together — but they are not always compatible. Hard hats and safety glasses can get in the way of ear muffs, for example, and not all goggles will fit with half-face masks. The result is discomfort and inadequate protection.

It is TUC policy that all protective clothing and equipment, should be provided free of charge by the employer, but if it is not possible to achieve this immediately, advantage should be taken of subsidised schemes run by the employer.

There are British Standards for most types of protective clothing — some approved by the HSE (for example in Codes of Practice etc). Remember that clothing and equipment bearing the British Standard symbol have been tested under artificial conditions and protection may not be as good when used in real life.

As part of the creation of the open market in the European Economic Community, their is now to be a European Directive on personal protection equipment (PPE) requiring the provision and use of PPE when risks cannot be avoided by other means. The advent of the Directive is likely to mean major changes in the way workwear and PPE are provided and used in the UK.

OVERALLS AND WORKWEAR

Because existing legal obligations are often vague, the provision of overalls and general workwear is poor. In this area of hygiene, Britain is well behind other European countries. In Belgium, employers must, by law, supply their workers with a full set of work clothes designed to standards approved by the Government. In Sweden all clothing introduced into industry is vetted by the unions and in West Germany, too, clean overalls are provided more often than in Britain.

Overalls and workwear should be made of the right material. Ordinary cotton is no use against oil, water or most chemicals, for instance. They must also be cleaned regularly. Workers should not be expected to clean their own overalls at home. Work clothing can contaminate the home and puts others at risk — for example women have died from washing their husbands' asbestos-laden overalls.

It is difficult to be specific about the frequency of changing workwear because of the wide variety of tasks performed. In many work situations that are excessively dirty, the ideal would be to establish the practice of wearing a clean pair of overalls every day. For those workers who have to be provided with overalls there should be a minimum change of clothing once or twice a week as well as regular cleaning facilities. However, due to the apathy and indifference of many employers, and in spite of the efforts of trade unions in the UK, only about half the workforce in this country have a regular supply of clean workwear.

PROTECTIVE CLOTHING

As with overalls and workwear, there are few specific legal requirements to provide some of the more specialised forms of protective clothing. Some exceptions to this are the Foundries (Protective Footwear and Gaiters) Regulations 1971, which say that footwear and gaiters must be provided; the Asbestos Regulations, which say that employers must provide protective clothing; the Chromium Plating Regulations 1931 and 1973, which say employers must provide aprons with bibs, rubber gloves and rubber boots; the Chemical Work Regulations 1922, which say overalls and protective footwear must be supplied; and the Agriculture (Poisonous Substances) Regulations (1975) which require protective clothing for crop spraying. (Figure 17.2 gives a list of regulations made under the Factories Act containing references for protective clothing and equipment).

Some guidance on protective clothing has been issued by HSC Industry Advisory Committees. For example the Construction Industry Advisory Committee (CONIAC) have issued guidance on the provision of protective clothing and safety footwear in Construction. This guidance, which is relevant to many other industries, relates to basic body, hand and foot protection which should be provided for those employed on construction work. It also summarises the general principles to be considered by management, safety advisers, safety representatives and others, for the selection, supply and use of protective clothing but it excludes consideration of equipment such as life jackets, helmets, harnesses, respirators, and eye and ear protection. The CONIAC guidelines say that those responsible for providing protective clothing should: identify potential hazards in the first instance at the planning stage and, before protective clothing is considered, control hazards at source whenever possible. Where hazards cannot be controlled by other means, employers should consider what form of protection is needed against:

a) physical injury;

b) chemical injury, ill health, irritancy or nuisance;

c) electrical risks;

d) temperature and humidity extremes (weather, fire, confined spaces, tunnelling etc); and

e) wet conditions (weather, tunnelling etc).

They should make sure protective clothing supplied complies with relevant standards and bears the BSI 'kite' mark where appropriate. They should also consider the compatibility of protective clothing with any necessary protective equipment (eg respirators, life jackets, helmets) and before selecting protective clothing, consult with those at risk and their safety representatives about its comfort and convenience, considering features such as durability, weight, warmth, windproofing, and waterproofing. They must also provide information, instruction, training and supervision for those using protective clothing and make sure there are adequate arrangements on site for the care, maintenance, inspection, replacement and storage of protective clothing.

Although the above points only constitute guidance, when considering protective clothing, attention should be drawn to the employer's duty under Section 2 of the HSW Act to:

a) provide clothing where necessary as part of a safe system of work and ensure that it is used;

b) provide information, instruction, training and supervision in the use and care of such clothing;

c) give an account of the arrangements in the firm's written safety policy; and

d) consult safety representatives on the choice, use and care of protective clothing.

Under the HSW Act, employees are also required to co-operate with their employers in the use and care of protective clothing.

SELECTION OF PROTECTIVE CLOTHING

When discussing the selection of protective clothing, it is important to consider the following principles:

- **cleaning, laundering** — this not only removes contamination but prolongs life and effectiveness;

- **inspection** — ensures protective clothing is in good condition and is repaired or replaced as necessary; and

- **storage and drying** — an important part of 'good housekeeping' on site to ensure that protective clothing is looked after systematically.

It is important to remember that a high standard of cleaning and maintenance is needed on all occasions, particularly for example to avoid irritancy where materials may enter gloves at the wrist (eg cement) or by direct permeation (organic solvents).

The type of protection afforded by protective clothing differs according to the materials used. Some examples are given in the tables over page.

FOOTWEAR

Although foot injury at work is very common, the provision of safety footwear in this country is by no means universal. It is a common sight to see workers wearing scuffed old work shoes, sometimes even sandals or 'trainers' — even though they may be

Figure 17.1: Features affecting selection of protective clothing

Protective materials	Protection afforded	Typical uses
Uncoated cotton, material such as terylene with water repellent finish	Protection from occasional splashes from dilute acids and alkalis and innocuous chemicals.	Overalls.
PVC coated nylon or *terylene*	Resistant to abrasion, cracking and tearing; protection from most oils and chemicals, including acids; weather protection.	Jackets, trousers, leggings, aprons.
Neoprene or *polyurethane coated* or *nylon* or *terylene*	Protection from very strong solvents, oils, greases, etc.	Coats, overalls, aprons.
PVC impregnated with fluorescent pigments	Improved visibility (for roadworks etc).	Bib type waistcoats, sleeves, jackets.
Chrome, leather or *heat retardant man-made materials*	Fire resistant (for welding etc).	Jackets, trousers, aprons, sleeves, gloves.
Chainmail	Protection from penetration and abrasion.	Gloves.
Terrycloth	Protection against heat, cold, penetration and abrasion.	Gloves.
PVC	Protection from chemicals,	Gloves.
Rubber	Sensitive touch, wet grip, electrical protection.	Gloves.
Neoprene	Good for handling oils and low temperature work.	Gloves.
Nitrile	Good for handling hydrocarbons. Resistant to acids, cuts and abrasions.	Gloves.
Steel	Prevention of penetration and crushing.	Midsoles and toe-caps for safety footwear.

Figure 17.2: Regulations made under the Factories Act 1961, containing references to protective clothing and equipment

Regulations	Clothing required
Aerated water	Face guards, gauntlets, waterproof aprons, boots.
Asbestos	Respirators, protective clothing.
Blasting castings	Protective helmets, gauntlets and overalls.
Bronzing	Overalls, headcoverings.
Cement works (WO)	Boots, goggles, coats, overalls, head coverings.
Chemical works	Overalls, 'protective coverings', respirators, boots, goggles, etc.
Chromium plating	Aprons, boots, gloves.
Clay works	'Suitable protective clothing', aprons.
Construction (GP)	Respirators if necessary.

Construction (H&W)	Adequate and suitable protective clothing.
Dyeing (WO)	Suitable protective clothing, gloves.
Electric accumulator	Overall, apron clogs, head coverings.
Electricity	Insulating boots, gloves.
Vitreous enamelling	Overalls, head coverings.
Filo cutting	Long aprons.
Flax and tow	Waterproof skirts, bibs (or splash guards).
Foundries (footwear, etc)	Footwear, gaiters.
Fruit preserving (WO)	Suitable protective clothing.
Glass bevelling (WO)	Protective clothing.
Gut scraping (WO)	Overalls, aprons, boots, clogs.
Hides and skins, hollow-ware and galvanising (WO)	Finger stalls, gloves, aprons, clogs.
Horsehair	Overalls, head coverings, respirators.
India-rubber	Overalls.
Ionising radiations (IRRs)	Personal protective clothing, breathing apparatus.
Iron and steel, and foundries.	Gloves, respirators, and molten metal splash protection.
Jute	Respirators, overalls and head coverings.
Laundries (WO)	Suitable protective clothing, boots, clogs, overalls, aprons, armlets.
Lead compounds	Overalls, head coverings, respirators.
Lead smelting	Overalls, respirators.
Magnesium grinding	Overalls, aprons.
Non-ferrous metals	Suitable protective equipment, gloves, respirators.
Paints and colours	Overalls.
Pottery (H&W)	Protective clothing (schedule), respirators.
Shipbuilding	Hand protection, welding gauntlets, breathing apparatus.
Tanning (two-bath WO)	Aprons, boots, leggings, gloves.
Tanning (WO)	Protective clothing (schedule).
Tin or Torno plates (WO)	Aprons, clogs.
Woodworking machinery	Ear protectors.
Wool, goat and camel	Overalls.
East India wool	Overalls, respirators.
Yarn heading	Overalls, head coverings.

S.75 of the Factories Act 1961

Young persons in lead processes	Protective clothing.

standing on steel swarf, operating machines, packing bottles, standing on broken glass, lifting heavy weights or working on slippery surfaces. This kind of footwear is worn despite accident statistics, which continue to show around 14 per cent of all accidents happen to feet or toes, causing a loss of over 3 million working days each year. The amount of pain, suffering and disability as a result can only be guessed at!

Even so, only a minority of the workers in this country wear safety footwear. And most safety footwear in the UK is still privately bought — often through schemes subsided by employers — whilst on the continent, 90 per cent is purchased by companies and issued free to their workers.

Work shoes should always be strong and in good repair, and, in many industrial situations, boots and shoes should have protective steel toecaps and insteps. People working with water and acids will need rubber or neoprene boots to protect their legs up to the knee, and these should also have steel toecaps and insteps. Rubber boots are hot to wear for long periods, so leather may be preferable.

The Health and Safety Commission have issued a number of Codes of Practice on the design of safety footwear which endorse relevant British Standards. Wherever necessary appropriate safety footwear should be provided. Safety representatives should be consulted about situations where it is required, types to be provided and arrangements for free issue, checking, storage and replacement.

GLOVES

Gloves should be worn as much as possible to protect the hands not only from cuts, but also from contamination (see *Chapter 11: Skin hazards*). The kind of gloves needed will depend on the hazards of the job and the type of injury to be prevented — puncture, cuts, heat burns, chemical burns and electric shock. But it is important to remember that it is dangerous to wear gloves when working with machines like drills and power presses where gloves might get caught.

EAR PROTECTION

Ear muffs and plugs are discussed in Chapter 12. Ears should also be protected from sparks, extreme cold, and flying particles etc.

EYE PROTECTION

This is dealt with in detail in Chapter 15.

PROTECTIVE HEADGEAR

Safety headgear is used in mining, in parts of construction, shipbuilding and maintenance work. In fact, it should be worn anywhere where workers are likely to be struck by falling or flying objects. Even relatively minor impacts to the head can cause death or serious injury, so head protection should be provided wherever the risk of such injury is identified — but design and comfort are very important to ensure such protection is acceptable.

It is becoming increasingly common to see workers wearing 'hard hats' in industries and activities where previously it was not generally considered to be the 'done thing'. These include forestry, agriculture, fishing, and many other outdoor jobs. Although safety headgear is often regarded as a badge of safety consciousness, it should always be remembered that it will not protect above a certain threshold of kinetic energy. The first line of defence therefore must always be prevention of falls of objects and material. Helmets also provide useful protection from impacts due to falls on the level or lateral impacts.

Even though prevention comes before protection, employers who do not provide suitable hard hats where necessary, or workers who refuse to wear them, may still be breaking the Health and Safety at Work Act 1974. Also, a hatless worker who suffers head injury may lose compensation for injury.

The Health and Safety Commission have recently agreed new regulations for the mandatory provision and use of safety helmets in the Construction Industry. The Commission's Construction Industry Advisory Committee have also issued advice on safety helmets including factors relating to comfort. Key features to be considered are:

- a terylene (as opposed to moulded plastic) suspension;
- a sweat band;
- adequate adjustment;
- adequate retention around the back of the skull;
- a chin strap; and
- a rain gutter.

These features are incorporated in all helmets which meet British Standard Grade 2 — as opposed to Grade 1, the basic standard, which merely covers impact resistance.

Wherever head protection is to be used, safety representatives should be consulted about the type of protection to be used (trials are often useful) and these discussions should include arrangements for issue, storage, inspection, replacement of helmets as well as issues such as supervision, information and training.

RESPIRATORY PROTECTIVE EQUIPMENT (RPE)

This is probably the most frightening form of protective equipment. It is certainly the most uncomfortable to use and can give even the most hardened of industrial veterans a sense of unease. There are a number of difficulties in using respirators and breathing apparatus, but the most important is ensuring that they really are safe. A further problem is the discomfort suffered by those who have to work in this kind of equipment for any length of time. Because of both these problems, respirators should only be used when the equipment is well fitting and designed for the particular job, and even then, only for short periods.

Recommendations for selection, use and maintenance of respiratory protective equipment can be found in British Standard 4275 (see *Further information* for details). There are two types of RPE – respirators, and breathing apparatus.

RESPIRATORS

These purify the air by filtering out harmful dusts and gases. Filters designed for dusts will not protect against gases and vice versa, so it is very important to make sure the right filter is used. Respirators should never be used where there is a lack of oxygen – breathing apparatus is necessary here. Respirators can have full face-pieces or half-masks that cover nose and mouth only. Eye protection may be needed with half-masks. The filter is often made quite useless by the amount of air that leaks in between the mask and the face, especially when talking masks must be issued individually to each worker and checked for a tight fit against the face; if the filter is to work, the mask must be worn so tightly that it is uncomfortable. Masks with a pneumatic seal can be more effective and less comfortable.

Canister respirators — the canister contains absorbent chemicals which remove gas or vapour from the air before it is breathed in. The correct canister *must* be used for each contaminant or there will be no protection; colour coding of canisters shows what they are for.

These respirators will not remove concentrations of contaminants which are greater than 1 per cent by volume and the absorbent material is quickly exhausted — usually in 30 minutes, some in only 15 minutes. They should never be used in confined spaces and, of course, they can do nothing in situations where there is a shortage of oxygen. Canisters will not trap dust particles unless a special filter has been added.

Cartridge respirators — these give even less protection than the canister type and for shorter periods, and they are often issued in conditions which they have no hope of coping with. Workers should be very wary of this equipment and if it must be used, it is vital to make sure the cartridge is right for the type of contaminant, its concentration and the length of time the wearer is exposed.

Dust respirators — with this equipment the wearer draws air in through one or two filter cartridges fixed to a mask. Filters are designed to stop dust but cannot stop gases and vapours. None will trap 100 per cent of any dust — if they did, not much air would get through. The filter must trap the size of the dust particle which is producing the risk and not let enough through to endanger health.

BREATHING APPARATUS

This provides air or oxygen from an uncontaminated source, either through an air-line or from a portable container. This should not be confused with respirators which only filter out toxic dusts or fumes. The right type of apparatus can be an effective protection for short periods of exposure to toxic gases, dusts and insufficient oxygen. It is very important that breathing apparatus is checked and maintained on a regular basis, and that workers are properly trained. There are two main types of breathing apparatus – airline and self contained.

Compressed air-line — with this equipment air is pressure fed through a flexible hose to a hood or facepiece. Air is supplied by a compressor fitted with filters to remove oil and toxic gases. In corrosive or irritating atmospheres skin and eyes must be protected as well. Positive pressure suits, fed by an air-line, can give all-over protection. This type of equipment gives good, if extremely restricting and oppressive, protection but it is important to remember that, in very poisonous atmospheres, equipment failure may mean death.

Self-contained apparatus — there are various kinds of apparatus that have built-in suppies of oxygen, or liquid or compressed air. They have a limited capacity ranging from 25 minutes to two hours. Self-contained apparatus is heavy, tends to become hot and puts a strain on users' lungs and heart.

'RESCUE' APPARATUS

All of the above types of RPE can be used in emergencies. But it must be the right type: in good condition, near to hand *and* used only by people who have been fully trained. There are also 'self-rescue' respirators and canisters available for emergencies only. These have a very limited life and must never be used for normal working.

CHECKLIST: PERSONAL PROTECTION

1. Are overalls provided for everyone who needs them?

   - Are overalls changed frequently, at least once a week?
   - Are overalls cleaned and maintained by your employer (either on the premises or by a rental service)?
   - Do overalls give proper protection against specific hazards, *eg* chemicals, water, oil etc?

2. Are gloves provided when they are needed?

   - Do the gloves give proper protection against hazards, *eg* chemicals, heat, cuts, electric shock etc?
   - Are gloves provided in a range of sizes?
   - Are gloves replaced before they are worn out, punctured or saturated?

3. Is safety footwear provided, either free or at discount price?

   - Does the footwear protect against hazards, *eg* crushing, slipping, heat, chemicals etc?
   - Is the footwear the correct size and comfortable to wear?

4. Is protective headgear provided where necessary?

   - Does the headgear protect against falling-object hazards?
   - Is it the correct size and comfortable to wear?
   - Is headgear cleaned, maintained and replaced regularly?

5. Are respirators or breathing apparatus provided only where control of hazard at source gives insufficient protection?

   - Are respirators or breathing apparatus the right type for the job?
   - Do they fit properly and are they tested regularly?
   - Are users fully trained to use this type of equipment?

6. Are union members involved in decisions about all protective clothing and equipment?

7. Is protective clothing and equipment worn by both management and workers?

SOURCES OF FURTHER INFORMATION

Further advice on personal protective clothing and equipment may be obtained from local safety groups, safety consultants, employers' federations, trade unions, industry training boards, safety journals and magazines. The following are a selection of addresses.

- **British Footwear Manufacturers' Federation**
  72 Dean Street, London WIV 5HB; 01-437 5573.

- **British Standards Institution**
  2 Park Street, London W1A 2BS; 01-629 9000.

- **Golden Shoe Club**
  PO Box 11, Holt, Norfolk NR25 6RL; 0263 712721.

- **Industrial Safety (Protective Equipment) Manufacturers' Association**
  69-75 Cannon Street, London EC4N 5AB; 01-248 4444.

- **Royal Society for the Prevention of Accidents**
  Cannon House, Priory Queensway, Birmingham B4 6BS; 021-200 2461.

- **Shoe and Allied Trades Research Association**
  Satra House, Rockingham Road, Kettering, Northants NN16 9JH; 0536 410000.

General

- **ILO Encyclopaedia of Occupational Health and Safety:** Volume 2 (third revised edition); 1983.

- **The selection, use and maintenance of respiratory protective equipment:** British Standards Institution; BS4275.

HSC/E guidance notes

- **Entry into confined spaces:** GS5.

- **Protection Clothing and Footwear in the Construction Industry:** CONIAC IAC c/6.

18: Welding hazards

Welding is, simply, making a union between two pieces of material by heating and/or pressing them together. However, what started out hundreds of years ago as a reasonably straightforward operation, has today become an increasingly complex process with the development of a wide variety of new techniques. These new developments have created many potential health risks for welding workers. The hazards can be roughly divided into two categories. Firstly, there are the dangers of burns, damage to the eyes, electric shock and possibly explosion. Secondly, there is a more insidious hazard, with both possible short term and long term health effects from fumes and gases. The latter problem is particularly acute with newer types of welding such as argon arc (TIG), metal inert gas (MIG), electron beam, resistance, laser and plasma-arc.

PREVENTION OF EYE INJURIES, BURNS AND EXPLOSIONS

The brilliant light given off by an electric arc contains a high proportion of ultra-violet radiation, which may produce painful conjunctivitis (known as 'arc-eye' or 'eye-flash') after even momentary exposure. This can be prevented by using a shield or helmet fitted with the correct grade of filter, and by avoiding stray flashes from other adjacent arcs. Adequate screening therefore to protect nearby workers is essential.

Excessive exposure to ultra-violet radiation may also cause over-heating and burning of the skin, so the face, nape of the neck and any other exposed parts of the body should be protected. In addition, the high temperature created by the arc can cause deep burns if concentrated at one point on the skin. If welding is being carried out in the presence of flammable gases or liquids there is the danger of explosion. All tanks and vessels containing flammable materials should be thoroughly purged before welding takes place.

PROTECTIVE EQUIPMENT

For all arc welding work, either a helmet or a hand-held face shield (handshield) is essential for protection against radiation, spatter and hot slag. For the gas-shielded arc welding process, flat handshields may not provide sufficient protection from reflected radiation. When working on aluminium or other reflective structures, or close to other welders, protection for the back of the head should be arranged. When slag is being removed from welds, for instance by chipping, the eyes should be protected by goggles or some other reliable method.

Leather gauntlet gloves with canvas or leather cuffs, must be worn to protect the hands from heat, spatter and radiation. Rubber gloves are unsuitable, but asbestos substitute gloves may be used.

Welders should wear aprons made of leather (or other suitable material) both to protect their bodies and clothing from heat and burns and to avoid damage from ultra-violet radiation and ozone. An apron is also necessary where the operator is seated at a bench for welding. If the welder is wearing ordinary clothes and welding in certain positions, leather or asbestos sleeves and leather spats, as well as an apron, may be required.

SCREENS AND BOOTHS

All arc welding operations should be screened to protect others who are working nearby. If the work is carried out at fixed benches or in welding shops, permanent screens should, where possible, be erected. Otherwise temporary screens should be used.

IONISING RADIATION

In welding shops where welds are radiographically inspected with X-ray or gamma-ray equipment, the customary warning notices and instructions must be strictly observed. Workers should keep at a safe distance from such equipment. Radioactive sources must be handled only with special tools which should be provided and then only after all the necessary special precautions have been taken. (For further advice on radiological protection, see *Chapter 9: Ionising radiations.*

NOISE HAZARDS

Certain specialised types of welding create excessive noise levels. For example, in plasma-arc welding, the jet is ejected at very high speeds producing intense noise (up to 90 dB) particularly in the higher frequency bands. This is also the case with certain resistance welding machines. To protect hearing from damage, ear protection must be worn. (For further information, see *Chapter 8: Noise*).

FUMES AND GASES

All welding produces fumes and gas. The numerous types of fumes and gases that are produced during welding depend on the composition of the metal being welded, including any surface coating, and the composition of the electrodes. Among the main gases produced are:

- carbon monoxide;
- carbon dioxide;
- nitrogen dioxide; and
- ozone.

  Fumes which may be encountered include:

- zinc;
- iron;
- cobalt, nickel and manganese (where present in stainless and alloyed steels); and
- copper and lead (usually in the electrodes).

  The short-term effects from exposure to welding fumes may vary from minor throat irritation, to catarrh, nipping of the eyes, slight cough, and possible metal fume fever – a flu-like condition which lasts usually only about 24 hours – and is caused by exposure to finely divided particles in the air.

  Welding fumes contain a wide variety of elements which are known, or are suspected, to have potential toxic effects in man. Some experts claim that they are not a serious long term danger to health while others believe that breathing in these toxic substances can pose a significant threat. It is important, therefore, that precautions should be taken to avoid exposure to these fumes and gases as far as possible. (For further advice on controlling exposure to toxic fumes, see *Chapter 5: Chemicals and toxic substances*).

EXPOSURE LIMITS

Experts have decided on the amount of toxic fume from each substance which should be regarded as too much and this is called the 'exposure limit'. A list of exposure limits is published by HSE in a Guidance Note called EH40 and this is revised annually. These limits are used by the HSE to assess compliance by employers with their general duty under the Health and Safety at Work Act to control risks to workers' health as well as their specific duties under the Control of Substances Hazardous to Health (COSHH) Regulations. The list also contains a shorter list of what are called 'maximum exposure limits' and these must not be exceeded under any circumstances.

  Over 700 substances have been given exposure limits and the Inspectorate use them when deciding whether employers are conforming to the law in protecting their workers from 'injuries' or 'offensive' impurities in the air. Testing the atmosphere to decide whether the limits are being exceeded is a specialised task, normally carried out by a specialist factory inspector, or an occupational hygienist. On no account however should fumes be visible in the atmosphere away from the immediate vicinity of the welding point, and steps should be taken to ensure that any visible fume near the arc is rapidly dispersed.

VENTILATION

Proper ventilation is the key to safe working with welding, and this is particularly important in confined spaces, such as large tanks.

  For most types of welding, other than MIG, high speed local exhaust ventilation (by exhaust fan, flexible ducting or elongated hood which remove the fumes at the point of the weld) is the most effective in making the job safe. Recent research indicates that an air velocity of not less than 100 linear feet per minute should be maintained at the weld point. There are a number of types of portable exhaust equipment available on the market, including a magnetic type that can be clipped to the job.

  With inert gas types of welding – *eg* MIG – there are special problems because of the difficulty in detecting these gases and because local exhaust ventilation cannot be used in many of these operations. This is because the arc is shielded by the gas to protect it against atmospheric contamination that might produce faults in the weld material. Where argon or carbon dioxide is being used as the shielding gas, particularly in confined spaces, breathing apparatus of the airline type should be worn. This, of course is a last line of defence and such protection should only be used as a temporary measure.

CHECKLIST: WELDING

1. Is adequate protective equipment available – for example:

    *   eyes – goggles or shields;
    *   neck – kepi or scarf;
    *   forearms — leather sleeves;
    *   hands – appropriate gloves or gauntlets;
    *   feet – leather spats, safety shoes;
    *   respiratory systems – fans and exhaust ventilation, air-fed respirators;
    *   ears – ear plugs or muffs.

2. Has the work-environment been measured for fume and gas contamination? If not, why not?

3. If contamination measurements are taken by a government inspector or occupational hygienist, check that the maximum readings are below the level of the appropriate Exposure Limit.

	8 hours	10 mins (short-term limit)
Ozone	0.1 ppm	0.3 ppm
Nitrogen dioxide	3.0 ppm	5.0 ppm
Carbon monoxide	50 ppm	40.0 ppm
Carbon dioxide	5,000 ppm	15,000 ppm
Chromium oxide	0.5 mg/cum	
Nickel oxide	1.0 mg/cum	
Zinc oxide	5.0 mg/cum	10 mg/cum
Lead	0.15 mg/cum	
Beryllium alloys	0.002 mg/cum	
Cadmium oxide	0.05 mg/cum	

4. Eyes need protection from ultra-violet light, and special filters should be provided. Are the filters supplied adequate for the task?

FURTHER INFORMATION

Health and Safety Executive

*   **Hot work : welding and cutting on plant containing flammable materials:** Health and Safety Guidance Booklet HS(G) 5; 1979.

Guidance notes

*   **Carbon monoxide poisoning:** EH 43; 1984.
*   **Welding:** MS 15; 1978.
*   **Entry into confined spaces:** GS 5; 1977.

Cautionary leaflets

*   **Hot work on tanks and drums:** IND(G)35(L); 1985.

General

*   **The health of welders**: AT Doig and LN Duguid; HMSO, 1962.
*   **Health and safety in welding and allied processes**: The Institute of Welding.

19: Fire precautions

Every year hundreds of people die and thousands are burned in fire related incidents which could be easily prevented with just a little thought and action by all the people concerned. Fire is one of the biggest causes of death and severe injuries in the community. Fire and explosion at work account for some 2 per cent of major injuries reported annually to the HSE. The law on fire safety at work is quite well developed but can appear complex and confusing to people not regularly using it.

It is sometimes difficult to enforce by Authorities outside the workplace simply because of the scarcity of resources in the form of inspectors and the number of premises they have to inspect, so safety representatives have a most vital role to play in monitoring existing fire safety measures and looking for improvements as the need arises.

Safety representatives should find out what fire safety standards ought to apply in their workplace and press for any improvements which are needed. All safety representatives need to be aware of potential or existing fire hazards and fire safety precautions at the workplace; the legal situation on fire safety at work; how to use and interpret Fire Certificates effectively; and how to develop a Union strategy for promoting fire safety.

ENFORCEMENT OF FIRE SAFETY AT WORK

The law on fire safety at work is fundamentally split between three enforcing authorities as shown below; safety representatives therefore need to identify which Authority they should be dealing with:

Fire authorities

Fire authorities are elected bodies of Local Councillors and thus run on behalf of the local community the Fire Service, they normally delegate their legislative powers for fire safety to the Fire Service. They are responsible for the enforcement of fire safety standards in respect of life and personal safety from fire in places of work which are normally run commercial or industrial premises.

Section 18 of the Fire Precautions Act 1971 requires the Fire Authority to enforce the Act in their area and for that purpose to appoint Inspectors.

The inspectors appointed are generally serving fire service officers and are usually known as Fire Prevention Officers. The 1971 Act gives them very wide sweeping powers of entry and inspection to premises plus the ability to require any person to give them assistance in their inspections.

Safety representatives should try to make contact with Fire Prevention Officers when they visit their workplace, however, unlike HSE Inspectors, Fire Prevention Officers are not obliged to liaise with safety representatives or to make information available to them because the 1971 Act is not a relevant statutory provision for the purposes of the HSW Act 1974. Nevertheless they may respond to general enquiries from safety representatives and to any complaints regarding infringements of fire safety standards. The Fire Prevention Officer can be contacted through the local fire service in most cases.

There are fixed penalties for breaches of fire safety standards or law on 'summary conviction' in a magistrates court, and if convicted on indictment in a higher court the potential for an unlimited fine and up to two years imprisonment or both to be imposed exists. Failure to keep a fire certificate or copy of it on the premises to which it relates can also lead to a fine.

Safety representatives should also note that a provision applies in the 1971 Act whereby anybody who is proven to have contravened a fire safety standard or condition of a fire certificate can be liable for prosecution not just the employer or occupier of the premises. Persons who wedge open fire doors should beware!

Home Office Fire Service Inspectorate Inspectors

Home Office Fire Service Inspectorate Inspectors are normally seconded, or retired, fire service officers, and either work from the Home Office in London or from Regional Centres around the Country. They are responsible for the enforcement of fire safety standards in respect of life and personal safety from fire in places of work owned or occupied by the Crown.

Health and Safety Executive

The Health and Safety Executive is a national body with Regional Centres around the Country whose Inspectors are normally graduate entrants, but, may have work experience in their particular field of enforcement. They are responsible for the fire safety standards in certain high fire risk places of work and the control of the storage of certain flammable liquids.

THE LAW ON FIRE SAFETY AT WORK

The law contains many vital standards of fire safety. There are a number of sources of law as shown below, with the Enforcing Authority indicated as a heading.

Health and Safety Executive

- Health and Safety at Work etc Act 1974;

- Highly Flammable Liquids and Liquefied Petroleum Gas Regulations 1972; (this only applies to factory premises, in commercial premises the Regulations will be enforced by the Local District Authority under delegated powers from the HSE); and

- Fire Certificates (Special Premises) Regulations 1976.

Fire Authority

- Fire Precautions Act 1971;

- Petroleum (Regulation) Acts 1928 & 1936; this only applies in Metropolitan areas eg London, West Midlands, Merseyside etc – in County areas it may not be enforced by the Fire Authority.

- Fire Services Act 1947

Home Office Fire Service Inspectorate

- Fire Precautions Act 1971 (as amended) where it applies to Crown owned or occupied places of work.

APPLICATION OF FIRE SAFETY LAW

Fire Precautions Act 1971

This Act which has been extensively amended by the two Acts detailed below – the Health and Safety at Work etc Act 1974 and the Fire Safety and Safety of Places of Sport Act 1987 – applies at the moment to places of work, being either factories, offices, shops and railway premises as defined in Schedule 2 to the 1971 Act, and hotels and boarding houses as defined in the Hotels and Boarding Houses Order 1972 (Statutory Instrument 1972: 238).

The 1971 Act provides *only* for life safety in case of fire – it does not cater for process or building safety. Those areas are the concern of either the Health and Safety Executive, the Building Control Department of the Local Authority or the Company Insurers. Insurers will often insist on such fire suppression measures as sprinklers or similar devices being installed which the Fire Authority can only recommend. However, the fire prevention officer will take these matters into account when inspecting a building for the purposes of assessing whether it is safe for people to get out if there is a fire.

Any factory, office, shop or railway premise in which persons are employed to work (or a building containing a number of workplaces) must have a fire certificate if:

a) more than 20 persons work in the building as a whole; or

b) more than ten persons are employed to work above or below the ground floor of the premises; or

c) in the case of factory premises *only* highly flammable or explosion materials are stored or used in or under the premises.

In the case of factories which only store or use very small quantities of flammable or explosive materials the Fire Authority *may* exempt them from the requirement for a fire certificate if the materials stored or used are not considered a risk to the persons employed to work. Fire Authorities *may* also exempt from the requirement to have or to hold a fire certificate, premises which in their opinion do not on the basis of fire risk need one. In other words low fire risk premises may be exempted from holding a fire certificate irrespective of how many persons are employed if the Fire Authority are satisfied they are safe.

Premises which do not need a fire certificate or have been exempted from holding one are still covered by other fire safety requirements, relating to the provision of adequate means of escape in case of fire and the provision of means for fighting fire and the onus is on the owner or occupier of the premises to comply with these requirements.

Fire certificates lay down the Fire Authorities requirements for fire precautions in the workplace and are individually tailored for each workplace. It is important therefore that each certificate is examined to find out the standards that apply at each site or premises. The following types of fire certificates are to be found:

a)   Office, Shops and Railway Premises Act 1963 certificate;

b)   Factories Act 1961 certificate;

c)   Fire Precautions Act 1971 certificate; and

d)   Special Premises Regulations 1976 certificate.

Old means of escape certificates issued under The Factories Act 1961 and The Offices, Shops and Railway Premises Act 1963 covered only means of escape in case of fire, limitations on numbers employed and in the case of factories *only* details of any highly flammable or explosive materials stored or used, nevertheless the documents are deemed to be Fire Certificates for the purposes of the Fire Precautions Act 1971. Safety representatives should press for the old 1961 and 1963 Act certificates to be replaced by a 1971 Act certificate.

Fire Certificates issued under the 1971 Act are far more detailed and very powerful in control of fire safety measures in premises and it is important safety representatives understand them. They will specify the particular use or uses of the premises which it covers, the means of escape in case of fire (mainly by reference to a plan), the means for ensuring that the means of escape can be safely and effectively used at all material times. (This would cover such matters as fire doors, fire resisting walls and ceilings, exit signs and notices and emergency lighting). The means for fighting fire, the means for giving warning in case of fire, and in the case of factories *only* the amounts of highly flammable or explosive materials stored or used, and any other matters taken into account by the Fire Authority when granting the fire certificate.

In addition, the following aspects may be dealt with, maintenance of the means of escape and keeping them free from obstruction or combustible storage, the maintenance and regular testing of other fire precautions specified in the fire certificate, the regular and ongoing training of those employed to work in the premises on the action to be taken in case of fire and the keeping of proper records recording training sessions, fire drills and the regular testing and maintenance of fire safety measures, any restriction or limitation on the number of persons who can safely work or be in a particular area and any other relevant fire precautions taken into account.

The fire certificate, or an approved copy of it, must be kept on the premises to which it relates – failure to do so is an offence. Safety representatives should have access to the fire certificate and should be able to have a copy of it, although strictly speaking this applies only to a fire certificate issued under The Fire Certificates (Special Premises)

Regulations 1976 by the HSE, since the 1971 Act is not a relevant statutory provision under the HSW Act 1974.

Some workplaces may not have a fire certificate. This may be because the employer has applied for one but it has yet to be issued – this frequently happens and it is quite legal for business to continue under these circumstances. It does not, however, mean that no fire safety precautions are taken. The employer/occupier must ensure that whilst their application is pending, any means of escape in case of fire that exist must be properly maintained as must any fire fighting equipment and the employees must be trained on what action to take if there is a fire. Failure to do so is an offence. These measures are known as the Interim Duty.

The second reason why a premises/workplace may not have a fire certificate is because there are not sufficient persons employed to work there. Once again this does not mean that there is no requirement for fire precautions to be taken or made. Small workplaces are covered as is shown below.

The third reason why a workplace may not have a fire certificate is because the Fire Authority have exempted it from the requirement to hold one, in which case the same fire precautions as for small non-certificated workplaces will apply, see below.

The fourth and final reason why a workplace may not have a fire certificate is because it is not put to a designated use, *ie* as an office, shop, railway premise, factory or hotel and boarding house. For instance schools and colleges are workplaces but they will not usually need a fire certificate because they are not a designated use.

NON-CERTIFICATED AND EXEMPT WORKPLACES

In small workplaces, and exempt (from the requirement to hold a fire certificate) workplaces, the owner/occupier must ensure that:

- a means of escape in case of fire is provided; and

- a means for fighting fire is provided.

To see whether they are complying with this duty they may use a Code of Practice for such premises issued by the Home Office and implementation of which can be used to prove that the duty has been discharged properly. If the Fire Authority inspect the premises and find that either the duty to provide means of escape or fire fighting equipment has not been met or they disagree with the way the duty has been discharged they can either issue an improvement notice or prosecute the person concerned immediately or do both.

Safety representatives should also note, that there is no requirement for fire alarms, staff training or fire drills in small or exempt workplaces. This is a matter therefore for local negotiation to seek improvements in these areas. They should also note that Fire Authorities are generally willing to assist in staff training and fire drills whether or not the law requires such things to be done.

EMPLOYER'S DUTIES

The responsibility for applying for a fire certificate rests with the owner or occupier of the premises. It is an offence to use a premise that requires a fire certificate without having applied for one.

Fire Authorities are, since January 1, 1988, able to charge for the issue of and any amendment to a fire certificate and will take into account their administration costs in so doing, other than the cost of the actual inspection.

Once a fire certificate is issued, any material changes or alterations affecting any of the fire safety matters detailed in the fire certificate must be notified in writing to the Fire Authority prior to implementing or carrying them out. Failure to do so is an offence.

The same criteria apply to premises which should have a fire certificate but which the Fire Authority have granted an exemption from holding one. Any material alterations or changes to the premises must be notified in writing to the Fire Authority prior to carrying them out. Failure to do so is an offence and may also result in the withdrawal of the exemption from holding and therefore complying with a fire certificate.

The best advice that can be given on this matter is:

- **If in doubt, *always* ask the Fire Authority first.**

'SPECIAL PREMISES' FIRE CERTIFICATES

As already indicated, in certain high risk premises, fire certificates are issued by the HSE rather than by the Fire Authority. These instances are quite clearly prescribed in and covered by The Fire Certificates (Special Premises) Regulations 1976.

In general, these are large scale hazards which are closely tied in with a system of production including processes where large quantities of flammable material(s) are stored or used – very specialised processes, *eg* nuclear plants, explosives factories or large temporary site buildings on construction sites.

They also cover smaller premises not requiring a fire certificate on building sites and lay down basic regulations for them. Guidance on the Regulations is contained in the HSE leaflet "The Fire Certificate (Special Premises) Regulations 1976: Twenty Questions", which is available from HMSO.

Process fire precautions, including precautions relating to the storage and use of flammable materials and processes involving significant fire hazard may be required under the HSW Act 1974 or its relevant statutory provisions. The situation is complicated by the fact that general and process fire precautions may interact or indeed be interdependent, *eg* the presence of flammable materials will be taken into account by the Enforcing Authority when assessing the means of escape in case of fire and similarly the means of escape is relevant to the suitability of the storage area.

FIRE INSTRUCTIONS AND FIRE DRILLS

Employers using premises where a fire certificate is in force must ensure that their employees are familiar with the action to be taken in the event of fire and in most cases this will mean that regular training and fire drills will be required to be undertaken. The frequency of fire drills and training periods will normally be included in the fire certificate, and there should also be a requirement for such training and drills to be recorded in a log book.

The Home Office Guides to the Fire Precautions Act 1971 (see bibliography) indicate that the following records should be kept:

a) date of the instruction or exercise;

b) duration;

c) name of the person giving the instruction;

d) names of the person taking part; and

e) the nature of the instruction, training or drill.

The Home Office Guides also indicates the range of topics which should be covered by instruction and drills. Instruction and training generally should provide for the following:

- the action to be taken upon discovering a fire;
- the action to be taken upon hearing the fire alarm;
- raising the alarm, including the location of alarm call points, internal fire alarm telephones and alarm indicator panels;
- the correct method of calling the fire brigade;
- the location and use of fire fighting equipment;
- knowledge of the escape routes;
- appreciation of the importance of fire doors and of the need to close all doors at the time of a fire and on hearing the fire alarm;
- stopping machines and processes and isolating power supplies where appropriate; and
- evacuation of the building.

This means that certain types of staff will need additional training, for example supervisors, engineering and maintenance staff, chemists, security staff and telephonists. Special instruction may also be needed for people who work outside normal working hours, *eg* night watchmen, cleaning staff, maintenance staff.

Fire drills should be held at least once a year (depending on the degree of risk). In some cases the drill should be unannounced. The Home Office guide suggests that certain emergency conditions (*eg* obstructing one or more of the escape routes) should be simulated during the drill. Notices should be prominently displayed indicating the action to be taken on discovering a fire or hearing the alarm.

Training should also cover the use of fire extinguishers. Not all extinguishers are suitable for all types of fire (*eg* water should not be used on electrical fires or burning liquids). So training should include the correct choice and use of extinguishers.

Special consideration must be given to the needs of disabled staff in fire situations. Some aspects for consideration are:

- identification of everyone who may need special help to get out;

- allocation of responsibility to specific able-bodied staff to help disabled staff in emergency situations;

- consideration of the best escape routes for disabled staff;

- developing procedures to enable lifts to be used where possible (*eg* to identify unaffected lifts, to prevent power loss to lifts being used to evacuate the disabled); and

- procedures for disabled staff to summon assistance in emergencies.

Note: normally, lifts should not be used as a means of escape in the event of fire. If the power fails due to effects of fire, the lift could stop between floors, trapping occupants in what may become a chimney for fire and smoke.

While the safety of disabled people needs to be considered, the problems this raises are seldom great, and management should not refuse to employ disabled staff.

USING THE FIRE CERTIFICATE

Safety representatives should inspect fire certificates or exemption documents and make up checklists to monitor whether they are being correctly applied. The following list can be used in conjunction with a fire certificate or exemption document to develop a list of questions relevant to a particular workplace:

- is the use of the premises as laid down in the certificate?

- are all the means of escape as set out in the certificate?

- are the means for securing escape routes as set out in the certificate? (*eg* fire resistance, signs, notices, emergency lighting, smoke control measures etc)?

- is fire fighting equipment as set out in the certificate? Is it the right type? Has it been tested and maintained? Is it in the right place?

- is the fire alarm equipment as set out in the certificate? Is it tested regularly? Are records kept of tests?

- are any provisions in the certificate governing storage and use of flammable materials properly applied?

- is appropriate training in general fire precautions and fire drills given to employees?

- are the limits on numbers employed obeyed?

- has there been any significant change in the workplace which could affect fire safety since the certificate of exemption was issued? (*eg* in structure, layout of the workplace, numbers employed, flammables used, etc). Have these changes been notified to the fire authority?

STORAGE OF FLAMMABLE MATERIALS

There are special requirements for storing flammable materials laid down in Health and Safety legislation. The Highly Flammable Liquids and Liquefied Petroleum Gases Regulations 1972 set standards for the storage of highly flammable liquids at factories, construction sites etc, and provide a guide to standards of compliance with Section 2 of the Health and Safety at Work Act at other places of work. The basic standards apply other than to suitable small closed containers containing not more than 500 cc of highly flammable liquid and that all flammable liquids must be stored:

a)   in suitable fixed storage tanks in safe positions; or

b)   in suitable closed containers:

- in a safe position in the open air (protected where necessary against direct sunlight); or

- in a storeroom which is in a safe position or is a fire-resisting structure (half-hour fire resistance); or

- in a workroom in a suitably placed cupboard or bin which is a fire-resisting structure (half-hour fire resistance), subject to a maximum quantity of 50 litres.

Storerooms should be adequately ventilated and should have means to contain any spillage, *eg* sills or drainage to a safe place. Guidance is contained in HSE Guidance Note CS 2, The Storage of Highly Flammable Liquids.

Storage of petroleum spirit and mixtures is controlled separately through a licensing system under the Petroleum (Regulation) Acts 1928 and 1936. Requirements for each storage premises are laid down in Conditions of Licence by Petroleum Authorities or, at sites subject to the Major Installations Handling Hazardous Substances Regulations 1982, or the Control of Industrial Major Accident Hazards Regulations 1984, by the Health and Safety Executive.

The Highly Flammable Liquids and Liquefied Petroleum Gases Regulations 1972 also set standards for the storage of LPG. Generally the Regulations require that all LPG not in use must be stored:

a) in suitable underground reservoirs or storage tanks in safe positions in the open air; or

b) in pipe-lines and pumps or other appliances forming part of a totally enclosed pipe-line system; or

c) in suitable cylinders kept in safe positions in the open air, or where this is not reasonably practicable, in a storeroom constructed of non-combustible material.

Storerooms should be adequately vented and either be in a safe position or a fire resisting structure (half-hour fire-resistance).

Advice on the storage of LPG is contained in the following HSE guidance notes:

- **The keeping of LPG in cylinders and similar containers:** HSE Guidance Note CS 4.

- **The storage of LPG at fixed installations:** HSE Guidance Note CS 5.

- **The storage and use of LPG on construction sites:** HSE Guidance Note CS 6.

- **Small-scale storage and display of LPG at retail premises:** HSE Guidance Note CS 8.

Advice on the storage and use of polyurethane foam is contained in HSE Guidance Booklet HS(G)1, Polyurethane Foam. Further advice is contained in HSE Guidance Note GS 3, "Fire risk in the storage and industrial use of cellular plastics".

General advice on storage of dangerous substances, including flammable substances, is also contained in HSE Guidance Note CS 17, "Storage of packaged dangerous substances".

Where they apply, safety representatives should be made aware of the requirement of the Notification of Installations Handling Hazardous Substances Regulations 1982 and the Control of Industrial Major Accident Hazards Regulations 1984, particularly the on and off-site emergency plans required under this legislation.

CHECKLIST

1. Obtain a copy of the fire certificate for your workplace.
2. Make a checklist summarising the requirements of the fire certificate.
   Does the fire certificate give details of:
   - what your workplace is used for?;
   - means of escape?;
   - fire-fighting equipment?;
   - fire alarms?;
   - limits on the numbers employed?;
   - training and fire drills?;
   - storage of flammable and explosive materials?; and
   - any other matters?
3. Use the checklist to inspect your work to see that precautions are being properly applied.
4. Check whether any changes made since the certificate of exemption document was issued have been notified to the fire authority. Have there been any significant changes in the structure of the building, layout of machines, use of flammable substances, or numbers employed since the certificate was issued?
5. Check whether management is keeping adequate records of alarm tests, extinguisher maintenance, fire drills and training.
6. Is adequate training provided in use of means of escape, fire fighting equipment, fire safety in working procedures, etc?
7. Are drills held regularly? Are proper notices outlining procedures in case of fire displayed?
8. What would you say are the biggest fire hazards in your workplace? Are relevant precautions adequate? Are they understood?
9. Is your workplace covered by major hazards regulations? If so, have you been consulted about emergency plans?

FURTHER INFORMATION ABOUT FIRE

The following sources offer more detailed guidance about specific fire problems:

- **Safety representatives' guide to fire precautions:** Dave Bennett, 45p; WEA 9 Upper Berkeley Street, London W1H 8BV; *very useful general guide.*

- **Guides to the Fire Precautions Act 1971** (HMSO):

   1. Hotels and boarding houses;

   2. Factories; and

   3. Offices, shops and railway premises.

- **Dust explosions in factories:** Health and Safety at Work Booklet 22.

Health and Safety Series guidance booklets

- **Polyurethane foam:** HS(G) 1.
- **Highly flammable materials on construction sites:** HS(G) 3.
- **Highly flammable liquids in the paint industry:** HS(G) 4.
- **Hotwork:** HS(G) 5.
- **Flame arresters and explosion reliefs:** HS(G) 11.
- **Evaporators and other ovens:** HS(G) 16.
- **The Fire Protection Association:** 140 Aldergate Street, London EC1 4HZ; *01-606 3757; also publishes material on fire precautions for different processes, including checklists for industry, shops etc.*

HSE guidance notes

- **Fire risk in the storage and industrial use of cellular plastics:** GS 3.
- **Entry into confined spaces:** GS 5.
- **Gas Flooding fire extinguishing systems, toxic hazards and precautions:** GS 16.
- **General fire precautions aboard ships being fitting out or under repair:** GS 19.
- **Assessment of radio frequency ignition hazards:** GS 21.
- **Industrial use of flammable gas detectors:** CS 1.
- **The storage of highly flammable liquids:** CS 2.
- **Storage and use of sodium chlorate:** CS 3.
- **The keeping of LPG in cylinders and similar containers:** CS 4.
- **The storage of LPG at fixed installations:** CS 5.
- **The storage and use of LPG on construction sites:** CS 6.
- **Petroleum based adhesives in building operations:** EH 7.
- **Small-scale storage and display of LPG at retail premises:** CS 8.
- **Spraying of highly flammable liquids:** EH 9.
- **The cleaning and gas freezing of tanks containing flammable residues:** CS 15.

HSE leaflets

- **Fires and explosions due to misuse of oxygen:** HSE 8; (free from HSE Offices).
- **Dust explosions in factories:** SHW 830; HMSO.
- **Use of flammable liquids in factories:** SWH 1447; HMSO.

- Fire Certificates (Special Premises) Regulations 1976: Twenty questions: HMSO.

Other organisations

- **The Fire Protection Association:** 140 Aldergate Street, London EC1 4HX; 01-606 3757; *also publishes material on fire precautions for different processes, including checklists for industry, shops etc.*

20: Electrical safety

Electricity properly used is a safe and efficient form of energy but improperly used it can be a source of danger. The main hazards of electricity are shock, burns, fire and explosion and, in some circumstances, arc eye. However, even if the electrical shock a person accidentally receives is not in itself directly harmful, it can have disastrous consequences, *eg* while working at a height or up a ladder, a mild shock may well cause a fall to the ground; while the shock may not cause injury, the fall probably will.

It must also be remembered that electricity is in constant use in *all* workplaces; not just factories but in offices, banks, schools, etc and its use in such places is growing all the time as new technology and the 'electronic office' become more common. So, while the material in this chapter talks mainly about factories and construction sites, the lessons to be learned and the precautions to be taken, will be just as relevant to those who work in offices, etc.

EMPLOYER'S DUTIES

It is the duty of the employer to ensure that adequate precautions are taken for the exclusion of these hazards firstly by satisfying himself that all electrical equipment is designed to ensure that in normal operation live parts are inaccessible, that protection against fault current is provided by such means as earthing devices or, in the case of portable tools, that reduced voltage systems with all insulated or double insulated tools are used. Where electrical equipment forming part of a system has to be worked on for maintenance etc, it is vital that a 'permit-to-work' system is in operation and supervised by a person with sufficient training and competence to ensure that the equipment being worked upon is dead. This means that it must be not only switched off but totally isolated and locked off from any other part of the system by which it can become, inadvertently, live. Before work commences the equipment etc should be tested with an approved device to 'prove dead'.

ELECTRICITY REGULATIONS

The requirement to prevent danger from electricity is part of the Electricity (Factories Act) Special Regulations to which every employer responsible for electrical equipment under the Factories Act has to work. In addition to these Regulations, non-statutory regulations commonly known as IEE Wiring Regulations are issued by the Institution of Electrical Engineers. These Regulations are an excellent source of information for the installation, inspection, testing and maintenance of electrical installations in buildings and contain many clauses about earthing, such as the provision of earth terminals and earth continuity conductors, the earthing of such metal work as cable sheath conduit and trunking and the earthing of exposed metal-work of plant and apparatus.

New Electricity at Work Regulations have been proposed by the HSC. These regulations, which will replace earlier Factories Act regulations, will include a number of general requirements and will be backed by Codes and Guidance.

PREVENTING ELECTRIC SHOCK

Properly designed electrical equipment in good order is safe. When it is damaged or poorly maintained, it can be lethal even at 240 volts. Hand held lamps and portable tools are particularly vulnerable. Frayed or damaged connecting cable should be replaced without delay and if tools or lamps have become damaged they should be sent for repair at once. The use of reduced voltage equipment, *eg* 110 volt system with the centre point earthed will reduce the hazard of serious electric shock and is to be recommended.

If reduced voltage equipment is not in use, as is usually the case in offices, one of the best means of protection is the use of some form of earth leakage circuit breaker. Unlike a fuse, which is designed to protect equipment, *not* people, in the event of an earth fault such a breaker will switch off the current so quickly that there should be no danger of injury.

If neither reduced voltages nor earth leakage breakers are in use, wherever possible, miniature automatic circuit breakers or cartridge fuse holders should be used. The use of rewireable fuse holders should be avoided if possible because of the danger of them being rewired with the incorrect size of fuse wire.

The chances of electric shock will be greatly reduced by a competent person carrying out the following checks:

- at least a weekly test of the continuity of the earth conductor between metal-clad portable tools and plug – this will ensure that the conductors in the earth wire remain adequate to effectively carry sufficient fault current to blow the fuse; in addition, the insulation resistance of both tool and flexible lead should be checked;

- at least a weekly inspection of fuse boards;

- a quarterly test of miniature automatic circuit breakers;

- a weekly inspection of rubber gloves, insulated mats, sheets etc used for electrical purposes;

- a six-monthly test of electrical rubber gloves;

- replacement of metal-clad tools in favour of suitable all insulated tools and appliances where practicable;

- routine inspection of the electrical installations;

- regular tests and inspections of all office equipment; and

- regular tests on all wall sockets.

A simple method to ensure that the routine maintenance and inspection of electrical equipment takes place, would be to label and date all equipment at the time it is inspected. If the date on the label shows that the equipment has not been inspected within the appropriate time span, the equipment is taken out of service until it is checked.

As well as inspecting and testing equipment to be used, thought should also be given to the positioning of sockets and to the amount and type of equipment plugged into them. Too often, especially in offices, sockets are either in an inappropriate position, causing wires to be trailing about the room, or there are too many appliances using too few sockets. In this latter case there is the risk of fire to be added to the risk of shock.

OVERHEAD WIRES

There are one or two areas where, even though people are not working directly with electricity, they may still be at risk. One is that of overhead electrically driven cranes using bare electric down shop and cross shop wires to supply power to overhead cranes. Danger from shock can be avoided by using flexible cables on self-reeling drums, down shop and cross shop wires enclosed in metal or insulated guards or self-kinking wires suspended on a catenary.

Where painting or maintenance is to be done in proximity to such wires, it is important to ensure that proper precautions are taken so that the work can be carried out safely *eg* by isolating the wires before access is permitted (see *Chapter 21: Safe maintenance*).

The other hazard is the presence of overhead uninsulated wires owned by the Electricity Boards but crossing open spaces which may include workplaces. They will be positioned correctly at a safe height from the ground in accordance with the Overhead Lines Regulations, but remember – metal ladders, mobile crane jibs etc can reduce that distance and even make contact, with possible tragic results in either case. Make sure that employers mark these hazards clearly (see HSE Guidance Note GS6).

It must also be remembered that with high voltage sources or wires it may not even be necessary to make contact with them before a circuit to earth is made.

Overhead lines are a particular hazard for crane drivers on construction work. There are arrangements for consultation with Electricity Boards where cranes are to be used in the presence of their lines. Those driving mobile cranes or similar vehicles, should make sure that their employers have followed these procedures, since they have been prepared for their safety. Whenever possible 'goal posts' and warning tapes should be erected.

UNDERGROUND CABLES

Another particular hazard for construction workers arises when excavations are being undertaken. Underground cables may lie in the path of excavations. Once again procedures exist for the identification of these hazards. Make sure that employers follow these and that cable routes are properly identified by the authorities, by means of plans, cable location devices etc, are marked and if necessary, that the cable is made dead before work commences (see NJUG Publication under item 2 of *Useful Publications*).

ELECTRICAL WELDING

Arc welding utilises electricity which may be *ac* or *dc*. Given similar conditions and circumstances, *dc* welding is safer than *ac* and is to be preferred in confined and awkward places. With *ac* welding the workpiece should be earthed and this must be the only earth to the welding circuit.

All insulated electrode holders attached to the welding lead by plug and socket are recommended. The return lead should be clamped to the workpiece. The return lead is necessary in order to control the path of the current returning from the job to the transformer. Without it, the current, which is of the order of at least 80 amps, may take a random path through structural steelwork, railway lines, pipes etc, which could include high resistances (say, a loosely bolted connection) resulting in the generation of heat and the possibility of fire.

The welding circuit should be earthed at the job. If the earth was at the transformer winding and a break occurred in the return lead, the path of the return current would be uncontrolled. Therefore, it is very important that adequate earths must be available to the welder at each workplace. Alternating current welding sets can be fitted with a device that prevents the voltage at the electrode holder rising above 50 volts during the period when no arc is being struck. Without this the voltage can rise to levels that would be dangerous to the operator.

There are further references to general safety precautions in the chapter on welding.

BATTERY ROOMS

In work which uses *dc* current, either for tools or emergency lighting, there will probably be a battery room where batteries are being charged. Batteries give off hydrogen when being charged and this can form an explosive mixture when mixed with air. Ventilation of battery rooms must be such that no concentration occurs. Since hydrogen is lighter than air, ventilation holes or ducts should be flush with the ceiling and precautions should be taken against the collection of pockets of hydrogen. (BS 6133 gives further guidance).

Forced ventilation may be necessary. However, ordinary electric fan motors may produce sparks and would create a hazard in an explosive atmosphere. Where necessary, expert advice should be sought before such ventilation is provided.

Electrical fittings in battery charging areas should be acid resistant and not fixed to the ceiling but to the walls about six feet or so above the floor, to ensure that they are well below likely concentrations of hydrogen, assuming that ventilation is adequate.

Smoking or the use of naked flames must be prohibited in battery rooms, and where any work is being undertaken which is likely to involve a source of ignition, it should be done under the direct supervision of a competent person. This also applies to the use of hand held lamps and tools which are not intrinsically safe. Suitable insulated tools for batteries will be available and should be used.

Finally, lead/acid type batteries contain sulphuric acid which is a hazard in itself and minimum precautions are the wearing of eye protection and the use of suitable gloves. Eye baths and a suitable supply of sterile water or saline solution should also be immediately available.

MOBILE GENERATORS

Mobile generators driven by petrol engines to provide a temporary supply of electricity are frequently in use in works. So far as safety requirements are concerned, the supply should be treated in the same way as a normal supply *eg* the generator neutral and all exposed metalwork that could become charged should be earthed. In general, before a mobile generator is used to replace the public supply, all conductors from the public supply must be isolated (totally disconnected) and remain so while the generator is in use and until the mobile generator is disconnected. This applies even where the generators are being used because of a failure of the public supply. There can be danger, not only to those directly involved but to fellow workers working in the Electricity Board if a generator feeds into the public electricity supply system. This must never happen without the agreement of the Electricity Board. The earlier comments about adequate maintenance also apply to mobile generators.

FIRST AID AND RESCUE

Suppose that, in spite of all the precautions that have been taken, someone has received an electric shock. Do you have to stand helplessly? No, you do not. To assist the victim, speed without panic is essential. The current must first be switched off or send someone to do it for you. Send for a Doctor or your first aiders but do not await their arrival.

When the current has been switched off, commence artificial respiration immediately, and persist in trying to restore natural breathing until qualified help arrives and instructs you otherwise. Lives have been needlessly lost by not starting artificial respiration soon enough and stopping it too soon.

If there is no one available who knows where to switch off the current, it is possible to free the victim from contact with the electricity at normal voltage met with in the place of work, *ie* 415/240, by using rubber gloves or a rubber mat. If these are not available, use a loop of rope or coat or cap to drag the person free. Avoid skin contact between yourself and the injured person. Whatever is used, it must be dry and non-conducting.

If it is known or suspected that the victim is in contact with live conductors much above 415v, it is particularly dangerous to attempt to free that person unless a suitable article insulated from the system is available or until you are sure that the current has been switched off. If any part of the electrical system is above 250v, the employer is obliged by the Electricity Regulations to display a poster giving instructions as to treatment of persons suffering from electrical shock.

These posters are available from the Health and Safety Executive directly or from booksellers. First Aid Organisations publish very useful and lucid posters which cover gassing, drowning and suffocation as well as electric shock.

Finally, it is advisable that workers should receive training in artificial respiration at regular intervals, and that, wherever possible, means of disconnection of electricity should be clearly indicated.

CHECKLIST: ELECTRICITY

1. Is all electrical equipment in use in your workplace regularly examined by a competent person?

2. Are there any signs of faulty electrical equipment?

3. Is reduced voltage equipment available in damp situations?

4. Are all overhead and underground cables clearly marked?

5. Is all electric arc welding adequately earthed?

6. Is there a battery room at your workplace? If so check ventilation, prevention of sparks and ignition, prohibition of smoking and first aid.

7. Are all workers trained in first aid and rescue techniques for electric shock?

USEFUL PUBLICATIONS

General

- **Beckinsale's safe use of electricity:** Edwin Hooper; ROSPA.

- **Recommendations for the avoidance of danger from underground electricity cables:** National Joint Utilities Group.

- **IEE wiring regulations – Regulations for electrical installations:** Institution of Electrical Engineers.

Department of the Environment advisory leaflets

- **Powered hand tools – electric tools:** No. 18.

- **Powered hand tools – safety and maintenance:** No. 20.

- **Electricity on building sites:** No. 59.

- **Site lighting:** No. 71.

- **Electric ring and radial circuits:** No. 81.

Health and Safety Executive: (available from HMSO)

- **Electricity on the farm:** AS17.

- **Buried cables – beware:** ING(G)30(L).

- **Avoidance of danger from overhead electrical lines:** GN.GS6.

- **Electricity on construction sites:** GN.GS24.

- **Protection against electric shock:** GN.GS27.

- **Avoiding danger from buried electricity cables:** GN.GS33.

- **Flexible leads, plugs, sockets etc:** GN.GS37.

- **Electrical test equipment for use by electricians:** GN.GS38.

- **Electrical hazards from steam/water pressure cleaners etc:** GN.PM29.

- **The safe use of portable electrical apparatus:** GN.PM32.

- **Electrical installations in motor vehicle repair premises:** GN.PM37.

- **Selection and use of electric hand lamps:** GN.PM38.

- **Electrical safety in arc welding:** GN.PM64.

- **Electrostatic ignition – hazards of insulation materials:** OP5.

- **Electrical testing – safety in electrical testing:** HS(G)13.

- **Electrical apparatus for use in potentially explosive atmospheres:** HS(G)22.

British standards

- **British Standard Code of Practice CP 1017:** 1969.

- **Specification for safety of electrically energised office machines:** British Standard BS 5850, 1981; British Standards Institution.

- **Code of Practice for safe operation of lead-acid stationary cells and batteries:** British Standard BS 6133, 1982.

Statutory documents

- **Memorandum on the Electricity Regulations:** SHW 928; available from HMSO.

21: Maintenance hazards

Safe systems of work are absolutely essential to prevent workers who are carrying out maintenance work, being killed or injured – for example through being trapped in conveyor belts, process lines or by entry into tanks, stills and other confined spaces containing poisonous substances that have not been detected.

The need for such systems was highlighted in 1985 in a special HSE report "Deadly Maintenance" which analysed 106 fatal maintenance accidents involving plant and machinery which occurred in 1980, 1981 and 1982. This emphasised that, in most routine tasks in industry, people are protected from danger by the design of plant, by physical safeguards or by safety devices. But maintenance, whether emergency repairs, routine servicing or cleaning, usually involves access into hazardous areas not normally approached. Such work is more than likely to be done under pressure to hand back plant for normal production and this combination of circumstances can prove fatal if a properly planned approach to safety is not adopted.

HSE have concluded that well over three quarters of fatal maintenance accidents at plant and machinery could be prevented by taking reasonably practicable precautions. About two thirds of such accidents occur during breakdowns or scheduled repairs. The remainder tend to happen during cleaning operations or during examination, lubrication and painting.

MANAGEMENT'S RESPONSIBILITIES

Maintenance, like other aspects of business, needs proper management and a planned approach. For example in "Deadly Maintenance", the HSE state *"It is quite clear that the main responsibility for reducing the death toll lies with management. If people are not to die in what, in a lot of cases, are tragic and horrific circumstances, management must plan and control its plant and machinery work.*

TYPES OF ACCIDENTS ASSOCIATED WITH THE MAINTENANCE OF PLANT AND MACHINERY (from "Deadly Maintenance", HSE, 1985.)

Accident type

		Total number of fatal accidents	
Machinery		*Individual totals*	*Sub-totals by group*
•	crushed by gravity fall machine parts or residual energy motion:	11	
•	entanglement in powered moving parts of machines:	17	
•	crushed between fixed and powered moving parts of machines:	12	
•	crushed between moving machines and structure:	10	50
Falls from			
•	work platforms:	7	
•	ladders:	2	
•	plant machinery:	8	
•	plant due to rupture of vessel		2
Falls through			
•	fragile roof/ceilings:	2	19
Burns		10	
Hot liquids/gases/dusts/metal:			
Gassing		9	
Electrocution		6	
Asphyxiation		5	
Struck by falling materials		4	
Struck by falling plant due to tackle failure		1	
Total		**106**	

Proper safe systems of work do not just happen, they must be developed. If they are not, a further hundred or so lives may be lost in the next three years!"

The Health and Safety at Work Act 1974 requires employers to provide and maintain a safe place of work, and the Factories Act 1961, says quite clearly that it is the management's responsibility to make sure that work is always done safely and to see that specific precautions are adopted when necessary. These precautions apply equally to maintenance operations carried out by a contractor and to those carried out by workers employed directly by a company.

KEY PRINCIPLES

The HSE advise that any maintenance system should take account of the following principles:

a) *Design:* good initial design can do much to minimise maintenance problems. The need to approach dangerous parts may be reduced by the use of proximity guards or translucent materials, and the provision of external lubrication points or adjustment devices. Means of controlled manual cranking, true inching or slow crawl can be a considerable aid to safe maintenance practices where guards have to be removed. Suitable means of isolating the hazards are important, such as lockable electrical isolators or props to prevent gravity fall. Safe access and working platforms for maintenance purposes should not be ignored. This may mean permanent walkways, or, for infrequent access, fixtures for attaching temporary structures. Tanks should be provided with adequately proportioned manholes to aid the entry and escape of people, possibly wearing breathing apparatus.

b) *Management:* maintenance needs to be properly managed. High risk activities require supervision by suitably experienced staff if failure and death are to be avoided. There will undoubtedly be occasions when local expertise is limited and specialist outside assistance will need to be obtained. The tendency for maintenance departments to attempt to cope must be avoided. Their boundaries of performance must be recognised, and strictly enforced.

c) *Information:* clear information about correct safe procedures should be available to the people actually doing maintenance work. Accurate plans and circuit diagrams with valves and controls of the plant or machinery correctly identified need to be provided. The hazards associated with the normal process materials should not be overlooked.

d) *Training:* maintenance often involves work in situations where normal production safeguards no longer apply. Training to a high standard is invariably required, with particular attention to safe working practices in hazardous environments.

e) *Planning:* the existence, nature and extent of hazards can be more accurately assessed in a calm atmosphere, rather than in the heat of the moment of a faltering maintenance operation. Clear and appropriately detailed procedures should be drawn up for all foreseeable maintenance operations.

The extent of those plans will obviously vary with the type of hazard. It may be a simple manufacturer's manual, a basic plant isolation procedure or a full written permit-to-work procedure. A system should define the extent of the maintenance activity and not only the precautions required to safeguard the people involved but also any others working in the premises. Contractors' activities should not be ignored. Whatever system is adopted, it is essential that the hazard remains isolated for the full duration of the work.

f) *Equipment:* a wide variety of special purpose testing or safety equipment may be necessary for maintenance operations. A tendency to use home-made devices has sometimes been noted. Such equipment can be deadly. Safety equipment should be compatible with the type of work or it may not be used. It must be appropriate for the hazards involved or the dangers will be increased. If it is to function as designed it must be kept in good working order. Hence the importance of regular inspection and servicing. It is equally important that personnel are trained in the correct procedures for its use.

The correct equipment should be readily available for use so that the temptation to make do is avoided.

g) *Implementation:* the benefits of planning can only be gained if procedures are fully implemented. If that is the case, plant or machinery should be promptly returned to production without loss of life.

The laid down systems must be applied in every detail and checks made to ensure that safe conditions have been achieved before work commences.

If the planned procedures are found not to isolate the hazards, then work should stop immediately, until appropriate expertise can be applied to solve the problem.

h) *Monitoring:* people must be protected throughout the duration of maintenance work. Conditions should be monitored periodically, or in some cases continuously. Inspection by experienced management with appropriate authority should be adequate in most situations, but more exhaustive checks may be necessary, *eg* atmospheric testing.

i) *Rescue:* in theory the meticulous application and monitoring of a planned safe working procedure should make the need for emergency/ rescue systems either superfluous or at least rarely applicable. But mistakes do happen and the rapid removal of unconscious or badly injured people from still dangerous situations may be needed.

If a multiple fatality is to be avoided, it is important that the range of possible failures has been considered and plans laid to stabilise the situation, so as to achieve a rescue without risking further lives. It is essential that training in rescue procedures is given if people are to act calmly when required.

PERMIT-TO-WORK SYSTEMS

The use of effective 'permit-to-work systems' is an important part of a planned approach to safe maintenance. The permit is usually a form completed by the person in overall charge of maintenance at the workplace or a person with special knowledge of the particular hazards. Its purpose is to:

- grant authority to certain individuals to carry out maintenance;
- identify plant or equipment and its associated hazards;
- identify the nature, and extent of work to be carried out;
- to ensure that precautions are taken before work starts; and
- to provide basic information to maintenance staff on safe working procedures.

For example, a permit-to-work may stipulate that the following general precautions should be taken before work is started:

- electrical and/or mechanical isolation of plant from all sources of danger;
- locking off isolating valves and blanking off of steam, acid, water, gas and compressed air supplies and pipework;
- erection of scaffolding or other means required to give safe access to all work areas;
- provision of temporary guards or other action required to make the job safe, *ie* guard rails around holes in floors;
- isolation of machine areas, indication of limits of safe working *ie* danger notices on adjacent equipment.

An efficient permit-to-work system will include all these precautions. Ideally, the permit-to-work system should also include:

- the signature of the person authorised to release the plant from production:

- the time period from which the permit is valid;
- details of isolation and other precautions/ procedures or prerequisites necessary for the job to be done safely to be filled in and signed by the plant engineer responsible;
- the signature of the person who carried out de-isolation procedures preparatory to the restoration of power supplies after checking that all work has been completed and signed off; and
- the signature of the person authorised to accept the plant back for production.

Persons should not issue permits-to-work to themselves unless they themselves are the sole person responsible for carrying out the work. The contents of each permit-to-work should be clearly drawn to the attention of the person receiving it and assurance received that it is understood. No-one should be expected to receive permits-to-work if he/she has any misgivings. If they have, such misgivings should be referred to a higher authority than the person issuing the permit-to-work. Where more than one permit-to-work is issued for example on connected systems, such permits should be cross-referenced accordingly.

The whole system of permit-to-work is, of course, based on a formal document. The format and details of the document will vary according to circumstances in each plant. It would be a worthwhile exercise for safety representatives to examine such documents being used in their own workplace to see if they fulfil all the necessary safeguards and principles outlined above.

MULTI KEY 'LOCKING OFF'

Where equipment has only one source of power (*eg* a machine driven by a single electric motor), it is often possible to adapt the isolation switch to the motor so that it can be locked in the 'off' position with a multi-key locking device. Each person employed on this equipment is then supplied with a key which they keep in their possession and the lock cannot be opened until all the keys have been turned. This enables several people to work on the equipment without the fear of one of them finishing their work and switching on the machine, thus avoiding the need for a full permit-to-work procedure. For this system to be safe, however, it is essential to adhere to the following rules:

- each machine and its isolation box must be numbered;
- the special padlocks and keys should be kept under control, *eg* of the Plant Engineer and only be issued to people authorised to lock the equipment off;
- each lock must have only one key which must be given to the person working on the

equipment and each kept by him until the job is finished, when it must be returned to the person in control; and

- where more than one trade works on equipment, a separate lock must be used for each trade.

CONTROL

Overseeing and monitoring of maintenance systems throughout a workplace should be in the hands of a suitably experienced person, who should be identified in the employer's written safety policy. They should have the authority to co-ordinate the duties and responsibilities of everyone who may be involved or affected by maintenance activities. Finally, this person must make sure that everyone understands that the terms of any permit-to-work system are followed in every detail.

Occasionally, it may be impossible for one nominated person to be responsible at any given time for all maintenance activities. In this case some other responsible person should be able to assume authority if the nominated person is absent.

The appointment of more than one nominated person will often be necessary. Separate people may be needed to deal with different classes of risk (mechanical, electrical, chemical or radiological) so that there is time not only to draw up the safe systems but also to check that all necessary precautions have been taken and the people controlling the work knows exactly what they have to do.

ENTRY INTO CONFINED SPACES

Entry into confined spaces can be, and often is, a highly dangerous operation with no outward sign of hazard. Tests are normally carried out to ensure that there are no dangerous gases, explosive atmospheres present or a lack of oxygen. The results of these tests decide whether the area is safe, or whether protective equipment must be worn. Such information may be recorded on a permit-to-work. In certain work situations, such as those covered by the Chemical Works Regulations, Shipbuilding Regulations, and Sections 30 and 34 of the Factories Act, certification of a safe atmosphere is compulsory by law.

The Chemical Works Regulations (Section 7) for example are quite specific in that they require that a responsible person shall certify in a book kept for that purpose, that he has personally examined the place to be entered and that it is isolated and sealed from gas or fume, or not free from gas or fume as the case may be. No person shall enter such a place that has not been certified as free from danger unless they are wearing breathing apparatus and a

life-belt, the free end to be left with a person outside, whose duty it is to keep watch and to draw out the wearer if they appear to be affected by gas or fume.

The provision of proper rescue facilities is vitally important, and these facilities should include someone trained in first aid and the provision of breathing apparatus. The type of breathing apparatus should be either a face mask with a supply of air from cylinders outside the danger area or self-contained with a supply of air carried on the person working in the confined space.

OVERHEAD CRANES

Often maintenance and other work must, of necessity be carried out near overhead travelling cranes (see also *Chapter 14: Cranes and lifting gear*). In these circumstances a reliable permit-to-work or lock off system, will ensure not only that the law is fully observed but, more importantly, that safe working conditions are actually achieved.

There are many hazards attached to such work. There are two main ways in which an overhead travelling crane can be effectively prevented from entering a particular zone. The first is the complete electrical isolation of both the crane area in which the maintenance work is to be done, and when necessary, of adjacent bays in which cranes operate. The second is the electrical isolation of the zone affected plus the fitting of stop blocks on the crane tracks to restrict any excessive overrun due, for instance, to faulty brakes. Stop blocks must, however, be used with discretion – the abrupt halting of the crane might endanger people working below. This could happen, for example, in a steel works in which cranes are used to transport heavy loads of molten metal; a sudden stop could cause the ladle to tip and shower molten metal over the workers below.

Records of accidents which have occurred in connection with overhead travelling cranes prove that, to be reliable at all times, the safety system must positively prevent an overhead travelling crane from entering the 'danger area'.

Methods which have failed when used on their own include use of signallers or lookout men, warning lights or flags, the use of detonators placed on the track to warn of an approaching crane, and the issue of verbal or written instructions to crane drivers.

Any system of work designed for use during maintenance of overhead cranes must, therefore, make it clear that it is forbidden to approach the crane, under any circumstances, until a permit has been issued or a lock off procedure implemented. The system must ensure that all cranes are kept out of the operation zone and also that all bare electrical conductors remain dead until the permit has been cleared and cancelled.

MAINTENANCE CHECKLIST

1   Make a list of all maintenance activities and hazards.

2   Who within management is responsible for safety of maintenance activities? Are they competent? When are specialist maintenance contractors needed?

3   How can maintenance hazards be reduced through design?
    - *eg* external adjustment or lubrication points; lockable isolators; props to prevent gravity fall; or safe means of access.

4   How are maintenance activities planned?

5   Are permits-of-work needed? Do they provide necessary information and conditions to ensure a safe system of work?

6   If entry is being made into a confined space, have tests been carried out to find out if the work area is free from fumes and gas?

7   Is adequate information and training provided for all maintenance staff?

8   What special safety equipment is required *eg* safety equipment, monitoring equipment etc?

9   How are systems of maintenance work monitored?

10 What rescue arrangements are necessary *eg* breathing apparatus, fire fighting equipment, harnesses and lifelines etc? Have all maintenance staff been trained in rescue techniques?

- **Entry into confined spaces:** GN. GS5.
- **Roofwork: prevention of falls:** HSE Guidance note GS10; HMSO.
- **Prevention of falls to window cleaners:** Guidance note GS25; HMSO.
- **Manhole access to enclosed plant:** HMSO.
- **Safety at lift landings:** Guidance note PM26; HMSO.
- **Escalators: periodic thorough examination:** Guidance note PM45; HMSO.
- **Lifts: thorough examination and testing:** Guidance note PM7; HMSO.

- **Work on fragile roofs:** free leaflet IND(G)21(L); HSE.
- **Fragile Roof covering:** Cautionary notice, Form 901; HMSO.
- **Preventing falls to window cleaners:** Free leaflet Ind(S)4L; HSE.
- **Dangers from carbon monoxide:** SHW 395; HMSO.

FURTHER INFORMATION ON SAFE MAINTENANCE

Legislation

- **The Chemical Works Regulations 1922,** HMSO.

Health and Safety Executive reports

- **Deadly maintenance – plant and machinery:** *a study of fatal accidents at work.*
- **Deadly maintenance: roofs**
- **Dangers during maintenance work in health and safety:** *Manufacturing and Service Industries 1982 Report; HMSO.*

Guidance

- **Hot work – welding and cutting on plant containing flammable materials:** HSE guidance booklet HS(G)5; HMSO.
- **Access to road tankers:** Guidance note PM26; HMSO.
- **Safety aspects of industrial maintenance:** technical information leaflet, hazard analysis 1; HSE.

22: Stress

Stress at work can be damaging and can adversely affect the mental and physical health of workers. It can have important implications both inside and outside the workplace. Some people are subjected to stress both in work and in society. Low paid workers are often in jobs which are less secure and have to cope with the stresses of poor housing, restricted education opportunities and family break up. Women who have a dual role with responsibilities in employment and for dependants are often in low paid, part-time, low graded jobs and face sexual harassment and restricted job opportunities. Trade unions have policies aimed at reducing some of these causes of stress such as poverty, poor housing and unemployment. Trade unions are also active in seeking to help those members whose personal circumstances present additional pressures for them in work. Such help may be the provision of details of the sources of professional counselling and support; negotiating more flexible working hours and special leave; and the negotiation of workplace nurseries.

But safety representatives are also concerned about the aspects of jobs which people do and the way in which work is organised which can create stress and lead to ill health. It is now known that, when the level of stress is continuous and becomes unmanageable, ill health will be the result. Therefore, trade unions want to investigate what it is about work that creates intolerable stress and identify the changes which the employer could make to reduce the risks to the health of their members.

It is often difficult for safety representatives and their members to get the problem of stress taken seriously. This is partly due to the fact that the effects of stress will vary from one person to another and the level of stress may be difficult to measure. More often employers will see signs of stress as an individual rather than a collective problem.

DEFINITION OF STRESS

Stress is a very commonly used term but difficult to define. However, if trade unions in investigating the risks to the health of their members are to effectively show the extent of stress, identify the causes and highlight the changes which are needed, then they will need a working definition. Stress is something to which we are all subjected and yet our understanding of it is far from complete. It is a word which is often used to describe distress, fatigue and a feeling of not being able to cope. Others see it as a driving force which helps them to survive more effectively. People respond to the same situation in very different ways. Some will find a repetitive job comfortable, others frustrating because it provides no challenge. Some will manage a stressful situation for a period of time and then find it intolerable.

Also while it is possible to measure the physical causes of stress, such as noise and temperature levels, it is much more difficult to measure workload and conflict. Stress will be the result if the demands made on the individuals do not match the resources available (in the person or provided by the organisation) or meet the individual's needs and motivation. For example, stress will be the result if the workload is too large for the number of workers and the time available. Equally, a boring repetitive task which does not use the potential skills and experience of some individuals will cause them stress.

This chapter should assist safety representatives to tackle the causes of stress and help to control and eliminate them.

CAUSES OF STRESS

Stress at work may arise from a variety of sources. Often there will be more than one factor responsible.

Sources of stress

Environment

- noise
- poor lighting
- poor ventilation
- overcrowding
- vibration
- incorrect temperature
- toxic fumes and chemicals
- badly designed furniture
- open plan offices
- poor maintenance
- poor canteen facilities
- poor childcare facilities

Contractual

- low pay
- shift work
- flexitime (when abused by employers)
- unsocial hours
- excessive hours of overtime
- job insecurity including temporary/ short term contracts and redundancy

Job Design

- boring work
- too much/little work
- pace and flow of work
- too much/little supervision
- job isolation
- lack of direction and decision-making
- lack of job control
- constant sitting
- lack of adequate rest breaks
- under-utilisation of skills
- working with VDUs or other machinery

Relationships

- bad relations with supervisors/workmates
- sexism/racism/ageism (including harassment and discrimination)
- customer/client complaints
- impersonal treatment at work
- lack of communication

Source: APEX Journal, November 1984

WHAT IS IT ABOUT WORK THAT CAUSES STRESS?

Insecurity

For many workers one of the largest sources of stress is rising insecurity and fear of unemployment. The threat of redundancies may be real, or used to put pressure on the workforce and weaken union organisation. Announcing redundancies and closures at short notice can lead to shock, depression, even mental illness with the consequent effects on social and family life. Employers may increase this by not announcing closure plans until the last moment. Unemployment itself is a source of stress. As well as the obvious financial hardship, unemployed people suffer loss of self-esteem, boredom, social isolation and social stigma. Recent research has found a whole range of stress-induced diseases amongst the unemployed.

However, in workplaces where the union is well organised, membership of the union does give individual workers some means of gaining control over what happens to them in their working lives. Trade unions can, through negotiation, seek to influence management decisions about such things as change and job security. Trade union membership also means that individuals know they can rely on representation and protection by the union in cases of discipline, dismissal or if they have a special problem.

The stress of insecurity is often linked to that of low pay and often it is the low paid who are first to be made redundant in a recession. The stress of unemployment will also affect those who remain at work. Employers often increase the pressure of work for those who keep their jobs.

Insecurity can also occur if people do not feel confident about their ability to do the job well and do not have enough time, information, training or support to do the job without making mistakes. If they have no confidence that support will be forthcoming if mistakes are made and disciplinary procedures are rigidly applied, this increases individuals' feelings of insecurity. Also, if there have been too many changes in the organisation, jobs, equipment layout and style of supervision and very little information is given in advance of the changes being made or any training in new methods or equipment, people will feel insecure.

Long hours

One key way of dealing with the stresses of work is to limit the length of exposure to them. Increased leisure time and opportunities to relax are a crucial aspect of social progress. Unlike wage increases, reductions in working time cannot be eroded by inflation.

The TUC has mounted a campaign for reduced working time which is also linked to the need to reduce unemployment, and to ensure that the benefits of greater productivity are distributed fairly. Overtime and low pay often work together to cause stress. To deal with one, people find that they have to face the stress of the other. Overtime can lead to disruption of family and social life, fatigue, and increased accident risks as concentration and attention fail.

The TUC has published guidelines entitled "Working Time" for trade union negotiators to help efforts to cut working hours.

Shiftwork

Members on 'twilight' or night shifts face stress problems on top of those faced by other workers. The most obvious is the social cost of working when family and friends are at home. Women working shifts will often have to cope with domestic responsibilities as well as the need to earn a living. All shiftworkers are at risk from:

- disturbed and inadequate sleep;
- fatigue;
- depression and neuroses;
- dependence on sleeping pills, tranquillisers, smoking and drinking;
- more sickness; and
- disturbed family and social life.

The main reason for many of these problems is that shiftwork involves a disruption of the body's natural rhythms. These "Circadian Rhythms" (24 hour rhythms) control:

- temperature, pulse rate, blood pressure;
- breathing, lung capacity, intake of oxygen;
- cells and chemicals in the blood; and
- hormone levels.

During the normal pattern of work and rest, these rhythms prepare the body for maximum activity during the day time, and make it ready for sleep at night. The shiftworkers – particularly those on complex shift systems – lifestyle goes against these rhythms. Although the body can adapt, it takes time and is subject to stress, and can never adapt completely.

Low pay

Many workers particularly women, members of ethnic minorities and young workers, are forced into low paid jobs. In many cases the low paid face a 'poverty trap' where any increase in their income is lost because of reduced entitlement to state benefits.

Pay is the most important method of recognising the individual's contribution to the

organisation but other forms of recognition can also be important in helping the individual to avoid stress. If the job has no status or the work of the individual is undervalued or not valued at all with little feedback from colleagues or management then this can contribute to a sense of stress.

The TUC has produced guidelines to help negotiators tackle the problems of low pay.

Lack of job satisfaction and control

This is one of the most important areas of occupational stress – and one of the slowest to improve. Many workers are at risk from boring monotonous or over-demanding jobs. Without some 'job satisfaction' work becomes much more stressful. Job satisfaction and control is often lacking because work pressure is too great; the job involves no creative thought or responsibility; there is no 'pride' in the work; and the work does not seem useful. The control of occupational stress must start from the recognition that the main changes must be in the design of jobs and the way work is organised. Attention must be paid to the following checklist, produced by the Work Research Unit.

CHECKLIST: JOBS AND WORK ORGANISATION

Well designed jobs with properly developed work organisation should:

- provide opportunity for learning;
- lead to some future desired by the job holders;
- enable people to contribute to decisions affecting their jobs and the goals of the organisations;
- ensure that the goals and other people's expectations are clear;
- provide a degree of challenge; and
- provide training and information adequate to perform at acceptable levels.

Tasks should:

- combine to form a coherent job, either alone or with related jobs whose performance make significant and visible contributions;
- provide a variety of pace, method, location and skill;
- provide feedback on performance in a number of dimensions both directly and through others;
- provide a degree of discretion in carrying out successive tasks; and
- carry responsibility for outcomes and particularly control of work.

Tasks should not:

- require completion in a time determined not by the workers but the machine or system;
- be short cycle; or
- create social deprivation.

BAD WORKPLACE DESIGN

A well arranged workplace is comfortable to work in with all the necessary tools and equipment to hand. Cramped conditions, badly spaced machinery, and untidiness can all cause stress.

Machinery and equipment should be designed and installed to suit the *users*. Badly designed equipment can cause physical or mental problems. Repetitive actions such as stretching over a machine, typing, twisting of joints can cause muscle fatigue, cramp and tenosynovitis.

The people who work in badly designed workplaces are often the last to be asked about what should be done – if asked they often can come up with answers to the problem.

WORK HAZARDS

Other factors which need to be looked at carefully in the workplace which could be causing illness and adding to stress include:

Noise and vibration can cause stress even at levels where there is no damage to hearing. Studies have found that workers in noisier factories have more diseases of the heart and circulatory system – as well as hearing damage.

There is also evidence that noisier factories have higher accident rates – partly due to fatigue.

Toxic chemicals in a stressful workplace will multiply the problems. Some chemicals – affecting the heart and nervous system for instance – attack parts of the body already vulnerable to stress. Occupational exposure limits take no account of this. The use of any toxic chemicals at work should be carefully controlled to protect the health of workers but they can also add to the level of stress experienced in work.

Biological hazards are more dangerous as part of the stress reaction is the suppression of the body's ability to fight off infection.

Temperature, ventilation and lighting are also environmental factors which – if not properly controlled – will increase the pressure on workers. Good standards of temperature and ventilation are basic essentials of any working environment but if they are not properly maintained and controlled they add to the parcel of physical pressure on the individual. Research has shown that there are likely to be more complaints of discomfort and ill health where the individual has no control over the temperature and air quality in the workplace.

The quantity, quality and siting of lighting are essential if jobs are to be done effectively. Many people work continuously in artificial lighting with very little access to natural light. Some have to take up uncomfortable and stressful postures in order to do their jobs well because the lighting fitments are badly sited. For others the amount and quality of light is so harsh that it is not an aid to work but just another source of 'painful pressure'.

EFFECTS OF STRESS

The body's reaction

The body itself has a built in mechanism which is designed to combat attack. These reactions to stress are based on a well established response of 'fight or flight'. While they may have been very relevant to our ancestors, they can be unacceptable and ineffective in coping with stress at work.

This physiological response is useful if it is called into play rarely and only for a short time. The increasing heart rate and muscle tone, the effect on blood sugar levels and the ejection of fats into the blood, do prepare the body against assault or for escape. But if these responses are repeated and become a regular or chronic reaction to the demands of working life then they will be harmful.

The hormones released can themselves cause damage. The links between adrenalin and coronary heart disease are known. Also, while in the short term adrenalin will help the body to react quickly, too much adrenalin will have an effect on the brain and produce the sensation of tiredness.

The symptoms of chronic (long-term) stress are wide ranging. They can include indecision, loss of appetite, reduced weight, headache, backache, skin rashes and difficulty in sleeping and may lead to heart diseases, and ulcers.

Below are listed some of the body's reactions to stress, some aspects of the alarm reaction – from Women's Work, Women's Health, Jeanne Stellman.

Diseases of the blood circulation system are probably the best known of the stress-related illnesses. Stress is known to cause:

- hypertension;
- coronary heart disease;
- angina; and
- coronary thrombosis (heart attack).

Several factors can increase the effects of stress, these include smoking, alcohol, lack of exercise and a diet rich in animal fats.

Diseases of the digestive system are also clearly linked to stress. The increase in stomach acids and the decrease in stomach activity which accompanies the emergency response can lead to:

- ulcers; and
- colitis (inflammation of the bowels).

Stresses, strains and their long-term consequences

Stress	Strains	Long-term consequences
• Poverty, insecurity of work and unemployment.	• *Physical reactions:* headaches, backache, poor sleep, indigestion.	• *Physical health:* coronary heart disease, hypertension, gastro-intestinal disorders.
• Excessive overtime, shiftwork.	• *Psychological reactions:* fatigue, anxiety, tension, irritability, depression, boredom, inability to concentrate, feelings of unreality, low self-esteem.	• *Mental health:* poor mental health, chronic anxiety, depression, insomnia, neuroses.
• Pressure of work – excessive pace, mechanical pacing, production deadlines.		• *Social consequences:* family and marriage disharmony and breakdown; breakdown of social and community relationships.
• Work that is monotonous and requires little skill but demands constant attention.	• *Behavioural effects:* heavy indulgence in smoking, alcohol and drugs; impulsive, emotional behaviour accidents.	
• Working in danger.		
• Interpersonal conflicts and tensions.	• *Social effects:* poor relationships with others at home and at work; inability to fulfil social and family roles; social isolation.	
• Uncertain responsibilities.		
• Social isolation at work.		
• Poor physical environment at work, *eg* noise.		

Source: "Stresses of Work", McDonald and Doyle, W.E.A.

Again these stress factors can be made worse by an inadequate diet (which is why good canteen facilities are important particularly for shift workers) and lack of proper opportunities to recover from the stress.

Other illnesses associated with stress include:

- bronchial asthma;
- nervous rashes;
- some cancers; and
- the triggering of diabetes.

STRESS AND MENTAL HEALTH

Mental strain caused by stress at work is one of the most common but least understood aspects of the problem. Psychological reactions include:

- fatigue;
- anxiety;
- depression;
- hostility and aggression;
- psychosomatic complaints; and
- neuroses.

Illnesses associated with mental strain are not usually classified as 'occupational diseases'. Few records are kept, even though their origins may be clear to the millions of workers who are suffering every day.

Mental strain or mental ill health caused by stress in work is very rarely tackled. Society's attitudes to mental ill-health are very different from those to physical ill health. This can add to the pressure of the stressed individuals and may cause them to try and hide the effects until they become so great that the symptoms are unavoidable. The use of emotive terms such as 'breakdown' and 'burnout' do not help stressed people or their trade unions who are seeking to tackle the problems created by work. Symptoms of stress such as fatigue, depression or headaches are not usually classified as occupational ill health, even though their cause could be occupational.

Just as the ways which the body reacts to stress can be harmful if stress is prolonged, so too are some of the ways which people use to try and reduce stress symptoms. As levels of stress increase so does consumption of alcohol, cigarettes, and tranquillisers.

TACKLING OCCUPATIONAL STRESS

This is a very difficult job for trade unions to undertake but it is a necessary and valuable one. It needs to be tackled at two levels. Firstly, unions should ensure that their stressed members are represented and cared for. So it is essential that individual grievances are effectively dealt with and special arrangements negotiated to protect the needs of people who have already been damaged by stress. However, trade unions do not see their role as being limited to only looking after those who have been damaged. They want to prevent ill health occurring.

Like other occupational hazards, stress needs to be controlled at source. Because stress arises from a variety of factors, and because there is no measurable 'danger level', it is important for safety representatives to think about their priorities, and investigate ways of dealing with the problem.

Trade unions in the workplace can organise a number of activities which will give them the information they need to tackle their employers about the risks and causes of occupational stress:

- a special inspection (under the SRSC regulations) to check on all the potential physical sources of stress;

- a survey of members either using a questionnaire or through organised discussions between members and their safety representatives to determine

  – attitudes to job content and work organisation;

  – feelings of ill health;

  – increased use of nicotine etc;

- an investigation of:

  – sickness absence figures

  – causes of death of people still at work or who have retired within the last two years.

Some employers have tried to reduce the effects of stress by 'lifestyle' campaigns – promoting healthy eating and fitness. These campaigns can help workers relieve the strains caused by stress, but they cannot remove the source of the stress itself.

Many workers may be reluctant to talk about stress, or admit the problems they face. They may even feel that their problems arise from their own weakness or inadequacy, unions have a clear job to do in showing members that they believe that occupational stress is a legitimate problem which arises from the demands of work and how it is organised. It is important to involve trade union members, get them to discuss problems with each other, and to make them aware that stress is a shared problem which can be tackled through the union. Union members will have ideas about how their stress can be reduced. Discussing the issue of stress within the union will help but also persuading management to implement the solutions suggested will give workers an immediate feeling of having regained some control over their working lives.

FURTHER INFORMATION

- **TUC guidelines on VDU's:** TUC.

- **Health and safety in the office:** TUC.

- **Low pay:** objectives and guidelines for trade union negotiations, TUC.

- **Working time objectives:** guidelines for trade union negotiators, TUC.

- **Sexual harassment at work:** guidelines for unions, TUC.

- **Mental health at work:** HSE; HMSO price £1.25.

- **Stress at work:** Labour Research.

- **Videos:** NALGO, CPSA, BIFU and NUCPS have formed a consortium to produce three videos exploring the issues of stress, job design, and the use of VDUs. Further details from NALGO: 01-388 2366.

23: Office hazards

WHAT COULD BE SAFER THAN AN OFFICE?

A recent report by the Royal Society for The Prevention of Accidents (ROSPA) shows that more than 5,000 serious injuries are sustained in offices. Many thousands of less serious injuries go unreported and often unrecorded.

Careless workers **can't** be held to account for all these accidents. You can only be as safe as the conditions you work in allow. Cramped, unventilated and badly lit offices are the real source of hazards. Work pressures can also put you at risk. You spend a third of your time at work, during your working lifetime. How do you feel? If you've got aches or pains or are absent sick from work, could it be something to do with your job?

It is often said that the products of office automation are making the office a more comfortable, less demanding and much safer place to work in. But is this really true? In fact new technology has brought a whole new range of hazards into the office. The office environment may be made more comfortable for the machines but for the workforce it usually means more fumes, more eye strain, more shiftwork and much more pressure. Moreover equipment is often first added to the office without any consideration for the people who use it, nor its effects on noise, heat or space available.

DO YOU KNOW THAT YOUR OFFICE IS SAFE?

There is no such thing as a typical office. Some are small, others immense. Offices are found both in old and new buildings. Some of these buildings may have been specifically designed for use as offices. In other instances the office will only be one part of a workplace which is not primarily concerned with office work. People work in offices which are attached to building sites or coal mines, or part of factories and hospitals and therefore share the same health and safety problems as other workers.

Look around the office you work in. Are you hemmed in between desks, filing cabinets, machinery and boxes?

Cramped conditions not only cause discomfort but increase the hazards of office workers tripping over wires or bumping into equipment. Overcrowding is usually worse when the office is in an unsuitable building, but even purpose-built offices can be 'outgrown' and need careful planning to avoid accidents, and ensure that workers' health is not put at risk.

Electrical safety is as important in offices as in factories. Faulty electrical equipment can cause shock to users and may be a fire hazard. All electrical equipment should be regularly maintained and any unsafe equipment immediately taken out of service.

Fire precautions are poor in many offices. Fire exits may be locked or obstructed; extinguishers may be old and fire drills non-existent. Overcrowding increases the hazards, by making it more difficult to escape, should a fire occur.

More and more new machinery is being introduced into offices. Equipment such as this can cause problems of noise, lack of space, and fumes. It also brings a wide range of mechanical hazards. There should be proper procedures for you to follow if the machine breaks down and no-one other than a trained mechanic should attempt to investigate the internal workings of any piece of equipment.

HEALTH HAZARDS

Many offices are too hot, too cold, draughty and airless (stuffy). People who work in such conditions talk of always feeling below par and having constant headaches, lethargy, dry throats and skin problems. Some cannot wear their contact lenses comfortably in the office and many say that their eyes are sore and itchy.

List of common office equipment

- Electric typewriters
- Photocopiers
- Printers
- Litho machines
- Transparency-making machines
- Stapling and binding machines
- Switchboards
- Lettering machines
- Teleprinter machines
- Comptometers
- Telex machines
- Stencil machines
- Visual display units/Word processors*
- Franking machines
- Dictaphones
- Shredding machines
- Guillotines
- Collating machines
- Duplicators

*For further information, see *Chapter 24: Visual display units*

Such offices are most likely to be air-conditioned and open-plan, with screens, partitions and banks of filing cabinets blocking the flow of air round the building. They are also likely to be overcrowded and depend on artificial lighting and the jobs done there will be the repetitive type of clerical work which is not given any status and is usually done by women.

NOISE

Another 'invisible' health hazard is noise. Many offices are built on streets where there is constant heavy traffic. Others may be next to a major building site or factory. The increasing use of machinery in offices can make noise levels intolerable and yet office workers are told what pleasant, quiet places offices are to work in.

Noise interferes with concentration and makes working stressful. A noise level of 60 dB (A) is thought to be about right for office work, but many offices are much noisier than this. One survey found that 80 per cent of office workers in an open-plan office were disturbed by noise.

There are several ways to make offices quieter:

- double-glazing can reduce noise coming in from the street;

- safety representatives can negotiate an agreement with employers to ensure that they will not purchase any equipment which produces more than a certain maximum level of noise;

- acoustic hoods can be purchased for any noisy printers;

- the amount of shiny surfaces which reflect noise can be reduced; and

- decisions about the number of people, the amount of furniture and equipment to be in any room must take account of the effect on the overall noise level.

LIGHTING

Lighting can cause many problems and consideration must be given to the amount and type of lighting and where desks and working areas are placed in relation to the lighting fitments. In some offices people work totally in artificial lighting and very far away from windows. Lighting fitments are often broken, flicker and are not kept clean. Lighting can be inadequate in store rooms and on staircases and many offices do not have an emergency system for staircases and corridors in the event of a power cut.

Some office jobs require extra task lighting to give the workers sufficient light to do the job well.

VDU screens are too often placed in offices without any understanding of the importance of avoiding glare and reflection from windows, lights and other screens. This means that the image on screen could be unclear and much harder to read.

Conditions like these add up to a stressful workplace. The nature of some jobs themselves don't help either. Constant interrruptions from telephones and bosses, or long hours of monotonous work, can result in headaches, tiredness and a whole range of stress-induced illnesses. The message is clear: reduce the causes to reduce the stress. The Checklist on page 154 will help you in this.

HOW CAN THE LAW HELP?

The Health and Safety at Work Act 1974 applies to all workplaces including offices. Section 2 of this Act says that employers have a general duty to ensure the health and safety of their employees. Section 7 outlines duties of employees.

The Offices, Shops and Railway Premises Act 1963 applies specifically to those such workplaces. This Act covers (for example) overcrowding, temperature, ventilation, lighting, toilets, and washing facilities, and seating. It also spells out more specifically what your employer must do about all of these problems.

The Fire Precautions Act 1971 and the Health and Safety (First Aid) Regulations 1981 also apply to offices.

Some of this legislation is rather vague (for example, 'adequate and sufficient' lighting) and the minimum standards laid down can and should be improved on by negotiating with your employer.

Enforcement of legal standards in most offices is usually the responsibility of Local Authority Inspectors. Some offices will be inspected by Health and Safety Executive Inspectors, so it is best to check who is responsible for your office by asking your union representative or by contacting the Environmental Health Office of your local authority.

Useful guides to the OSRP Act and First Aid Regulations have been published by the HSE and are available from HMSO. Ask your union for advice on the law applying to offices and health and safety generally.

GETTING ORGANISED

Safety representative can do much to improve your working conditions. They have special rights and functions which make it easier to deal with health and safety issues (see *Chapter 2: Safety representatives and safety committees*).

Here are some of the steps they can take:

- check your office for potential hazards, using the Checklist at the end of this chapter as a start; you may find additional hazards which can be included; make out a list of unsatisfactory points, decide on priorities and raise them with management through usual procedures;

- do a simple survey to find out if anyone is suffering from signs of ill health that may have been caused by work, *eg headaches, eyestrain, skin rashes, etc;*

- get your employer to agree to tell you of any changes in the office *before* they happen, and the possible implications for health and safety — new office machinery, for example, should be vetted by safety representatives for potential hazards; you may also wish to insist on a health and safety agreement before any new machinery or process is introduced;

- arm yourself with further information by getting on a TUC or union approved health and safety training course; your own union or the TUC will provide information on health and safety (colleges and local libraries can also be a useful source); and

- ensure that health and safety is a regular item on union branch and workplace committees.

CHECKLIST

Are any or all of these problems familiar? Check for hazards in your office using this list as a guide.

Lack of space

1. Is the amount of space adequate? for people and machinery? Has it been measured?
2. Could proper storage help to clear floorspace?
3. Could a better-planned layout give more space?
4. Could office space be shared out more fairly?
5. Are floors clear of wires and small objects which may be a tripping hazard?
6. Are sharp edges and projections covered and enough space allowed around these?

Electrical safety

7. Are all wiring, sockets and electrical equipment regularly checked and serviced?
8. Is damaged or faulty equipment immediately taken out of service?

Machinery hazards

9. Is machinery properly guarded?
10. Is the noise level as low as possible?
11. Are chemical fumes removed by ventilation?

Fire precautions

12. Is there a fire certificate for the building?
13. Are fire escapes and exits clear and properly labelled?
14. Are fire extinguishers available and in working order?
15. Does everyone know what to do in an emergency and are regular drills carried out?

Environmental

16. Is the temperature comfortable?
17. Is there enough air without draughts?
18. Does the atmosphere feel dry and stuffy?
19. Is the ventilation/air conditioning system in clean, working order?
20. Are noise levels at or below 60 dB(A)? — for example, can you hear clearly what people are saying to you at normal conversational levels?
21. Are lighting levels adequate in all areas?
22. Is different lighting provided for VDUs and paper work?
23. Are stairs, corridors and toilets/rest rooms also adequately lit?

FURTHER INFORMATION

- See *Chapter 22: Stress.*
- **TUC Guidelines on VDUs**
- **Guide to the 1963 Office, Shops, and Railway Premises Act:** HMSO.
- **Lighting at Work:** HS(G)38; HMSO.

24: Visual display units

Over the past ten years there has been a rapid and continuing growth in the use of VDUs in all sections of industry and commerce. In Britain alone there are now an estimated 1.5 million visual display units and by 1990 more than half the workforce in the industrialised countries will be using visual display units on a regular basis.

This growth has been accompanied, however, by growing concern about a range of health and safety problems that may be associated with VDU work.

POSSIBLE HEALTH AND SAFETY PROBLEMS

VDU work can produce a wide range of different physical and psychological health problems amongst those who do it. Some of the symptoms produced are relatively minor and disappear when the source of the problem is removed but can, in combination with other factors, produce longer term health damage if they persist over a period of time. Other symptoms are more serious and can either produce the risk of serious health damage or increase the severity of problems which already exist.

Not all these problems can be attributed to the effects of the VDUs themselves. Many arise as a result either of bad work environment or bad job design and may equally well be found in some non-VDU workplaces. The present state of scientific research on a great many of the problems which have been observed amongst VDU operators and which are suspected of being occupational in origin, does not permit firm conclusions to be drawn about either the role of the VDU or the precise precautions to be taken. This means firstly that further detailed research, should be carried out into the problems raised, and that VDU health and safety standards should err heavily on the side of caution whenever there is the slightest doubt about possible hazards.

VISUAL PROBLEMS

The single most common health problem reported by VDU workers is eye strain (asthenopia). This can result in deterioration in visual acuity, tiredness and soreness of the eyes, headaches, neckaches, backaches, etc. Although it is sometimes argued that visual performance can be affected in the long term by use of VDUs, there is little medical evidence yet to support this. What is clear, however, is that workers with uncorrected, or imperfectly corrected visual defects, will suffer much greater eyestrain from using VDUs than those with properly corrected vision. Since eye defects become worse with age, this problem crops up more and more in older workers.

EYE TESTS

At commencement of the job and annual intervals thereafter, it is recommended that all VDU workers should be given a thorough eye examination by a qualified ophthalmologist.

VISUAL CORRECTION

The cost of any visual correction which is necessary in order to work in VDUs should be borne by the employer. This is particularly the case where existing spectacles are unsuitable for viewing at a typical VDU viewing distance of 50-60cm.

JOB GUARANTEE

The purpose of eye tests for VDU operators is to identify and correct any pre-existing visual defects which may aggravate discomfort or even cause long term deterioration in their eyesight as a result of the high degree of visual concentration needed to do many VDU jobs. In no circumstances should eye tests be used by employers to screen out people who are unsuitable for VDU work.

MUSCULOSKELETAL PROBLEMS (REPETITION STRAIN INJURY)

In a number of countries reports have been made of an increase in repetition injuries, such as tenosynovitis and carpal tunnel syndrome usually of the fingers, hands, wrists, and/or arms, amongst data entry and word processing operators who are expected to use keyboards to enter material into computer systems at high speeds and for long periods. Such problems are not restricted to users of VDUs but are also observed with mechanical typewriters and in other jobs requiring rapid repetitive work. TUC Guidelines on VDUs set out standards on good ergonomics which should be sufficient to protect workers against this type of injury. Any worker suffering from symptoms such as soreness or tenderness of the fingers, hands, wrists, arms, neck or elbow should notify their safety representative and seek medical advice immediately.

The objective should be to eliminate the causes of repetitive strain injury (RSI) through good ergonomic design of VDU workplaces and of jobs. Any change in job necessitated by the risk of repetition injury must be without any loss of pay or conditions. Where injury has occurred, workers' compensation or other legal remedies may be claimable for loss of earnings, pain and suffering, loss of enjoyment etc. A more detailed account of repetitive strain injury is given in Chapter 12.

REPRODUCTIVE HAZARDS

There has been widespread concern throughout the trade union Movement in recent years over reports, mainly from the United States and Canada, about cases of abnormal pregnancy outcome (miscarriages, premature birth, birth defects) which, it is suggested, are linked with the use of VDUs. There is no consensus about whether there is any direct casual link between VDU use and these occurrences or about what such a link might be.

The most commonly suggested cause of these problems has been radiation but the only measurable levels of radiation have been in the Very Low Frequency or Extra Low Frequency bands and, as yet, exposures to these have not been shown to induce biological changes in human beings. The VLF and ELF radiation, if it is being emitted, will not be coming from the screen but from the transformer which contains electrical windings.

Other possible causes suggested have included stress from high workloads and bad work environment, unsatisfactory working postures, infections such as rubella which have simply been spread amongst a group of workers in one workplace, or environmental toxins.

Until the results of more comprehensive research become available, many unions have negotiated agreements with employers giving pregnant women the right to move, if they choose to do so, to other equivalent work not involving the use of a VDU during their pregnancy, or to take leave during pregnancy without loss of employment rights.

TUC RECOMMENDATIONS

Given the present state of knowledge it is not easy to make definite recommendations on this subject. There is very little real evidence that radiation from VDUs causes miscarriages and birth defects, but it has not been demonstrated conclusively that some form of radiation (for example in the Extremely Low Frequency Band) might not be responsible. Since many women are now aware of the controversy over this subject, they quite understandably require advice and assistance from their trade unions about what to do. It is suggested that trade union policy in this field should be guided by the following principles:

a) Until more conclusive scientific evidence becomes available on the presence or absence of a link between VDU work and reproductive hazards, pregnant women who wish to do so, should have the right to transfer to non-VDU work during the course of their pregnancy without loss of pay, status or career prospects. This right should be conferred collective agreement.

b) Such an agreement must make it clear that it deals with the whole range of potential causes of reproductive hazards and is not restricted to radiation. Giving pregnant women the right to transfer is likely to be more effective in reducing potential hazards from bad posture, excessive workloads, stress, etc, than in protecting against possible radiation risks, since medical knowledge about foetal damage from radiation shows that the most critical period is the first weeks of pregnancy, a period when most women are not aware that they are pregnant. To be fully effective therefore, agreements should cover not only pregnant women but those planning to become pregnant.

c) Since the potential risks to men as well as women have not yet been identified, it is preferable that all workers, male or female, pregnant or not, should have the right to transfer away from intensive VDU work if they feel it poses a danger to their health. Where this right is extended only to pregnant women it should be viewed as an interim precautionary measure which should not be permitted to restrict employment opportunities in high technology jobs involving the use of VDUs in the future.

d) One of the most effective ways of reducing the risks of reproductive hazards as with other health problems encountered by VDU workers, is to limit the total time which all workers spend working on VDUs, and to ensure that jobs are designed in such a way as to avoid *intensive VDU use,* which is likely to result in the highest risks.

e) While serious concern continues to exist about the possible reproductive hazards of VDU work, the TUC will continue to put pressure on occupational health authorities to step up their programmes of experimental and epidemiological research in order to provide much firmer evidence to confirm or refute the hypotheses which have been made.

f) In the longer term, trade unions should press for the development and use of non-cathode ray tube VDUs, such as liquid crystal and plasma displays.

CATARACTS

A number of cases from the USA and Australia have been cited in support of the view that VDUs emit radiation which can cause radiant energy cataracts. Cataracts are opacities of the eye lens which normally only occur in older people or as a result of an inherited tendency. There is reasonable evidence to show that cataracts are induced by high levels of microwave radiation, for example in radar installations. VDUs (under normal conditions at least) do not emit microwave radiation. It has been suggested that non-ionising radiation in another frequency band (for example UV) may be responsible, but this is strongly disputed by other experts in the field. As with reproductive hazards it is impossible to say with certainty that there is or is not a connection between VDU use and cataract formation.

PHOTOSENSITIVE EPILEPSY

A further medical condition which has been claimed to be aggravated by using a VDU is photosensitive epilepsy. Approximately 0.5 per cent of the total population have epilepsy and, of those, up to 3 per cent – *ie* 0.015 per cent of the total population – have a sensitivity to flickering lights or certain patterns.

The condition is more common amongst children than amongst adults. The flicker level of most VDUs is higher than the frequencies usually associated with this condition although some special features of VDUs may encourage it. Most people with a photosensitivity epilepsy will know of their condition from watching television, before coming into contact with a VDU. Anyone who suspects that they may be susceptible to visually induced epilepsy should consult a doctor before working on a VDU. Their pay and conditions should be guaranteed if they are found to be medically unsuited for work.

DERMATITIS

There have been a number of recorded cases of rashes on the face or hands amongst VDU operators which have been linked to the VDU. Some VDUs build up an electric charge on the face of the screen. This electrical charge may contribute to facial rashes in sensitive workers.

RECOMMENDATIONS: VDU USE

Guidelines governing VDUs usually concentrate most of their attention on the VDU itself and the physical ergonomics of VDU workplaces. While these questions are undoubtedly of importance, the single most important source of the problems is an inappropriate and excessive use of the VDU. Serious health problems are much less common amongst workers who use VDUs for only a part of the working day and who have some control over how and when they use them, than amongst those who are forced to operate a VDU throughout their working day, at high speed and with their performance and behaviour closely monitored.

Types of VDU jobs

There are already thousands of different jobs which require the use of a VDU for at least some part of the working day. There will be many more in the future. It is difficult to classify them precisely but most fall into one of the groups shown opposite.

These jobs vary in a number of ways: firstly in the input rates. Some require a high rate of keyboard entry.

Work Organisation

By far the most effective way to avoid psychological and physical health problems arising from the way in which VDUs work is to use a participative approach to the design of VDU related jobs. This means that decisions about job content should be taken jointly by management and trade union representatives with the direct participation of the workers who are actually doing the jobs. Such an exercise is clearly much easier to carry out when major changes are taking place in technology and work organisation, but it can be done at any stage provided the employer accepts the principle that they should be redesigned. Participation in job design should be carried out at the earliest possible

Task	Input rate	Visual emphasis	Interruptions	Control over workplace	Decision making
Data entry	High	Document	Few	Very little	Very little
Data retrieval	Medium	Screen	Some	Variable	Some
Dialogue	Medium	Screen/keyboard	Time lags	Variable	Some
Word processing	High/intermittent	Screen/document	Few	Some	Variable
Programming	Low	Document/screen	Frequent	Much	Great
CAD/CAM	Low	Screen	Frequent	Much	Great

Sources: National Research Council, *Video Displays: Work and Vision, 1982* (USA).

stage, and wherever possible before any decision on the choice of VDU based systems or the design of software associated with them has been made. Union representatives should have the right to call on outside experts to assist them in the ergonomic design of jobs and software. Such experts should be provided at the employer's expense.

Work organisation and stress

Work which is not designed according to ergonomic principles or which involves excessive workloads, or insufficient control over the job by the individual worker, can give rise to very high levels of stress and mental, as well as physical fatigue. Persistent stress can not only result in psychological health problems, but is also associated with serious physical health problems such as muscular tension, back problems, high blood pressure, stomach disorders and coronary heart disease. The elimination of sources of stress from VDU jobs is therefore a priority area for trade unions.

VDU job design

No employee should be required to use a VDU constantly throughout his or her working day. Jobs with titles such as 'VDU operator' or 'word processor operator' should be strictly avoided. The objectives should be to achieve a mixture of VDU work and non-VDU work with the VDU element occupying no more than 50 per cent of daily working time. (If jobs are entirely VDU based, the provisions for rest breaks must be strictly adhered to but this is very much a second best solution.)

Avoiding monotonous work

Monotonous repetitive work requiring little or no judgement and providing no variety is extremely stressful and can thus result in serious risks to workers' health. Most jobs with or without VDUs involve some monotonous work, but the objective in job design should be to minimise its proportion in the overall job content. Techniques such as job rotation can be helpful in doing this although they can also carry the risk of substituting one monotonous job for another with no real advantage for the worker to compensate for the disturbance caused.

To eliminate the risk, job design techniques should aim not just to alternate VDU work with non-VDU work, but also to include in the overall job content more qualitatively interesting and challenging tasks leading to more highly skilled and qualified jobs.

Control over work pace and content

Workers in *some* VDU jobs have little control either over the pace at which they work or the way in which their work is organised. This too is a major stress-generating factor. Although work pace is often affected by outside influences (other workers, customers, etc) in most jobs there is plenty of opportunity for giving individual workers or small groups of workers the right to determine themselves how fast and in which way their jobs should be carried out, subject only to broad jointly agreed performance criteria. It is therefore recommended that agreements incorporating this principle should be negotiated with employers. Many workers do not object to working fast and intensively for a short time provided it is they, and not a machine or a supervisor, who decides when they will slow down or stop.

Training

Employers should, under conditions negotiated with their union, provide finance and give time off for adequate training for employees involved in work with VDUs. Such training should include:

- an overall appreciation of the system of which the VDU forms a part;

- phased training over an extended period of time in system principles and operation techniques, including training away from the workplace at least in the initial stages;

- general principles of ergonomics including the optimum adjustment of furniture, screen, keyboard, lighting, etc;

- skill development training to enable them to benefit from enhanced job design;

- trade union training;

- training for workers and union representatives

in the early identification of health programmes;

- training for managers in ergonomic and health and safety principles so as to enable them to better implement the standards established by regulations and/or collective agreements; and

- continuous retraining for older workers whose jobs are affected by technological change.

Performance and behaviour monitoring

Jobs which require intensive use of screen and keyboard and which offer little control to the employee are inherently stressful. They are rendered much more so, however, by employers' attempts to monitor closely the work done by employees. The significance of VDU-based equipment is that it frequently offers the technical possibility of recording work speeds, times of arrival and departure, error correction rates and other aspects of performance and behaviour and of identifying this data with individual employees. The information thus obtained can then be used, for example, as evidence in disciplinary proceedings, as the basic data for payment by results schemes or as one criterion in selecting employees for redundancy.

It should be clear that such applications are completely unacceptable to the trade union Movement. The following guidelines are therefore recommended to prevent abuse of monitoring systems.

Automatic performance monitoring

No VDU-based system should be used to collect or store individually identifiable data on arrival and departure times, work breaks, keyboard speeds, error corrections made, or other performance related data. No individually identifiable data of any type should be collected unless the prior agreement of the union representatives is reached on the principle of collecting it and on the type of data collected and the use to which it is to be put. Any information collected by these means should be made available to the employee concerned as well as to his or her union representatives. Agreements should include provision for the erasure of all personal information collected after a period of time to be jointly agreed by the employer and union representatives.

Incentive payment schemes

No VDU operator should be paid wholly or partly by means of incentive payment schemes based on keystroking error-free operation. Such schemes encourage excessive work speeds with greatly increased stress on the workers involved. For the same reasons keyboard speed 'competitions' with prizes should not be permitted.

Workload monitoring

One of the biggest problems arising from new technologies using VDUs is that employers frequently attempt to increase the workload on each employee. While some systems undoubtedly enable a higher output to be processed without increasing the work pressure on the employee concerned, this cannot be taken for granted. Trade union representatives should make a special point of monitoring workloads before, during and after the change to VDU working, of establishing acceptable output levels and of ensuring that they are not exceeded.

Undoubtedly the best way of reducing or eliminating the majority of negative effects of VDU work on employee's health and safety is by limiting the total time which they spend on working with the VDU screen. In view of the variation in VDU jobs referred to earlier, the following recommendations should be strictly applied to those jobs which involve constant use of the screen and keyboard. They should be adapted on a more flexible basis for jobs which already have a mixture of VDU work and non-VDU work.

Maximum daily work time

It is recommended that trade unions should aim at limiting intensive VDU work to a maximum of 50 per cent of daily working time. This guideline must not be used as an argument by employers for the conversion of full time jobs into part-time ones, and any such move should be strongly opposed. Where such a limit is precluded by the nature of the job, the recommendations on rest pauses must be strictly adhered to and, if necessary, extended.

Rest pauses

Frequent short rest pauses should be taken from VDU work. These pauses should be long enough for the eye muscles to recover from the visual effort of reading the VDU screen. Breaks of at least 15 minutes per hour of intensive VDU work and 15 minutes per two hours for other VDU work are recommended.

Rest pauses and job design

A properly designed job involving mixed VDU and non-VDU work will eliminate the need for rest pauses. If such jobs cannot be achieved, the rest pauses described above must be strictly adhered to. Likewise, if the ergonomic standards cannot be fully met, even longer rest pauses may be necessary.

Electronic homework

A growing problem experienced by workers in a number of sectors is the uncontrolled use of VDU terminals at home directly linked to computer systems on an employer's premises. Such electronic homework can often result in a total disregard for ergonomic and health and safety regulations, as well as high levels of stress, excessive working time, etc. Because of these risks, it should be avoided as far as possible and, where it exists, the conditions under which it is carried out should be strictly controlled by trade unions.

The arrangement of the VDU within the total work environment is of prime importance in ensuring that there are no risks to the health and safety of employees. One of the most attractive selling points of the newer generations of microelectronic-based computer systems is that they do not, unlike their predecessors, need carefully temperature-controlled, air-conditioned, dust-free conditions. One result of this is that the computers and the VDUs linked to them are often placed in offices suited to other tasks without any thought for the comfort or health of the people who are using them or with insufficient space for the job concerned to be carried out properly.

Lighting

There is a basic conflict between the level of lighting needed to do normal office tasks involving paper documents, and the level and quality of lighting most suited to operating visual display units. The ideal ambient lighting level for VDU work alone is around 300 lux; whereas general office lighting should be 500 lux or above. There are other aspects of lighting such as blinds, windows, wall surfaces that need to be taken into account.

Avoiding glare

Glare is a general term describing other light sources within the field of vision significantly greater than the luminance of the VDU screen vision which cause a reduction in the legibility of the VDU display and which can add to the visual load. This can cause eyestrain and visual fatigue. In medical terms severe glare which reduces operator efficiency is known as disability glare whereas less severe glare which 'merely' adds to the visual fatigue is known as discomfort glare. From the workers' point of view, however, both are equally unacceptable.

Glare can be either direct, from lights or windows, or indirect as a result of specular (recognisable image) or diffuse reflections either of light sources or of reflective surfaces. Positioning the VDU correctly should eliminate direct glare. Indirect glare can best be tackled by ensuring that, as far as possible, the reflectance of large surfaces in the immediate vicinity of the VDU result in luminance levels similar to those of the VDU screen. The desk in particular should be chosen in order to minimise reflections, ie it should not be too lightly coloured and the surface should be matt not glossy.

Temperature and humidity

A comfortable temperature and relative humidity is an important aspect of health and safety provision for workers of all types, not just for those who operate VDUs. VDUs produce heat, however, and if a number are grouped together, they can raise the ambient temperature in a room to a higher level than is comfortable and healthy unless extra steps are taken in terms of air conditioning and/or ventilation. Furthermore the visual and postural problems which arise from the operation of VDUs can be aggravated by unsatisfactory temperature and humidity. Heat from VDU screens and draughts from fans can also aggravate visual fatigue, headaches, etc, by drying out the mucous membranes of eyes and nose. For all these reasons it is particularly important to ensure that adequate standards governing temperature and humidity in VDU workplaces are observed.

Noise

VDUs themselves do not normally present a serious noise problem, most of them being much quieter than other office machines, eg typewriters. Nevertheless many VDU tasks require a significant degree of mental effort, and noise from related machines such as printers or even from the VDU cooling fan can be irritating. The placing of printers, telephones, telex machines, etc, is frequently decided without any thought for the problems which may be caused for VDU workers. VDUs may also produce high pitched noise or ultrasound which can be painful to those with acute hearing. Current occupational health standards for noise in most countries are set normally well above 70 db (A), a noise level at which concentration is virtually impossible and both job performance and health can suffer. A great deal can be done often at very little cost, to reduce noise in VDU workplace, for example by:

- positioning equipment (for example placing printers in a separate room);

- installing acoustic hoods;

- installing sound absorbing material on walls and ceilings;

- use of enclosures or partitions; and

- where ultrasound is a problem, use of padding around the terminal casing or flyback transformer.

THE WORKSTATION

General

One of the most critical factors affecting the health of VDU workers is the design and layout of the VDU workstation. A badly arranged workstation (desk, chair, wrongly positioned VDU and document holder) can lead to the adoption of a bad working posture with consequent back pains, neck pains, etc, as well as serious repetition injuries (tenosynovitis, carpal tunnel syndrome) and can aggravate visual problems.

Many employers, when taking decisions about the installations of equipment which involves

VDUs, pay little or no attention to the selection and layout of the furniture and peripheral equipment which goes with it. They tend either to adapt existing furniture or to buy the cheapest furniture which will do the job.

Union representatives should be sufficiently trained in ergonomic principles to be able to assess critically each employee's work position and make proposals to improve it. The recommendations made below should be treated as general principles to be adopted in the light of experience to each individual case, see *Chapter 12: Hazards of physical work*.

Adjustability

The most important factor in workstation design is adjustability. Reference has already been made to the need for adjustability of the screen and keyboard. Equally important is adjustability in the height of these units and in the support given to the employee's back by the chair which is used. Adjustment is important both because people of different shapes and sizes use VDUs and because different VDUs are used for different jobs. While important, however, it is not sufficient to have equipment and furniture which is adjustable. The workers concerned must also know how to carry out the adjustment so as to optimise the layout of the workstation. The adjustments should be easy to make, and it should be possible to make the most common adjustments from the working position.

Basic principles of workstation layout

Most VDU workstations consist of a desk/table and a chair. In some circumstances a footrest may also be needed. The dimensions of the various components of the workstation should be arranged and adjusted so as to fulfil the following objectives which are necessary for an ergonomically sound work posture:

- the feet should be touching the floor – or, if this is not possible, a footrest should be provided;
- there should be adequate leg room, both horizontal and vertical for comfortable working and stretching;
- there should be adequate support for the back;
- the VDU should be at a height which permits it to be viewed with the head at a comfortable angle;
- the VDU should be at a height and inclination which permits a viewing angle of 90°;
- the viewing distance should be comfortable and within the range specified below;
- the height of the desk and keyboard must be sufficient to prevent any significant flexion of the wrist (either up or down) during keyboarding;
- the document holder (as appropriate) must be positioned to minimise neck movement and at the same viewing distance as the screen and keyboard; and
- wrist or palm rests should be provided where necessary.

RECOMMENDATIONS: THE VDU

VDU screens come in many different types although the majority in use in data and text processing tasks are monochrome (single colour display) screens, usually with 25 lines × 80 character displays. To prevent eyestrain and visual fatigue in using a display screen it is important that the display be clearly legible and flicker free. The TUC Guidelines on VDUs set out standards which should be used as the basis for laying down acceptable standards for displays. Nevertheless the quality of the display (including freedom from reflected glare) should also be tested by direct reference to the people operating the VDU. The most important factor in VDU ergonomics is adjustability. The brightness and contrast must be adjustable; the screen must be adjustable (tilt and swivel) and the keyboard must be detachable under most circumstances so as to enable a correct work posture to be adopted.

Radiation

No single problem associated with Visual Display Units has received as much attention as the possible hazards arising from electromagnetic radiation. There are various possible sources of radiation in VDUs, chiefly the cathode ray tube which can produce a certain amount of X-ray (ionising) radiation, and various electronic components, which as a by-product of their functioning, produce radio frequency radiation (non-ionising). The illumination of the phosphor coating produces not only visible light, but also radiation in the bands immediately surrounding the visible spectrum (UV and IR).

The fact that the components inside a VDU produce radiation does not automatically mean that there are radiation induced health hazards for VDU operators. X-rays, which are by far the most dangerous potential hazard, for example, are almost entirely absorbed by the thick glass screen. Radio frequency radiations can be reduced greatly by the use of simple metal shielding over certain parts of the apparatus, notably the power supply (flyback transformers).

Although there is, as yet, no generally accepted scientific evidence linking radiation from VDUs with specific health hazards, there are a number of unexplained incidences of reproductive problems, cataracts, dermatitis and other phenomena, which cause legitimate concern to many people who spend a large proportion of their working day in close proximity to a VDU.

It is impossible to prove conclusively that any piece of equipment including a VDU is completely safe. It is only possible to test extensively all the theoretically possible sources of health problems in the light of present medical knowledge. Because of the mounting concern about VDU radiation, extensive testing of VDUs for radiation emission levels in the various parts of the electromagnetic spectrum is underway in a number of countries and epidemiological studies into the relationship between VDU use and some of the major health problems which have been attributed to VDU work are also being carried out.

FURTHER INFORMATION

- **TUC Guidelines on VDUs:** TUC; 1985.

- **Health and safety in the office:** TUC; 1985.

- **Visual Display Units:** HSE; 1983, HMSO.

- **Working with VDUs:** HSE; 1985; available free from HSE area office.

25: Violence

INTRODUCTION

The TUC has argued strongly for some years that the risk of a violent attack at work is a serious and very real occupational hazard for many working people. At the two TUC Conferences on Violence at Work, held in 1981 and 1987, it was seen that many occupational groups are affected by this risk, particularly those whose jobs bring them into regular contact with the public. The TUC cannot and will not accept that a risk of a violent attack at work is:

- something which comes with a contract of employment — in other words, something which has to be accepted as part of the job; or

- just 'bad luck'; or

- personal incompetence; or

- because of a worker's individual personality characteristics.

The TUC believes that the risk of violence at work arises from the jobs which many workers have to do and the circumstances in which they work. For some workers violence they have to confront at work may also be a 'law and order' issue and the violence may be an extension of vandalism and anti-social behaviour generally but for others this is not the case. In 1986 the Health and Safety Executive (HSE) published a guidance document which stated very clearly that *"the problem of violence is often associated with the main purpose of an organisation — providing a service to the public"*.

WHAT IS VIOLENCE AT WORK?

Defining what is meant by a violent incident is an essential (but difficult) task for anyone involved in the investigation, management and prevention of violence at work. Clearly it must include incidents which cause death or serious or minor injury but threats, especially with a weapon or an implement, are also important even if no injury occurs. Also, constant verbal abuse can cause health damage by being a source of stress. Sometimes violence is not limited to the workplace but follows workers to their homes or takes the form of attacks on their property such as the car they use to undertake their job.

The HSC's Health Services Advisory Committee, when carrying out a survey of the incidence of violence to workers in the NHS, defined violent incidents as those:

- requiring medical assistance (major injury);

- requiring only first aid (minor injury);

- involving a threat with a weapon/object but causing no physical injury; and

- involving verbal abuse.

The Association of Directors of Social Services, in their guidance, recommend that sexual and racial harassment should also be seen as violence at work. Reported injuries from violence have covered the whole range — from bruising to broken bones, stab wounds to death. Threats have involved guns, axes and broken bottles although the psychological effects of such attacks remain largely hidden and unrecognised.

THE SIZE OF THE PROBLEM

Discovering the number of workers who have already been damaged as a result of a violent attack has been very difficult but good figures do exist about public transport workers in a report prepared by the HSE and the Department of Transport. Also the survey carried out in the NHS found that the risk of violence was not limited to a few jobs. It found that, in the previous 12 months, one in 200 staff had suffered a major injury; more than one in ten, a minor injury; one in 21 had been threatened with a weapon or implement and more than one in six had been threatened verbally.

The most common question posed is whether or not the incidence of violence towards workers has increased. It is not possible to say 'yes' or 'no' to this question but the perception of the risk has increased and so has the unwillingness of many workers to tolerate it. It is not possible to assess whether or not there has been an increase because so many incidents are not reported by staff or recorded by management.

REPORTING OF INCIDENTS

People are often reluctant to report incidents for a number of reasons which relate directly to the way work is organised. Some fear it could be seen as their own failure — their mishandling of a situation and their professional incompetence. Some do not want the attention that a report would bring and, given the absence of counselling and support for victims, see no point in reporting it. There is still a 'macho' approach in many work groups where the 'I can handle anything' attitude is still common. Workers must be encouraged to report incidents and be given the confidence that employers will deal with the issue.

RECORDING OF INCIDENTS

Many incidents, even when injury is caused, are not seen by employers as 'accidents at work' and therefore are not recorded or counted. But even when a death occurs there is no guarantee that, if it was due to violence, the HSE will have been automatically told by the quickest means as is required in the reporting regulations for fatal or major accidents at work. This is simply because violence is still not seen as an occupational hazard.

Too often, even where it is acknowledged that violence does exist there is a tendency to see it as affecting only certain specific groups and there is an unwillingness to accept that a very large number of workers may face this risk at work. The HSE, in their 1986 report, said that an incident in one employing authority was regarded by management as isolated until soundings were made and it was found that violence was much more common and affected a wider range of jobs than at first thought.

While it is difficult to build up evidence of the extent of the risk from violence at work from reports of actual incidents, this is possible, from a careful analysis of the jobs which people do and the places where they work.

LEGAL STANDARDS

There is no actual mention of the word violence, in the Health and Safety at Work Act (HSW Act). Nevertheless all the general duties placed on employers by the Act still apply to the control of this risk. Under the Act employers must provide:

- safe systems of work (*ie* safe methods of working);
- safe workplaces;
- a safe working environment; and
- information, instruction and training for staff.

All these duties are very relevant where there is a risk of violence.

EMPLOYERS' RESPONSIBILITIES

Some violent incidents cannot be predicted but many are foreseeable and therefore employers have a responsibility in law to identify these and seek to prevent them. All employers have a responsibility to manage the health and safety aspects of their affairs. Thus, where a real risk of violence exists, employers must: if employers are to meet their statutory responsibilities:

- identify such hazards to the health and safety of workers arising from the jobs which they are asked to do;
- plan measures to remove hazards and reduce risks; and
- train and inform all workers affected.

Where violence is a problem, all employers should make a commitment to prevent predictable (*ie* foreseeable) incidents of violence and this commitment — which must come from the highest level in management — must be translated into arrangements which will ensure that they meet their legal duty to provide a safe system of work and a safe workplace. All workers at risk must be able to do their jobs with the confidence that their employer not only deplores acts of violence towards them but has developed a strategy with which to prevent, control or minimise the risks involved.

AUTHORITATIVE ADVICE

Even if employers acknowledge that a risk of violence exists, many fail to appreciate the need for a planned approach to the prevention of violence and do not understand how this issue can be tackled systematically.

Such arguments can no longer be accepted as several sources of authoritative guidance for

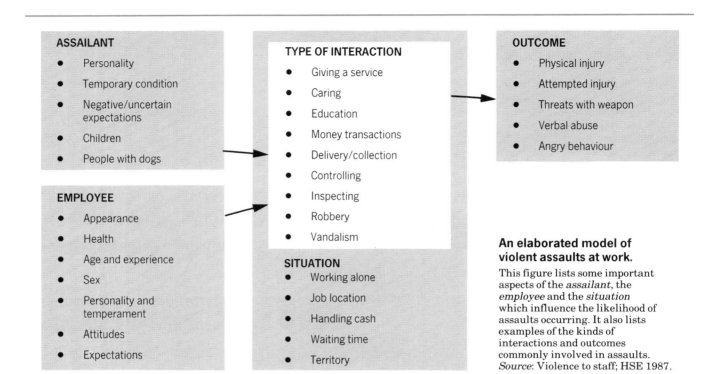

ASSAILANT

- Personality
- Temporary condition
- Negative/uncertain expectations
- Children
- People with dogs

EMPLOYEE

- Appearance
- Health
- Age and experience
- Sex
- Personality and temperament
- Attitudes
- Expectations

TYPE OF INTERACTION

- Giving a service
- Caring
- Education
- Money transactions
- Delivery/collection
- Controlling
- Inspecting
- Robbery
- Vandalism

SITUATION

- Working alone
- Job location
- Handling cash
- Waiting time
- Territory

OUTCOME

- Physical injury
- Attempted injury
- Threats with weapon
- Verbal abuse
- Angry behaviour

An elaborated model of violent assaults at work.

This figure lists some important aspects of the *assailant*, the *employee* and the *situation* which influence the likelihood of assaults occurring. It also lists examples of the kinds of interactions and outcomes commonly involved in assaults. *Source*: Violence to staff; HSE 1987.

employers on the prevention of violence have been published. The HSE document: "Violence to Staff — A Basis for Assessment and Prevention" sets out, for all employers, a procedure which will enable them to manage this problem effectively and it provides a framework for investigating the risk of violence at work, as shown above.

By assessing each component of a violent incident using the above model it is possible to identify the possibility of intervening to modify the circumstances which may contribute to a violent incident or to alter the possible outcome.

The TUC supports this approach but would argue that other factors may be present in the situation which are also relevant — such as poverty, unemployment, sexism, racism, and the general political attitude to the public sector as a whole.

In addition, specific advice has been published for various sectors including:

- transport;
- the NHS; and
- from the Association of Directors of Social Services.

A DHSS Committee was also established in 1987 to look at the common areas of concern for those employed in the social services, the NHS and the DHSS.

IDENTIFYING THE RISK

This must be the first step for any safety

representative concerned to ensure that their members are protected from the hazard of violence at work. In order to discover who is at risk, the TUC believes it is necessary to look closely at the jobs people do and the circumstances in which they work. As any such examination could produce a very long list of risk factors so it is important to try and group these under certain headings such as:

Jobs

- handling money;
- providing care, advice, information;
- working with violent people;
- dealing with complaints;
- having the power to act against the public, inspect premises and enforce legislation;
- working alone; or
- working unsocial hours.

Workplaces

- isolated — geographically, from other staff;
- out in the community;
- badly lit;
- not on own employers' premises; or
- on multi-occupied premises.

For most people the risk is more likely to arise because of a number of factors coming together rather than just a single cause — handling money in isolation (rent collection, emptying meters in private homes); operating a driver only bus service at the end of the school day or after pub closing hours; or coping with angry and distressed patients and their relatives or friends in isolated accident and emergency units at night.

Of course what goes on in work can never be separated from what is happening in society at large. In terms of attitudes, the risk of violence can be enhanced by factors such as sexism, racism and views on sexual orientation. Also the effect of government policy towards the public, which has brought a reduction in the amount and quality of many services has increased pressure on individual staff and clients — limiting the range of viable preventative solutions.

A PREVENTIVE STRATEGY

The risk of violence is an occupational hazard which must be tackled in a systematic way. The first step must be to discover where and why there is a risk. This will very often be different for each location and each job function. Without this investigation, any preventive measures adopted are unlikely to be effective. The effectiveness of any measure can only be assessed by its relevance to any one situation where violence is a possible outcome.

The question of violence must be taken into account when decisions are being made about such issues as:

- designing and altering buildings;
- setting staffing levels;
- job design and re-design;
- working practices;
- communication channels and procedures;
- recording of accidents at work;
- assessing training needs; and
- establishing an Occupational Health Service.

This list is by no means exhaustive.

AVOIDING INSTANT SOLUTIONS

When trying to solve the problem of violence at work there are no panaceas, easy solutions or short cuts. Whenever an incident occurs, the discussion can quickly turn to one particular proposal such as panic buttons, two-way radios, training, doubling up of staff, screens etc. All of these may be very useful but not in isolation from a planned and systematic approach. If these suggestions arise from an analysis of a specific situation and are deemed to be relevant to an overall approach then they can be useful but so often they are not discussed in these terms.

It is very important to look at the issues raised by some of these ideas. Safety representatives need to ask more in-depth questions about some of these ready-made solutions.

For example, on panic buttons the questions should be:

- are they checked regularly?;
- what actually happens when the button is pressed?;
- will workers be considered a nuisance/ incompetent if they press the button?;
- will they be encouraged to use them even if eventually the situation does not become violent?; and
- what about league tables? — for example "I only needed to press the panic button once last month".

On doubling-up of staff, which may be necessary in some cases, the important thing for safety representatives to consider is who decides when it is necessary. Is the decision to be made by senior staff because of the nature of the risk or are individuals going to be left to ask? Could it not be that in some cases, especially if it is the only change which is made to deal with the risk of violence, that it could lead to two deaths or two injuries?

On training, the first questions must be: for which staff; for what purpose; and who should provide it? Often, when a problem is found, the response tends to be "let's have some training" — as if training on its own can work miracles. Training must be part of an overall planned approach. Yet, in isolation from an investigation of the causes in any one situation, it could be wasteful and even give staff a false sense of security. Nevertheless, in their guidance produced for the Health Service, the Health and Safety Commission's Health Service Advisory Committee (HSAC) recommended that, for all staff working in an area where the risk of violence has been established, there should be a short course providing discussion of:

- the causes of violence;
- the recognition of warning signs;
- the relevant interpersonal skills; and
- the details of the arrangements devised by management.

In addition, HSAC recommended that, for those people who have the responsibility of handling violent or potentially violent people, special training courses should be provided.

Self-defence training is often raised when discussing the risk of violence but this throws all the responsibility for protecting the worker from the risk back on to the individual worker whereas in law the employer has the greater responsibility. Self-defence training will rarely if ever be appropriate, since it is not really acceptable for a worker to use violence against a member of the public.

Personal alarms have been recommended by some employers for their workers but there are several issues which need to be addressed. The use of a personal alarm may turn a potentially violent situation into an actual violence. Its use will only be helpful if there are people around to hear it and who know how to respond.

WHAT EMPLOYERS MUST DO

When launching the HSE document Dr John Cullen, Chairman of the Health and Safety Commission said *"The report makes clear that the way jobs are planned and performed can affect the occurrence of violence. It emphasises the importance of a systematic approach to the design and monitoring of preventative measures. It should help employers who are uncertain about the extent of violence to their staff as well as those who recognise the problem but are unsure of how best to devise effective measures to combat it."*

Some employers have produced policies on the prevention of violence but many of these are merely procedures informing their workers what to do after violence has happened. Others, who have thought the problem through carefully with trade union representatives, have produced policies which include detailed arrangements on how they are going to protect their staff from the risk of foreseeable violence.

Too many workers are left for themselves to identify situations in which they are at risk from violence and then to work out how to deal with the problem. To protect themselves, many are expected, simply to rely on their experience in a job and some are left to feel that they have failed in that job if they become a victim of a violent attack.

If this situation is to change, the trade unions require employers to make a top level commitment to deal with violence as a health and safety problem and to develop practical policies which include:

- investigation of risk areas and groups;
- proper reporting procedures;
- the development of safe systems of work;
- the creation of safer workplaces;
- information and training for all workers at risk;
- examination of the relevance of training and any training gaps;
- counselling and support for the victim and their colleagues; and
- effective monitoring.

COMPENSATION AND VICTIM SUPPORT

Despite efforts by employers and trade unions to prevent assaults on staff, assaults are unlikely to be eliminated completely and adequate compensation and support for victims whilst they recover from serious attacks is therefore important. Employers should be persuaded to provide aftercare arrangements involving visits to the victim with counselling and advice on a wide range of welfare issues. Unions have an important role to play here. The National Association of Victim Support Schemes, which uses local volunteers, can also give support and advice as can Rape Crisis Centres. If workers or their colleagues ask for counselling after an incident, this should not be seen as personal weakness.

Compensation can be obtained through the Criminal Injuries Compensation Board for injuries serious enough to warrant an award of at least £400. For lesser injuries, compensation can be awarded by Magistrates.

CHECKLIST: VIOLENCE

1. List all jobs where workers come into contact with the public and identify those where there is a risk of violence.

2. Analyse the problem in further detail. Take soundings.

3. Make a report to your members.

4. Urge management to establish a joint working party, chaired by a senior person in management, to develop a preventive strategy.

5. Persuade management to urge workers to report all incidents so that they can be recorded and analysed and support can be given to victims.

6. Consider a range of preventive measures for each problem area.

7. Make sure these are implemented and regularly monitored.

8. Review arrangements for compensation and victim support.

FURTHER INFORMATION

- **Violence to staff — a basis for assessment and prevention:** HSE/Home Office, 1986.
- **Violence to staff in the Health Service:** HSC Health Services Advisory Committee, 1987.
- **Guidelines and recommendations to employers on violence against employees:** Association of Directors of Social Services, 1987.
- **Assaults on bus staff:** Department of Transport, 1986.
- **A study of violence on London Transport:** GLC, 1976.

26: Hours of work

One of the original purposes of protective legislation in the 19th century was to limit the hours which people could be required to work — for example in factories and mines. Traditionally the employment of women and young people in industry has been restricted by numerous pieces of detailed legislation. However, by the introduction of the Sex Discrimination Act (SDA) 1986, the Government have now removed restrictions on the hours of employment of women in factories and other similar undertakings. The TUC has opposed this strongly arguing that essential requirements to prevent women working excessive or unsocial hours should be extended to men.

The effect of the SDA 1986 is that the only remaining restrictions on hours of work are those relating to young people. In December 1987 the Government issued a consultative document proposing removal of restrictions on the employment of young people and the removal of alleged sex discrimination in employment. Again the TUC has opposed the removal of essential protections for young people and has argued for their extension – particularly in view of the extra hazards faced by young people at work (see *Chapter 27: Young workers*).

A wide variety of legislation regulates the hours of employment of young people. This legislation has developed in a piecemeal fashion since the beginning of the 19th century and is highly complex. In some cases it can appear old fashioned or it may be obsolete because conditions and processes have changed or have gone out of use.

YOUNG PERSONS

A young person means, where appropriate in the relevant law, a person who has ceased to be a child but has not attained the age of 18. A child means a person who is under minimum school leaving age which varies between 15 years 8 months and 16 years 7 months depending on the relationship between the pupil's birthday and statutory school leaving date. Children are mostly prohibited from employment in industrial undertakings and their hours and conditions of work are strictly regulated in other types of employment.

In their consultative documents, the Government have tried to suggest that there are few differences between 16 to 18 year olds and the rest of the adult employed population. However it is important to bear in mind that there are biological and age related differences, such as incomplete physical development, longer life expectancy, (which can affect young people exposed to long term health hazards), and immaturity (which is important when considering risks from machinery, or processes and accident proneness). Many of these things mean that young people need extra information, training and supervision. But restrictions on hours of work are important too.

HISTORICAL BACKGROUND

Protective legislation dealing with young people's and children's hours began to be introduced at the beginning of the 19th century in response to the appalling conditions then prevailing in factories and mines and the extremely long hours worked in factories, mines and shops. At that time, as a result of the industrial revolution, the textile trade changed from a domestic to a factory based industry, and the conditions under which children and young people were employed in textile mills gave rise to public clamour for reform. A complicated pattern of controls over young people's and women's hours was developed and eventually applied to most manufacturing industries. Legislation on the same lines was also developed to control the hours and conditions of work of children and young people working in mines and also as shop assistants. Protection for young people was also embodied in more general legislation dealing with health and safety, dangerous and unhealthy industries, the education and morals of children, homeworking and so on.

The 1833 Factory Act regulated the employment of older children and provided for enforcement by appointment of the first four salaried factory inspectors. The struggle for shorter hours for adult workers resulted in the 1844 Factory Act which then extended limitation of hours of work to women. A Commission, which had been set up in 1840 to investigate conditions in mines, led to the Mines Act which prohibited the employment of children under 10 underground, and restricted the kind of work, young people could do.

These principles were carried forward in the 1847 Factory Act which was followed later by the Factory and Workshop Act of 1878. In 1880 the Education Act brought in compulsory school attendance to the age of 10. Further restrictions were introduced in the Factory and Workshop Act 1901, which brought in the ten hour day for women and young children and the 55½ hour week for textile factories and the 60 hour week for other factories.

Later on in 1920 the Employment of Women and Young Persons and Children's Act raised the minimum age for full time employment in industry to 14. From then on a number of other acts including the Employment of Women and Young Persons Act 1936, the Hours of Employment (Conventions) Act 1936 and the Factories Act 1937 consolidated and enhanced protection for women and young people working in factories. In the '50s and '60s this was carried into the Mines and Quarries act 1954 and the Factories Act 1961. The Shops Act 1950 and the Young Persons (Employment) Act 1938 also laid down maximum weekly hours for those under 18 and specified holiday times, meal intervals and regulated overtime, night employment etc.

THE CURRENT POSITION

Government statistics estimate that there are about 900,000 16 to 18 year olds in the labour force. About two thirds work in areas which are subject to Acts governing hours of work. But even where these do not apply, Sections 2 and 3 of the Health and Safety at Work Act place a duty of general care on employers towards young people and this duty has been extended to trainees by further legislation (see *Chapter 27: Young workers*).

Since the middle of the last century there has been a gradual decrease in the length of the average working week for most people at work. In 1900 total weekly hours including overtime, averaged 54. By 1983 this had reduced to just over 40. But of course there are wide variations. Legislation covering hours of young people working in industry has played its part, but about 9.5 million manual workers are covered by national collective agreements, most of which contain references to hours (usually 39 or 40 hours maximum after which overtime rates apply).

EXEMPTIONS

The legislation relating to young people's hours in factories contains a large number of exemptions from basic general restrictions, and the Health and Safety Executive can grant special exemption orders (SEOs) by administrative means under Section 117 of the Factories Act. This Section is used quite extensively. In 1985 nearly 16,000 young persons (almost 10 per cent of those employed in manufacturing in 1984) were covered by 1,369 orders and many factory employers who want to employ young workers at night or at weekends do so through the exemption order procedure. Very few applications for SEOs are turned down, but the TUC has always insisted that HSE inspectors should consult with trade union representatives before such orders are issued. Also, SEOs should only be issued where the HSE vet the employers' practices. SEOs usually have conditions attached to them relating to matters such as welfare, adequate supervision, adequacy of transport arrangements etc and they usually set a maximum working week of 54 hours in total. In theory SEOs can be withdrawn but this rarely happens.

DUTIES ON EMPLOYERS

Several of the requirements relating to young people require employers to follow certain procedures. For example, employers must post notices in the factory giving details of the daily period of employment and intervals, details of overtime, dates of any holidays substituted for statutory bank holidays and information about proposed new shift systems. A register must be kept giving details of overtime worked by individual young people and employers must give advance notice to the HSE when they intend to make use of particular exceptions, seek advanced authorisation from HSE for overtime working, introduce a new shift system or they intend to obtain an SEO. Before introducing a system of shift working an employer has first of all to carry out a secret ballot of the workers affected (excluding adults required to work the same shift) and obtain the consent of the majority. Procedures for this kind of ballot are laid down in Regulations.

YOUNG PEOPLE'S HOURS OF WORK

Summary of the legislation

The main provisions restricting young people's hours of work and other questions such as meal and rest breaks and holiday times are set out in the following Acts:

- Factories Act 1961 (Factories);

- Factories Act 1961 (Certain occupations at docks, wharves, quays);

- Mines and Shops Act 1954;

- Shops Act 1950;

- Young Persons (Employment) 1938;

- Employment of Women, Young Persons and Children Act 1920;

- Children and Young Persons (Scotland) Act 1937; and

- Education Act (1944).

RESTRICTIONS ON HOURS OF WORK IN FACTORIES

The table opposite is a guide to the maximum hours of work permitted for young persons in factories. There are many exemptions to this general guide, some on a temporary or seasonal basis and others permanently.

As stressed above, if employers want an exemption from the various sections from the Factories Act restriction on hours of work, they have to apply to the Health and Safety Executive. The Inspector will usually visit the factory, and discuss the matter with both management and workers' representatives. Exemptions are granted for a limited period, on condition that the work is done voluntary. While an Inspector should not grant an exemption if the workers' representatives oppose it she/he has the power to do so. A copy of the exemption certificate is to be posted up in the factory and many include conditions such as arrangements for meals, transport, attendance at further education colleges etc.

In certain industries, for example fruit canning and certain food processing just before Christmas, the industry as a whole is exempted from some parts of the Factories Act. Where safety representatives are not sure what restrictions apply they should seek copies of appropriate legislation from management, contact their local union representative or the HSE.

SHOPS

The provisions contained in part 2 of the Shops Act 1950 regulate the hours of work and other conditions of employment of all persons defined as shop assistants employed about the business of a shop (as defined by Section 74 of the Act). These Sections of the Act which provide for half holidays, meal breaks, and restrict hours for all workers are amended in their application to young people by

Limits of normal factory hours of young people

Factory working a six-day week	**Factory working a five-day week**
Maximum period of employment Weekly other than Saturday: 11 hours Saturday: 6 hours	12 Hours
Maximum daily working hours (excluding breaks) 9 hours	10 Hours
Maximum weekly working hours	48 hours (44 hours for young people under 16)
Maximum continuous spell	4½ hours (4 hours for young people under 16)
Earliest starting time	7 am (the Secretary of State may under certain conditions make regulations or orders permitting a starting time before 7 am but not before 6 am)
Latest finishing time	Weekday other than Saturday: 8 pm for young people of 16 or over; 6 pm for young people under 16 Saturday: 1 pm

Note: Subject to certain exceptions, young people must not be employed in a factory on Sunday.

further Sections of the Act which apply more stringent restrictions on the employment of young people. These are broadly similar to those for factory employment. There are exceptions but there are no exemption procedures as in the 1961 Factories Act.

Section 24 of the Act requires that no young person between the ages of 16 and 18 be employed about the business of the shop for more than 48 working hours a week. All shop assistants are entitled to one half day's holiday a week and if they work more than four hours on Sunday, then they must be given a day off in place of that Sunday. The Act is a very complex piece of legislation with numerous exemptions and alterations for different trades and activities. It is enforced by environmental health officers employed by the local authority.

TRANSPORT DRIVERS

The hours of work of bus and coach drivers, drivers of other vehicles adapted to carry more than 12 passengers, and goods vehicle drivers (including locomotives, tractors, articulated units and other motor vehicles adapted to carry goods) are limited by transport legislation — including EEC transport regulations.

Although there are many exceptions, the driver must not drive any of these vehicles for more than 10 hours in any working day. A working day includes meal breaks and periods on duty until the driver takes an eleven hour rest period. Drivers cannot work more than 60 hours each week. There are many other exemptions to the Transport Act and it is interesting to note that tractor drivers are completely exempted.

CHECKLIST: YOUNG PEOPLE'S HOURS OF WORK

1. Check up on the hours of work which young people (aged 16-18) are required to do.

2. Find out which statutory restrictions, if any, apply, *eg* Factories Act 1961, Mines and Quarries Act 1954, Shops Act 1950.

3. Has the employer asked the Health and Safety Executive for an exemption? Were trade union representatives consulted?

4. Do young people have adequate rest periods, holiday time as well as time off for education and recreational purposes?

5. Are young people being asked to work during unsocial hours? If so, what special arrangements have been made for welfare, transport etc.?

FURTHER INFORMATION

- **Hours of employment of women and young persons:** Health and Safety at Work Series Booklet No 23; HSE; HMSO.

- **Protective legislation — should we distinguish between men and women?:** Equal Opportunities Commission.

- **Restrictions on Employment of Young People and Removal of Sex Discrimination in Legislation:** Consultative Document; Department of Employment, 1987.

27: Young workers

Accidents and health damage to adult workers are bad enough – but to young workers who may have to carry the scars or disability resulting from an accident or disease with them for the rest of their lives – the prospect is even more horrendous. Worse still is the prospect of a young life damaged or destroyed through an avoidable accident at work.

To many young people, the workplace is often a new environment where lack of experience and trained judgement can put them at particular risk. Historically the law has recognised this by restricting employment of young persons in certain high risk activities and requiring higher standards of instruction, training and supervision than for adults. From the very moment they enter the workplace, therefore, safety representatives must see that every effort is made to ensure that employers meet their obligations to protect young workers and train them about the hazards with which they have to cope.

KEY PRINCIPLES

The TUC has published comprehensive guidelines entitled *Protecting Young People at Work* designed to assist safety representatives in ensuring the health and safety of young people in the workplace — whether they are part of the Training Agency's (TA) training schemes or are in full time training or employment. These guidelines set out certain key principles as shown in the panel over page.

YOUNG WORKERS AND HEALTH AND SAFETY LAW

The Health and Safety (Youth Training Scheme) Regulations 1983 were introduced to extend the meaning of 'work' to include training under the Youth Training Scheme (YTS). This means that trainees at workplaces are given exactly the same protection as employees under the Health and Safety at Work Act. This includes regulations made under the Act and other requirements such as regulations applying to agricultural workers and the Offices, Shops and Railway Premises Act — the Factories Act 1961 already deemed young people under 18 to be employees for the purpose of the Act.

From a legal standpoint, therefore, the principal responsibility for ensuring the health and safety of young people at work rests with their employer – or in the case of non-employed YTS trainees, with their immediate provider of training under the scheme. At the same time, young workers, too, have legal duties, for example, to co-operate with their employer in meeting health and safety requirements and not to interfere with or misuse anything provided in the interests of health and safety. The Department of Employment is currently reviewing the need for special legislative requirements for young people.

THE ROLE OF THE TRAINING AGENCY (TA)

The TA is responsible for funding training schemes and has a duty to take care to see that trainees are placed with reputable providers who are aware of health and safety requirements. The TA has accepted for example that it must do all it reasonably can to ensure that trainees are not placed with sponsors where there are substantial health and safety risks and there are clearly inadequate arrangements to deal with them. Under the two-year YTS, TA insist that trainers and those seeking Approved Training Organisation status must demonstrate a commitment to health and safety.

In some cases TA have refused to accept or have closed down placements for reasons such as inadequate supervision; general untidiness and

- Young people may be at particular risk in the workplace because they **lack experience and trained judgement.**

- The health and safety of young workers should be a **standing and separate agenda item** on all trade union and workplace committees concerned with health and safety matters – both to review health and safety arrangements for young people and to monitor performance.

- Young people should not be required to undertake work tasks where their **lack of experience** may put their own or other people's health and safety at risk. All such tasks should be clearly identified in the employer's safety policy.

- **Particular care** should be taken when placing young persons in work involving use of dangerous machinery or harmful substances. Young people are often more susceptible to health damage from exposure to toxic substances – although harmful effects may not appear until later in life.

- Ensuring health and safety of young workers means **ensuring proper arrangements for supervision.** Work operations requiring constant supervision should be clearly identified – this may mean recruitment of more supervisors.

- **Supervisors** and **first line management** should always be **adequately trained** in understanding the risks and control measures connected with the work young people are required to do.

- Every young worker should be entitled to **adequate health and safety induction training** which explains the hazards of the job and precautions to be observed. Induction training should emphasise not only the young person's duty to co-operate – but what they are entitled to expect from their employer and others. Trade union safety representatives should be given the opportunity to take part in health and safety induction training programmes for young people.

- **Health and safety training** should be an integral part of job training programmes to explain health and safety hazards and legal requirements. Full information on health and safety matters should be made available – *eg* on articles and substances. Trade union safety representatives have the legal right to be consulted and to comment on the health and safety content of training programmes for young people.

- There should be **full consultation** with trade union safety representatives **about all training schemes** involving young people. They should be involved in the planning of schemes at the earliest possible stage rather than reacting to problems when training programmes have started.

- Trade unions should **encourage recruitment** into membership of all young people whether they are part of YTS or are in full-time training or employment. They should also encourage them to become fully involved in health and safety at work issues.

Note: Full details on the role of unions in influencing YTS are given in the TUC Handbook on the TC's *Youth Training Scheme,* available from TUC Publications, Congress House, Great Russell Street, London, WCIB 3LS.

lack of cleanliness on premises; unsafe working practices or poor attitudes to safety by employers/ providers; machinery in poor condition or inadequately guarded; poor hygiene, lack of toilet and washing facilities; and protective clothing not being used by trainees or not being provided.

In order to make sure that providers are made aware of their legal responsibilities and to assess whether they are prepared to discharge them, TA has appointed safety co-ordinators in its area offices as well as Regional Safety Advisors to provide specialist advice on health and safety appraisal.

The TA has also issued guidelines ("Health and Safety on the YTS – Guidance for Providers of Training, Education and Work Experience") and arranges for providers to give to each trainee a copy of the HSE Booklet "Mind How You Go". This tells trainees about common causes of accidents and how to prevent them.

The approval and monitoring of training schemes is supplemented in some instances by Programme Review Teams (PRTs), which are composed of management, union representatives and trainees which oversee individual YTS schemes. In guidance the TUC has stressed the importance of safety representatives keeping trade union representatives on these bodies fully informed about any health and safety problems that may arise.

BEFORE WORK STARTS

As soon as proposals for YTS begin to be discussed at the workplace, safety representatives should be involved and should be present at the initial briefing meeting with the TA programme assessor in order to discuss health and safety aspects. They should draw up their own written health and safety assessment for discussion with management, TA officials and fellow trade union representatives based on the seven points outlined below – this covers most of the main issues but may need to be adapted to suit local conditions.

1: Safety policy
The employer's safety policy should be examined to see what it says about the special problems which arise from employing young people. If the safety policy needs to be revised, prepare some suggestions.

2: Health and safety performance
The employer's health and safety record should be studied – including the accident record and any enforcement action by the HSE or local authority Environmental Health Officers. If the overall attitude to improving health and safety performance and working relationships on health and safety matters is poor, this should be drawn to the attention of TA officials.

3: Work tasks and risks

The work tasks which trainees are going to be required to undertake should be studied in detail. What are the inherent risks? How serious are they? Is the industry or process one which has a higher than average accident rate? Are there any obvious dangers such as use of powered machinery or tools, potential exposure to toxic substances or other harmful agents, working at heights, or working with or near site transport vehicles or in confined spaces? Safety representatives must be satisfied that the work tasks in any proposed scheme are safe for young people.

4: Restrictions

Having made an assessment of the risks safety representatives should work out:

a) those tasks in the workplace where young people should not be involved – for examples, see "Prohibitions Checklist" below;

b) those for which constant supervision by competent person is required – see "Dangerous machines Checklist"; and

c) those which require extra training and instruction.

Tasks in a), b) and c) should be clearly designated in the employer's health and safety policy. It should be remembered that workplace hazards are not always obvious to young workers and things which to them can seem harmless fun can sometimes end up in tragedy.

5: Induction

The next task is to look at the health and safety induction programme. A timetabled programme should be made available. This should be more than just a 'pep' talk. Safety representatives should be given the opportunity to explain their role and induction should meet the TA basic requirements.

6: Supervision

In addition to supervision of the potentially hazardous tasks identified under 4(b) above, safety representatives should look carefully at how trainees are going to be supervised in general during their time on a YTS scheme as well as arrangements made for training supervisors about health and safety problems when working with young people. The TA gives some guidance on this point in its document "Health and Safety on the YTS – Guidance to Providers of Training, Education and Work Experience." If there are insufficient numbers of suitably trained supervisors, officials should be informed.

7: Health and safety training

In addition to induction training, safety representatives should examine the health and safety content of the job training itself. This should be taken seriously by training staff and should not be limited to the rudimentary 'do's' and 'don'ts'. Although health and safety training should be an integral part of job training it should not be so 'built-in' that it disappears amongst everything else. Separate time should be regularly set aside for health and safety training throughout a scheme. Also, there should be an effective means to check on how much of what trainees learn about health and safety is actually retained by them in practice, *eg* assessed fire drills, questions and answer sessions, practical demonstrations. Safety representatives must be satisfied that the content of job training adequately covers health and safety aspects.

CHECKLIST: PROHIBITIONS

Under the Factories Act, the Offices, Shops and Railway Premises Act, the Agriculture (Safety, Health and Welfare Provisions) Act and related regulations, the employment of young people in the following trades or processes is prohibited; although these are currently under review by the Department of Employment;

1. Cleaning machinery in motion and exposing persons to risk of injury.

2. Working all prescribed dangerous machines unless fully instructed and either sufficiently trained or under adequate supervision by an experienced person.

3. As an 'appointed' machinery attendant at prescribed dangerous machines.

4. Lifting excessive weights specified in certain industries but prohibited in general terms in all factories.

5. Driving locomotives and operating capstans for moving wagons.

6. Operating cranes and lifting appliances on building and civil engineering sites and docks or operating a power driver capstan or winch.

7. Setting up tools and safety devices on power presses.

8. Operating certain woodworking machines – unless completed approved training course.

9. Working in certain shipbuilding processes.

10. As a competent person assisting an 'authorised person' on electrical work requiring technical knowledge and experience.

11. Doing certain work on electrical apparatus above 125 AC or 250 V DC.

12. Testing electrical circuits above 50 volts.

13. Painting using lead based paints.

14. The blasting of castings.

15. Cleaning of blasting enclosures or apparatus (castings).

16. Working regularly within twenty feet of a castings blasting enclosure.

17. Chrome, nitro or amino processes.

18. Working at a chromium plating bath.

19. Work at any lead or zinc manufacturing process or processes associated with the manufacture of lead or zinc compounds.

20. Manufacture of solder and certain other lead processes.

21. Specified processes in the manufacture or repair of electric accumulators.

22. Manufacture or repair of electric accumulators.

23. Cleaning of rooms where certain lead processes are carried out.

24. India rubber fume processes (a process where chloride of sulphur, carbon disulphide, benzole and certain other chemicals are mixed with rubber).

25. Certain processes in the pottery industry.

26. Workplaces where asbestos processes are carried out unless asbestos dust is prevented from entering the work area.

27. Working as a classified worker with radioactive substances including sealed sources of radiation and X-ray equipment.

28. Working with horsehair which has not been disinfected.

29. Working between the fixed and travelling parts of a spinning mule.

30. Melting or blowing of glass, other than lamp-blown glass.

31. Annealing glass, other than plate or sheet glass (females under 18).

32. Evaporation of brine in open pans or the stoving of salts.

33. Use of circular saws in agriculture.

34. Use of scheduled pesticides in agriculture or operations using a smoke generator.

35. Employment in an offshore installation.

Notes:

- The term young people applies to persons under 18 years of age.

- For guidance on manual handling safety, see *Lighten the load*, available from TUC Publications, Congress House, Great Russell Street, London, WC1B 3LS.

- Under the Factories Act and The Office, Shops and Railway Premises Act there are restrictions on the number of hours for which young people may be employed. For further information see Chapter 26.

DANGEROUS MACHINES

The TA reminds all providers that in accordance with Section 21 of the Factories Act 1961 and Section 19 of the Offices, Shops and Railway Premises Act 1963, young people must not work at any of the dangerous machines listed below unless

they have first been instructed in the dangers arising in connection with the machine and the precautions to be observed. They must also either have received sufficient training or be under adequate supervision by a person who has a thorough knowledge and experience of the machine. The cleaning and maintenance of these machines by young people is generally prohibited. The following checklist, which is also under review by DE should not however be regarded as exhaustive. Many of the machines listed were identified years ago and subsequently newer and equally dangerous machines have been introduced – so it is the general principles which are important.

CHECKLIST: DANGEROUS MACHINES

1. Brick and tile presses.

2. Machines used for opening or teasing in upholstery or bedding works.

3. Carding machines used in wool textiles.

4. Corner staying machines.

5. Dough brakes.

6. Dough mixers, bakers and confectioners.

7. Gill boxes used in wool textiles.

8. The following in use in laundries:
   - hydro extractors;
   - calenders;
   - washing; and
   - garment presses.

9. Worm pressure extruding machines.

10. Meat mincing machines.

11. Milling machines used in the metal trades.

12. Pie and tart-making machines.

13. Power presses including hydraulic and pneumatic presses.

14. Loose knife punching machines.

15. Wire-stitching machines.

16. Semi-automatic wood turning lathes.

17. Planing machinery, vertical spindle moulding machines and routing machines.

18. Machines of any type equipped with a circular saw blade.

19. Machines of any type equipped with a saw in the form of a continuous band or strip.

20. Rotary knife bowl-type chopping machinery.

21. Food mixing machinery when used with attachments for mincing, slicing, chipping and any other cutting operation, or for crumbling.

22. Vegetable slicing machinery.

23. Wrapping and packing machinery.

24. Guillotine machines whether powered or not.

25. Circular knife slicing machines used for cutting bacon and other foods.

26. Potato chipping machines.

27. Platen printing machines including such machines when used for cutting and creasing.

TUC ADVICE

Below are some examples of other hazardous activities which should be subject to restriction, although this list is not comprehensive:

- driving tractors and agricultural machinery;
- operating fork lift trucks;
- mounting of abrasive wheels;
- erection and dismantling of scaffolding;
- roofwork;
- Demolition work;
- working at height;
- use of corrosive substances; and
- use of flammable liquids and gases.

MONITORING

Once a commitment to key health and safety principles for protection of young people has been obtained on paper, safety representatives need to ensure that these are carried out in practice – for example by seeing that induction and other health and safety training programmes are implemented and that any proposed changes to schemes are subject to consultation and approval. In addition all accidents and incidents involving trainees should be reported and analysed. Here it should be remembered that the TA's requirements for reporting accidents are more stringent that those required by the HSE and that safety representatives are entitled by law to receive a copy of any notification sent to the HSE and to investigate the circumstances of any accident of notifiable incident.

Safety representatives should make sure they have sufficient time-off, assistance and facilities to enable them to monitor health and safety arrangements for young workers. They should make regular reports to appropriate union officials and where necessary, report problems through appropriate procedures to union and TUC representatives.

COMPENSATION

If a young person does suffer an injury or damage to their health whilst at work they should be told about their rights to compensation. Although YTS trainees are not covered by DHSS statutory Industrial Injury Benefit, the TA is empowered to pay equivalent benefits if it can be accepted by them that the injury arose out of an industrial accident. In complex cases the advice of DHSS may be sought.

CHECKLIST

1. Are all the young workers in your workplace members of a trade union? If not, organise a local recruitment drive to organise young people.

2. Organise a discussion with some of the young people in your workplace. Prepare a short report. Try to cover the following questions:

   - What safety training have the young workers had?
     Did they think that it was enough?

   - What do they think are the main health and safety problems in the workplace – what improvements would they want? What do you think this union should do?

   - Are problems concentrated in a few jobs or departments, or are they spread throughout the workforce?

3. Has young workers' health and safety ever been raised with management? Try to get hold of minutes of any meetings where the issue has been discussed.

4. Find out if there have been any recent accidents involving young people. Look at the Accident Book, and talk to other safety representatives. If there have, try to talk to the victim and to their safety representatives. Find how and why the accident happened – and what has been done to prevent it happening again.

5. Talk to members who have teenage children. What do they think are the biggest threats to young workers' health and safety? What do they think unions should do to protect young workers?

6. Organise a detailed inspection of the jobs which young people do – or will be expected to do – in your workplace.

   - What built-in risks are there?

   - How serious are any risks?

   - What training will be needed to deal with the risks?

   - Could the risks be removed at source?
     Discuss with other safety reps if there should be limits on the jobs which young people can do in your workplace.

7. Draw up a list of changes which you want see in your employer's safety policy to make sure that it covers the special needs of young workers for training, information, and supervision.

8. Use the checklist of prohibitions and restrictions to review whether there are any jobs or processes in your workplace which young people cannot do, or can only do after training and under proper supervision. Draw up a report for your union committee.

9. Look carefully at all health and safety training provided for young people. Does training include:

   - work which will be done by young workers, and by other people in the workplace?

   - details of the employer's responsibilities for dealing with health and safety at work?

   - possible hazards that could arise – including hidden hazards?

   - precautions which need to be taken?

   - procedures for reporting accidents, fire alarms, getting first-aid and so on?

   - the job of the safety rep, and how health and safety complaints are dealt with?

10. Find out from the local TA office:

    - who the TA (or Careers Service) link officer is for your workplace;

    - the names of the trade union representatives on Programme Review Teams;

    - if the TA is running any health and safety courses for Supervisors of trainees.

11. Draw up a list of arguments on the need to improve monitoring and enforcement of health and safety for young workers. Discuss this matter with fellow union representatives.

FURTHER INFORMATION

- **Protecting young people at work:** TUC Guidelines; TUC, Congress House, Great Russell Street, London WC1B 3LS; *discussion of accident statistics, negotiating points, and useful checklists.*

- **Youth Training Scheme:** TUC Booklet; *negotiating points, and explanation of the way YTS runs.*

- **Health and safety on the Youth Training Scheme:** free from local TA offices; *guidance for providers of training, education and work experience.*

- **Mind how you go:** HSE; free from HSE Enquiry Points; *brief health and safety guidelines for young workers.*

- **Restrictions on employment of young people and the removal of sex discrimination legislation:** Consultative document; DE, 1987.

28: First aid and welfare facilities

Besides being required to take steps to prevent accidents and health damage at work, employers are also obliged by law to provide first aid facilities and certain basic welfare facilities such as toilets, washing facilities, messrooms and storage for clothing. These are all important aspects of a safe, healthy and civilised workplace. This chapter describes minimum legal requirements in this area and suggests steps which safety representatives can take to ensure that first aid and welfare needs at work are properly met.

FIRST AID AT WORK

The importance of taking proper first aid action following an injury at work cannot be over emphasised. Every cut, every bruise should get immediate attention from a trained first aider who knows what they are doing. Failure to provide proper first aid arrangements can mean minor injuries not being treated, perhaps becoming infected or not being recorded in the accident book. This in turn can give a false picture when accident statistics are analysed and could mean problems for the injured person later if complications develop and they decide to pursue a claim for damages. Sometimes the provision of proper first aid facilities can quite literally be the difference between life and death. This means that first aid arrangements at work should be reviewed regularly to identify problems and the scope for improvements. Some common problems with first aid cover include:

- not enough first aiders;
- no first aiders in more dangerous areas;
- not enough first aid boxes;
- empty or poorly maintained first aid boxes;
- no first aid facilities for workers travelling away from the workplace;
- no first aid facilities for shift workers;

- poorly equipped first aid rooms;
- not knowing who the first aider is or where the first aid box is kept;
- reduced first aid cover when work systems are reorganised;
- ignorance of first aid procedures; and
- outdated notices indicating names of first aiders and location of first aid boxes.

THE LAW

Since 1982 the minimum legal standard for nearly all workplaces has been the Health and Safety (First Aid) Regulations 1981 – usually called the "First Aid Regs". The old standards in the Factories Act, Offices, Shops and Railway Premises Act, and in many Regulations have been repealed. The First Aid Regulations also apply to many industries not previously covered, such as Education and the Health Service.

The First Aid Regulations put five clear duties on employers:

1: To provide adequate and appropriate first-aid **equipment** and facilities   Regulation 3(1)

2: To provide an adequate number of **trained and qualified first-aiders**   Regulation 3(2)

3: To provide an **'appointed person'** if the first-aider is absent   Regulation 3(3)

4: In some, smaller workplaces, to provide an **'appointed person'** instead of a first-aider   Regulation 3(4)

5: To provide **information** to all workers about the provision of first-aid location of equipment, facilities and personnel.   Regulation 4

The Regulations are supplemented by an Approved Code of Practice (under revision) and Guidance Notes. These explain in detail the minimum legal standards. The Regulations, Code of Practice and the Guidance Notes are all included in the HSE's booklet "First Aid at Work" HSE 11 – a copy of which should be made available for safety representatives.

WHAT IS REQUIRED?

The old legal standards on First Aid were simply based on the number of employees. Under the new Health and Safety (First-Aid) Regulations the employer has to take into account the following:

- **Nature of the undertaking:** in the Guidance Notes, workplaces are divided into 'low hazard', 'greater hazard' and 'special or unusual hazard'.

- **Size of the establishment and the location of employees:** where workers are scattered over a wide area, or there is shift working, more first aiders and facilities will be needed.

- **Location of the establishment:** workers in remote areas will need more first-aiders and equipment than those working in, or near, a hospital. But even in urban areas there could be long delays in getting an injured person to an accident department. Workers travelling away from the workplace may need first-aid kits.

- Part IV of the Guidance Notes, are designed to help **identify minimum requirements:** when using the Guidance Note it should be remembered that safety representatives have a right to be consulted (HSW etc Act 2(6)) on decisions about the level of hazard in the workplace. They should also be consulted about the implementation of the Approved Code of Practice and Guidance Notes. Consideration should also be given of the number of customers, visitors, residents and so on who may also be on the premises – and who may sometimes need first aid. The Regulations also allow for first aid cover to be provided by a full time Occupational Health Service. This is covered by paragraph 2 of the current Approved Code of Practice (ACoP).

FIRST-AIDERS

First-aiders are people who have been trained and have been given certificates to show that they are capable of administering first-aid. According to the Approved Code of Practice there are three types of first-aider:

- **first-aiders** who have been on an approved training course and hold a current certificate;

- **occupational first-aiders** who have received the same training as first-aiders plus extra training which covers the treatment of injuries such as poisoning, burns, and so on which might be a particular hazard of their workplace; and

- **other persons,** including medical practitioners, and occupational health nurses, who have qualifications recognised by the HSE as enabling them to be counted as first-aiders.

The Approved Code of Practice, which is being reviewed by the HSC, also gives guidance on the number of first-aiders required as a minimum. These standards should be seen however as a basic minimum from which to negotiate better arrangements.

APPOINTED PERSONS

Appointed persons are needed in two situations. If there are first-aiders in the workplace, the employer should have an appointed person to cover when the first-aider is temporarily absent (sick, on holiday) or is busy giving first aid. If there is no first-aider for a particular workplace then there must be an appointed person.

Appointed persons have two main tasks:
- to take charge of the situation (call an ambulance for instance) in the absence of a first-aider – ACoP 31; and

- to keep first-aid facilities and equipment in good order in the absence of a first-aider – ACoP 31.

TRAINING

The training of first-aiders can only be done by organisations or employers approved by the HSE. There is a list of approved organisations available free from the HSE. Training courses should last at least four days, and follow a syllabus approved by the HSE. Occupational first-aiders receive the standard course of training, plus more detailed training to deal with the first-aid requirements of their workplace.

First-aid certificates are valid for three years. A refresher course and re-examination are required before a new first-aid certificate can be issued. There is evidence suggesting that the frequency of refresher courses should be reviewed, possibly to every two years. Safety representatives should negotiate more regular training for first-aiders.

First aid facilities

Type of provision required

Type of establishment/ circumstances	First-aid box(es)	First-aid room	Supplementary equipment	Small travelling first-aid kits
All establishments	Approved Code of Practice Paras 23-25; GN 4-7			
Establishments with: First aider(s) or occupational first aider(s)	Approved Code of Practice Paras 23-25; GN 4-7			Approved Code of Practice Para 28; GN 9, 10
Dispersed working over wide area	Approved Code of Practice Paras 16, 23-25;	Approved Code of Practice Paras 16, 13		Approved Code of Practice Paras 16, 10
More than 400	Approved Code of Practice Paras 23-25; GN 4-7	Approved Code of Practice Paras 13, 26, 27; GN 11-13		Approved Code of Practice Para 28; GN 9, 10
Isolated location	Approved Code of Practice Paras 23-25; GN 4-7	Approved Code of Practice Paras 17, 26, 27; GN 11-13		Approved Code of Practice Para 28; GN 9, 10
Special or unusual hazards	Approved Code of Practice Paras 23-25; GN 4-7	Approved Code of Practice Paras 15, 26, 27; GN 11		Approved Code of Practice Para 28; GN 9, 10
Alone or in small groups, in isolated locations or using potentially dangerous tools or machinery				Approved Code of Practice Paras 18-21; GN 8
Larger groups with relatively low hazards, no other factors				Approved Code of Practice Paras 18-21; GN 8
Larger groups in isolated locations or using potentially dangerous machinery	Approved Code of Practice Paras 18-21; GN 4-7			Approved Code of Practice Paras 18-21; GN 8
Employees or two or more employers working together	Approved Code of Practice Paras 22, 25; GN 4-7	Approved Code of Practice Paras 13, 15, 17, 22, 26, 27; GN 11-13	Approved Code of Practice Paras 22, 28; GN 9, 10	Approved Code of Practice Paras 18-22; GN 8

Miscellaneous

Type of provision required

Type of establishment/ circumstances	Information to employees	Means of keeping records	Liaison with ambulance service
All establishments	Approved Code of Practice Paras 33-36	GN 24	—
Establishments with isolated location	—	—	GN 25

Instruction in emergency first-aid (resuscitation, control of bleeding, treatment of unconsciousness) should be given to all appointed persons, and to all workers who work in small groups away from the employer's main workplace (see Guidance Note 23).

PAYMENT

Payments for first-aiders are not covered by the Regulations, although Guidance Note 18 makes the point that employers who cannot find volunteers should try all possible ways of encouraging them. First-aiders are helping employers to do a job that the law and common sense says they have to do, so many trade unions have argued that first-aiders should receive extra payment for their skills and responsibilities.

The possible legal liability of first-aiders is another issue which may put people off volunteering for the job. Some employers have been persuaded to put in writing that they will take responsibility for the treatment given by first-aiders acting on their behalf.

EQUIPMENT AND FACILITIES

Although the most obvious type of facility provided under the Regulations is the first-aid box, safety representatives also need to consider the provision of travelling first-aid kits, and first-aid rooms.

Boxes						**Kits**
Item	*Numbers of employees*					
	1-5	6-10	11-50	51-100	101-150	
Guidance card or leaflet	1	1	1	1	1	–
Individually wrapped sterile adhesive dressings	10	20	40	40	40	6
Sterile pads, with attachment: an example of a suitable eye pad currently available would be the Standard Dressing No 16 BPC	1	2	4	6	8	–
Triangular bandages (if possible sterile)	1	2	4	6	8	1
Sterile coverings for serious wounds (if triangular bandages not sterile)	1	2	4	6	8	1
Safety pins	6	6	12	12	12	6
Medium sized sterile unmedicated dressings approx 10 cm × 8 cm: examples of suitable dressings currently available are the Standard Dressings No 8 and No 13 BPC	3	6	8	10	12	1
Large sterile unmedicated dressings approx 13 cm × 9 cm: examples of suitable dressings currently available are the Standard Dressings No 9 and No 14 BPC and the Ambulance Dressing No 1	1	2	4	6	10	–
Extra large sterile unmedicated dressings approx 28 cm × 17.5 cm: an example of a suitable dressing currently available would be the Ambulance Dressing No 3	1	2	4	6	8	–
If tap water is not available, sterile water or sterile normal saline in disposable containers, each holding at least 300 ml, needs to be kept near the first aid box. At least these numbers of containers should be kept.	1	1	3	6	6	–

Source: "First Aid Provision in Small Workplaces" HSE Leaflet IND (G) 3(L)

FIRST AID BOXES AND KITS

Guidance Notes to the Regulations (which are under review) give details of what should be in, or near, first aid boxes, and the quantities required. Guidance is also given on the contents of travelling first-aid kit. Whenever items are used, they must be replaced. The contents of first-aid boxes and kits need to be regularly checked. Every workplace must have at least one first-aid box, and the box – and all its contents – must be accessible *at all times* that workers are present. (See box on opposite page.)

Other first-aid equipment which could be necessary will include stretchers, blankets, and protective clothing if needed when first-aiders themselves might be put at risk going to the aid of an injured person. Any extra first-aid equipment must be stored near the first-aid box, protected from dust and damp, and regularly checked. (See Approved Code of Practice 28 and Guidance Notes 9 and 10).

According to the Code of Practice (paragraphs 13-17) a first-aid room is only necessary if there are 400 or more workers in the 'establishment'; if there is a special or unusual hazard; if workers are dispersed over a wide area; or if there is difficulty in getting the injured to hospital.

INFORMATION

The provision of information is an important part of the provision of first-aid. People need to be able to find the nearest first-aider, and the nearest facilities in an emergency. The Regulations include the following requirements:

- employers have to tell workers of the first-aid arrangements, the location of the equipment, facilities, and personnel – Regulation 4;

- new workers should be given this information as part of their induction training. Workers who move to other departments or areas need to be given information about the procedures in the area they move to – ACoP 34;

- there should be *at least* one notice in each workplace, giving locations of facilities and equipment, and names and locations of first-aiders — ACoP 34;

- notices should be in English and any other language commonly used in the workplace – ACoP 36; and

- the location of first-aid facilities should be clearly marked. Signs should comply with the Safety Signs Regulations 1980 – ACoP 36.

CHECKLIST

1. Use the HMSO book "First Aid at Work" to develop a checklist to use in an inspection of your workplace.

2. Compare first aid cover in your workplace with the minimum legal standards. Could cover be improved? How could you achieve this? Prepare a report to put to your safety reps or safety committee, and include the arguments that would have to be put to management.

3. Arrange an inspection of your workplace with other safety reps to check first-aid provision, and to identify areas for improvement.

4. Prepare a list of arguments which could be used to counter any attempts to reduce first-aid cover in your workplace.

FURTHER INFORMATION ON FIRST AID

- **Health and Safety (First Aid) Regulations 1981:** Approved Code of Practice.

- **First aid at work:** *the main source of legal standards, including regulations, Code of Practice and Guidance Notes;* HSE booklet HS(R)11.

- **First aid provision in small workplaces –** your questions answered: *useful summary;* HSE leaflet IND (G)3(L); free from HSE offices.

- **First aid at work:** *general first aid guidance for first aid boxes;* HSE leaflet IND(G) 4(P).

- **List of organisations approved for first aid training:** HSE leaflet IND(G)5; free from HSE offices.

- **Workplace health and safety services:** TUC; *outlines TUC policy on occupational health services;* TUC Publications, Great Russell Street, London WC1B 3LS.

- **Guidelines for occupational health services:** *practical guidance on the functions, staffing, and operation of occupational health services;* HSE booklet HS(G)20 from HMSO.

CANTEENS, MESSROOMS AND REFRESHMENT SERVICES

Although by law they are not obliged to do so, many employers provide some form of food service to their workforce. This now is an accepted social norm and is widely regarded as an essential feature of good working conditions. Provision of food and refreshment at work can take any form, for example:

- full meals and snacks in restaurants or canteens;

- messrooms providing the means of heating-up snacks, eating sandwiches and for making hot beverages, etc; and

- refreshment services, kiosks, tea bars or vending machines.

At first sight such facilities might appear to be outside the normal scope of health and safety at work but increasingly it is being realised healthy eating at work is an essential part of health promotion. Safety representatives should review food and catering provision at work. They should also remember that there are important health and safety aspects to be considered.

There are two distinct sets of (legal) requirements governing the provision of food services. The first relating to the actual service itself, and the second concerns the preparation, handling or storing of food. The statutory requirements on employers to provide canteens and messrooms are outlined in detail in the Department of Employment Handbook No 2 which indicates that section 62 of the Factories Act, 1961 contains two Regulations relating to canteens in special industries ie The Clay Works (Welfare) Special Regulations, 1948 and the Jute (Safety, Health and Welfare) Regulations, 1948.

Section 64 of the Factories Act, 1961 also requires the provision of mess accommodation for workpeople employed where lead, arsenic or other poisonous substances may give off dust or fumes. This also applies where silica or asbestos dust may be present in the working environment, which would make eating in such circumstances undesirable. This principle is embodied in a number of special Regulations and Welfare Orders which should be referred to for more detailed information.

As a general rule food should not be consumed in work areas and where there is potential contamination from any source (eg toxic or biological risks). In such cases special eating facilities should always be provided.

In offices and shops, whilst contamination from work processes may not be the same as in factories, section 15 of the Offices, Shops and Railway Premises Act nevertheless requires certain essential food services to be provided. It says that where persons are employed to work and to eat their meals in premises covered by the Act, suitable and sufficient facilities for eating them shall be provided. It should be noted however that this does not necessarily require a canteen to provide hot meals, etc, but would require provision of a messroom to satisfy the statutory requirements.

Where the food is prepared, handled or stored the Food Hygiene Regulations apply and such work is subject to inspection by Local Authority Public Health Inspectors. There are a number of specific Regulations and Codes of Practice laid down outlining standards that should be adhered to. Although these are outside the scope of the HSW Act, safety representatives should ask for

information and use their general rights under the SRSC Regulations to inspect food preparation, storage and serving areas.

It is not just enough to have a restaurant, canteen or messroom provided. Attention should also be given to the standards of lighting, heating, ventilation, noise levels, and the amount of space provided. The Department of Employment's Health and Safety at Work series Booklet No 2 suggests that the following amount of space is desirable:

Dining-room areas, including aisles and space between tables:

- to seat at tables for 4:   12 sq ft per person
- to seat at tables for 6:   10 sq ft per person
- to seat at tables for 8:   8 sq ft per person
- coffee-bar type seating: 4 to 6 sq ft per person

Areas for messrooms-seating space and equipment:

- up to 25 customers at one time: 14 sq ft per person
- from 25-50 customers at one time: 13 sq ft per person
- from 50-100 customers at one time: $12\frac{1}{2}$ sq ft per person

Areas for tea-making point (no seating):

- up to 25 teas served at one time: 2 sq ft per service
- from 25-50 teas served at one time: $1\frac{3}{4}$ sq ft per service
- from 50-100 teas served at one time: $1\frac{1}{2}$ sq ft per service

CHECKLIST: CANTEEN AND REFRESHMENT SERVICES

1. What kind of catering, food and refreshment facilities does your employer provide?

   - restaurant?
   - refreshment service?
   - mess room?
   - vending machines?
   - snack bar?

2. What is the employer's policy concerning consumption of food and drinks in working areas?

3. Are there any work areas or processes where contamination means food and drink should not be consumed, eg processes specified in Welfare Orders?

4. Are facilities adequate for numbers employed? What about environmental factors, overcrowding etc?

5. What food hygiene standards apply to food preparation, storage and serving areas? Who is responsible? Have staff been adequately trained?

6. Are safety representatives consulted about canteens, mess rooms, refreshment facilities and food policy at work?

LAVATORIES AND WASHROOMS

Proper lavatory and washing facilities which are clean and well maintained are an absolutely essential feature of a civilised workplace. Substandard facilities are still to be found in many (particularly small) workplaces (and are often non existent), so safety representatives should use basic minimum legal standards as a baseline to check up on facilities provided and whether they adequately meet members' needs.

Legal requirements for lavatories are covered by Section 7 of the Factories Act, Section 9 of the Offices, Shops and Railway Premises Act, Section 94 of the Mines and Quarries Act and various regulations. Detailed requirements are spelled out in the Sanitary Accommodation in Factories Regulations 1938 and, in the case of offices, shops and railway premises, by the Sanitary Conveniences Regulations 1964. The main points of the Factory Regulations are listed below.

- Where women are employed there must be at least one toilet for every 25. For men there must also be at least one suitable toilet (not merely a urinal) for every 25. In factories where the number of men employed is more than 100 and sufficient urinal accommodation is also provided, it is enough for there to be one WC for every 25 men up to the first 100 and then one for every extra 40.

- Every WC must be sufficiently ventilated, and must not lead directly into any workroom except through the open air or through an intervening ventilated space.

- Every WC (other than a urinal) must be under cover and partitioned off for privacy and have a proper, locking door. Urinals must also be placed or screened so that they are not visible from other parts of the factory. The lavatories must be arranged to be easily accessible to the people employed at all times while they are at the factory.

- Where people of both sexes are employed, the toilets for each sex must be placed or screened so that the interior is not visible, even when the door is open, from any place where people of the other sex have to work or pass. If the conveniences for one sex adjoin those for the other sex, the approaches must be separate and clearly indicated.

The Offices, Shops and Railway Premises Act Regulations are broadly similar to the Factories Act, with one rather curious distinction. These Regulations make requirements for the disposal of sanitary towels. This says that suitable and effective means for the disposal of towels must be provided where the total number of women exceeds ten. If these are provided they must be constantly maintained in proper condition and, where bins are supplied, the contents disposed of at suitable intervals.

Washing facilities are dealt with very briefly in section 58 of the Factories Act and just say that there must be a supply of clean, running, hot and cold water, and that soap, clean towels or other means of cleaning and drying must be provided, and that these facilities must be kept clean. Except in some special regulations, the Factories Act 1961 does not specify the minimum number of wash basins to be provided, but the Factory Inspectorate recommends one basin for every 20 workers. The Regulations dealing with the Offices, Shops and Railway Premises Act are roughly similar to the Factories requirements.

In addition to the general requirement of the Factories Act, there are a number of welfare orders made under the Factories Act 1961, which require special facilities for workers in particular jobs known to present a hazard to the skin, or traditionally known to be dirty. The industries covered are as follows:

- bakehouses;
- biscuit factories;
- cement works;
- dyeing;
- fruit preserving;
- glass bottle;
- gut scraping and tripe dressing;
- herring curing;
- hollow ware and galvanising;
- sacks (cleaning and repairing);
- sugar factories;
- tanning, tin or terne.

The orders generally say the employer must provide protective clothing, washing facilities (often to a higher standard than normally required), dining rooms, separate accommodation for clothing and, in some cases, first-aid facilities, baths and drinking water.

As in many areas of health and safety, modern practice and the recommendations of professional bodies often exceed the minimum legal standards; the same is true of washing facilities. One independent body has issued recommendations that are more comprehensive and generous than the Statutory requirements. For example, instead of one wash basin to 20 workers, two are recommended, and from 21-40 workers, three; 41-60 workers, four; 61-80 workers, five; 81-100 workers, six; and over 100, one for every 20 people. This example can be repeated in relation to other aspects of cloakroom, washing and toilet facilities.

CHECKLIST: LAVATORIES AND WASHROOMS

1. Are adequate numbers of lavatories and urinals provided for both sexes?

2. Are these facilities:
    - easily accessible?
    - properly ventilated?
    - private?
    - regularly cleaned?
    - well maintained?

3. Who is responsible for lavatories and washing facilities?

4. Are disposal facilities for sanitary protection provided?

5. Is there an adequate supply of soap, cleansing agents, hand creams (where necessary) and hand drying facilities?

CLOAKROOMS, CHANGING ROOMS AND SHOWERS

Besides providing lavatories and washing facilities, employers also have by law to provide 'suitable and adequate' facilities for storing clothing not worn during working hours – for example where outer wear is worn to the workplace, and where workers are required to change into workwear or protective clothing.

Arrangements must also be made for drying wet clothing. Section 59 of the Factories Act 1961, section 12 of the Offices, Shops and Railway Premises Act 1963, section 96 of the Mines and Quarries Act 1954, and the Docks and Harbours Act 1966 make these general requirements.

More detailed specifications for cloakroom accommodation are laid down in various regulations, for example, for iron and steel foundries, and the jute and pottery industries. Just exactly what the words 'suitable' and 'adequate' mean in practice is open to some doubt.

HSE Inspectors, for example, would not accept the provision of nails for hanging clothing as 'suitable'. Another difficulty is the definition of 'adequate', particularly regarding the possibility of theft from workers' clothing. There are no clear standards, but a High Court decision has stated that while there is no absolute obligation on an employer to keep the workpeople's clothes safe, the risk of theft is an element that has to be considered when deciding whether accommodation is adequate. The HSE suggests the following are essentials for satisfactory clothing accommodation:

- a separate peg or locker for each worker, which would have the worker's name or work's number;

- provision for drying wet outdoor clothes and overalls worn in wet processes;

- adequate space for changing clothes and footwear;

- adequate precautions against theft;

- a high standard of cleanliness; and

- adequate ventilation and lighting.

The provision of baths is required by special regulations in certain trades and processes such as are found in chemical works, electric accumulator manufacture, iron and steel foundries, lead smelting, oil cake works, patent fuel manufacture and sugar manufacture.

Many firms engaged in work that is hot or dirty provide baths even though they are not legally obliged to. The Department of Employment recommends that showers are most practical, as they are quick to use and easy to keep clean and maintain (but care must be taken to prevent legionella contamination – see *Chapter 10: Biological hazards*. The floor space within a shower should be not less than three feet by four feet, and the partitions between them not less than six feet high. Even for workers who are not engaged in physically demanding work, showers can nevertheless be beneficial and they can enable workers to take exercise or take part in sports activities (for example cycling to work or taking exercise at midday) without feeling sweaty and uncomfortable afterwards.

CHECKLIST: CLOAKROOMS, CHANGING ROOMS AND SHOWERS

1. Are storage facilities provided for hats and coats etc?

2. Do workers have to change into workwear? If so are facilities provided?

3. Are facilities provided for drying wet clothing?

4. Are facilities adequate – a cupboard or locker for each person? Are they big enough?

5. Are baths or showers provided – for example for hot or dirty work?

6. Who is responsible for cloakrooms, changing rooms and showers?

FURTHER INFORMATION ON CLOAKROOMS, CHANGING ROOMS AND SHOWERS

HSE guidance

- **Cloakroom Accommodation and Working Facilities 1980:** HSG(G)10.

29: Access to information

Knowing how and where to obtain basic information about health and safety at work questions is often the first step to solving problems in the workplace. The Health and Safety at Work (HSW) Act etc 1974 contains a number of important provisions which are designed to guarantee a wide range of information to working people and their safety representatives. Employers have a general duty under the Act to provide adequate information, instruction, training and supervision for all employees. They are also obliged to provide safety representatives with full legal and technical information to enable them to carry out their functions. This information includes for example:

- plans, performance and future changes in the workplace;

- technical information (vis information about articles and substances for use at work);

- accident and sickness records;

- survey results; and

- information issued to sub-contractors and home workers.

The Act also requires manufacturers, suppliers, importers and designers to provide employers with full information about hazards and precautions associated with their products as well as the results of any relevant research. Inspectors of the Health and Safety Executive are obliged to supply safety representatives with technical information, factual information obtained during visits (*ie* survey results) notice of prosecutions and correspondence and copies of any improvement or prohibition notice issued to the employer.

This chapter describes how safety representatives can gain access to certain essential information on health and safety issues and what sort of health and safety information should be provided for them by employers, inspectors and others concerned with the control of health and safety hazards in the workplace.

INFORMATION WHICH EMPLOYERS SHOULD PROVIDE

For all employees

The employer has a wide ranging duty to provide information, instruction and training for all his employees. In fulfilling this duty exactly what sort of health and safety information he provides will depend on the circumstances of the workplace in question.

Traditionally employers were required to display abstracts of health and safety legislation in the workplace. The HSC has since proposed new measures to require employers to display basic information about health and safety law in the workplace. The TUC view is that, in addition to this basic information, employers should make available for inspection copies of all relevant legislation (for instance: copies of the HSW Act, Factories Act 1961, Offices, Shops and Railway Premises Act 1963, special regulations, codes of practice), all relevant HSE guidance notes, copies of the employers' safety policy document and any information which individual employees need if they are to carry out their work safely (for instance, guidance notes from suppliers, pocket cards, warning signs, safety instructions and so on).

Employers should also provide adequate safety training for all employees (as part of job training). In addition safety representatives are entitled to on-going technical safety training in addition to time off for trade union organised training (for details of TUC organised training, see *Chapter 2: Safety representatives and safety committees*).

For safety representatives

In contrast to those they represent, safety representatives are entitled to receive a much wider variety of information. The Guidance Notes to the 1977 Safety Representatives and Safety Committee Regulations and the Code of Practice, point out that if they are to carry out their functions successfully, safety representatives require to be provided with information over and above that provided for employees generally. The Code of Practice to the Regulations indicates that this information includes:

- statutory information – Acts, Regulations, Codes of Practice;

- official publications – HSE Guidance Notes, Industry Advisory Committee publications;

- technical information about substances or plant and machinery;

- information from manufacturers and suppliers;

- directories of toxic substances and safety manuals;

- accident reports;

- accident and sickness records – statistical information and reports on notifiable accidents, dangerous occurrences and cases of industrial diseases;

- notices and reports from HSE Inspectors – improvement and prohibition notices, reports, survey results; and

- reports from safety consultants, doctors, safety officers, safety engineers.

While the employer has to provide all the above information, Regulation 7(2) of the Safety Representatives Regulations excuses him from providing the following:

- any information the disclosure of which would be against the interests of national security; or

- any information which he could not disclose without contravening a prohibition imposed by or under an enactment; or

- any information relating specifically to an individual, unless he has consented to its being disclosed; or

- any information the disclosure of which would, for reasons other than its effect on health, safety or welfare at work, cause substantial injury to the employers' undertaking or, where the information was supplied to him by some other person, to the undertaking of that other person; or

- any information obtained by the employer for the purpose of bringing, prosecuting or defending any legal proceedings.

INFORMATION IN SAFETY POLICIES

As mentioned in Chapter 1, under the HSW Act all employers with more than five workers have a duty to prepare and make available for their employees a written and up-to-date statement of their safety policy. The purpose behind this is to oblige employers to consider carefully, in each set of circumstances, the organisation and arrangements which they must create to ensure healthy and safe working conditions. Although HSC have published general guidance notes on safety policies, far too many employers have still either produced no statement or have produced statements which are so general as to be virtually meaningless.

If the employers' safety policy contains analyses of potential hazards, precautions and relevant legal standards that apply in each part of the workplace, this will increase its practical value. By urging the employer to carry out such an exercise in each part of his undertaking, safety representatives can ensure that they are informed about the application of safety standards to their members' work activities. In addition, if the analysis of hazards, precautions and standards is set out simply for each department, safety representatives can also use this part of the safety policy as a simple checklist with which to assess the employers' compliance with his legal obligations.

Where safety policies contain additional notes and guidance on particular hazards, it should also be remembered that there is nothing to prevent employers from reproducing relevant parts of HSE guidance notes in their policy documents.

HEALTH AND SAFETY LIBRARIES

One of the most practical ways in which employers can fulfil their duty to make available information is to provide a health and safety library at the workplace. The TUC wants to see new measures to require employers to set aside a suitable place where relevant information is kept available for employees. Such facilities, however, could then form the basis of an information bank for safety representatives. If such a facility is to be successful, however, it is important that it contains more than the bare minimum of statutory literature. Such libraries might contain relevant HSE Guidance Notes and Department of Employment's Health and Safety at Work Series of Booklets, directories of toxic substances, information from manufacturers and suppliers made available under Section 6 and so on. The titles listed at the end of each chapter in this book are a useful guide to publications which might be included in a health and safety library.

One way in which safety representatives can keep themselves informed of developments is by ensuring that their employers' safety library subscribes to the various health and safety periodicals. Some of these are:

- **TUC Health and Safety Bulletin:** available from unions and the TUC;

- **Health and Safety at Work Magazine:** Bofoers Publishing;

- **The Safety Representative:** published by ROSPA;

- **The Safety Practitioner:** journal of the Institution of Occupational Safety and Health;

- **Health and Safety Information Bulletin:** published by IRS Services;

- **Occupational Safety and Health** (Magazine): published by ROSPA;

- **Occupational Health:** published by Ballierie Tindall;

- **Occupational Health Review:** published by IRS; and

- **Safety Management** published by the British Safety Council.

FILMS

The use of health and safety films forms an important part of employers' training programmes. The Health and Safety Executive produce a range of films on the HSW Act and particular hazard topics. In addition, there are a number of other organisations which produce and/or supply a wide variety of health and safety films. Names and addresses of these organisations can be obtained from HSE. As part of joint discussions about selection of appropriate training films employers should be urged to provide safety representatives with up-to-date film catalogues.

INFORMATION WHICH DESIGNERS, MANUFACTURERS, IMPORTERS AND SUPPLIERS SHOULD PROVIDE

Under the HSW Act those who design, manufacture, import or supply plant and machinery or substances have a wide ranging duty to make sure that when their products are supplied for use at work, they are accompanied by adequate information. They also must make sure that their products are safe and without risks to health, and that articles are properly erected and installed and that their products have been subjected to adequate testing and research before they are introduced into the workplace.

When faced with a potential hazard from either plant and machinery or a substance, safety representatives should always, as a first step, seek from the employer the information which he in turn should have received from the supplier. Many suppliers produce comprehensive hazard data sheets (see *Chapter 5: Chemicals and toxic substances*). Others, on the other hand, may produce only scanty information. The HSC have published a series of guidance notes on how to comply with Section 6 which was amended with effect from March 1988 by the Consumer Protection Act 1987. Safety representatives can use this guidance when examining information from manufacturers and suppliers. For instance:

- Is the information in an easily understandable form, *ie* the hazard data sheets? Are potential hazards clearly outlined?

- Does the information describe testing and research which has been carried out to identify potential hazards? Does it include the results of tests and research?

- Is the information adequate; for example, in the case of a substance? Are details provided of: its chemical composition, possible poisonous effects, whether it can cause cancer, whether it can affect pregnancy, whether it is explosive or inflammable and so on?

- Are adequate precautions outlined? Is reference made to dangers of unusual uses?

- Does the information make reference to existing standards and recommendations in order to show that the article or substance is safe and without risks to health when properly used? – For instance HSW Act, Factories Act, Regulations, Code of Practice, British and International Standards and so on?

In addition to the requirements of Section 6 of HSW Act, regulations on labelling and packaging of dangerous substances require over 1,100 prescribed substances to be supplied in secure containers which bear labels showing certain basic health and safety information. These state that containers must be adequately constructed and that caps and stoppers must be made of the materials which are not affected by the substances in question. The regulations require labels to show the following information:

- the chemical name of the substance (as listed in schedule 1 of the regulations);

- the name and address of the manufacturer, importer or supplier;

- words and symbols indicating the broad category or risk;

- prescribed words specifying the precise hazard; and

- prescribed words indicating health and safety precautions.

The regulations also specify the dimension of labels according to size of container. In addition, there are a number of exemptions from the regulations – for example, where a prescribed substance is supplied as a motor fuel, munitions, a pesticide, a medicinal product, etc.

INFORMATION WHICH HSE SHOULD PROVIDE

As mentioned in Chapter 1, one of the aims of the HSW Act is to create a closer liaison between HSE 12 inspectors and safety representatives. Inspectors must contact safety representatives on their visits to the workplace and provide them with reports;

survey results, details of written or verbal warnings given to the employer; written undertakings from the employer; details on prohibition or improvement notices or other legal proceedings which have been issued against such notices. Inspectors are also a useful source of technical information and advice.

HSE have established a computer based information and advisory service based on a network of enquiry points located at HSE area offices. A full list of HSE area office addresses and telephone numbers is given in Appendix 1. The purpose of the information and advisory service which is linked to HSE's library services is to supply trade unionists and employers with a wide variety of statutory guidance material, including HSE guidance notes, posters, pamphlets, reports, regulations, codes of practice, explanatory booklets, etc. The HSE also produce free publication lists for particular industries. In addition it should be remembered that when health and safety problems cannot be solved satisfactorily in the workplace, in addition to seeking help from their own unions, safety representatives can also contact their local HSE area office.

LOCAL AUTHORITIES

As enforcing authorities under the Health and Safety at Work Act, local authorities also have a duty to provide information to safety representatives on their actions and observations. They have responsibility for enforcing health and safety legislation in a wide variety of non-industrial situations such as offices, shops, some warehouses, catering services, hotels and boarding houses, various consumer services and laundrettes. The precise range of activities covered by local authorities depends on agreement between such authorities and the HSE. Details of premises covered by local authority can be ascertained by contacting either the authority itself or the appropriate HSE area office.

EMPLOYMENT MEDICAL ADVISORY SERVICE

The Employment Medical Advisory Service (EMAS) (now the Medical Division of HSE), which was founded in 1973 consists of approximately 100 full time doctors and nurses, who are employed under the umbrella of the HSC. EMAS has the task of identifying health hazards related to employment, by monitoring studies and surveys; acting as a central information bank – advising trade unions and employers on how to deal with health hazards – and acting as a focus for medical aspects of employment problems, particularly in areas such as disablement and rehabilitation.

Employment Medical Advisers (EMAs) can be helpful in advising on problems in the workplace.

They are often prepared to carry out health screening, workplace surveys and, together with HSE's Technology Division, to give advice on work with toxic substances. Wherever occupational health (as opposed to safety) problems are concerned, one possible line of enquiry for safety representatives is to the local EMAS area office. EMAS telephone numbers can be obtained by contacting HSE area offices.

INFORMATION FROM UNIONS

Even though safety representatives may be able to obtain the information they require through the channels outlined above, they will also want to seek advice (via appropriate procedures) from their own unions. A number of unions have produced guides for safety representatives. Others have appointed health and safety officers or have access to specialist information via their research departments. Dissemination of information within unions is often a two-way process. In addition to serving members' requirements, requests for health and safety information enable officials to build up a clearer picture of the changing pattern of health and safety problems faced by their members.

INFORMATION FROM THE TUC

Where information cannot be obtained from employers, from manufacturers and suppliers, from inspectors, from EMAS, or from local universities and polytechnics or individual unions, then it may be necessary to seek advice from the TUC. The TUC produces a wide range of health and safety publications (see Appendix 3) as well as a regular health and safety bulletin. In addition, because of its involvement in the Health and Safety Commission and its advisory committees and other official bodies in the health and safety field, the TUC has access to a wide range of up-to-date legal and technical information. Requests for information, however, should not be sent directly to the TUC but should be made via individual unions.

INFORMATION FROM HMSO

Her Majesty's Stationery Office supply a wide range of useful publications on health and safety. Some of these include the Health and Safety at Work Series Booklets, HSE Guidance Notes and other Health and Safety Executive Annual Reports. A full list of health and safety publications is given in a reference booklet "Publications in Series" available free from HSE. Safety representatives can arm themselves with this little catalogue and use it as a starting point in finding out what Government publications are available on particular subjects.

INDEPENDENT ADVISERS

Guidance Note 26 to the Safety Representatives Regulations states that where technical matters are involved safety representatives and employers may wish to seek advice from appropriate universities or polytechnics. The HSC recommend that where such outside advice and expertise is necessary, safety representatives and employers should agree which persons and institutions are to be called upon and that copies of any reports made by them should be made available.

   Further advice on professional health and safety services to be provided or used by employers is set out in *Chapter 30: Workplace health and safety services.*

OTHER SOURCES

Amongst other sources of information and assistance useful to safety representatives are the facilities of local reference libraries, advice from general practitioners and the publications of the various safety organisations.

FURTHER INFORMATION

Advisory leaflets

* **Writing a safety policy statement:** advice to employers; HSC6.

* **Area office information services;** HSE9.

Guidance booklets

* **Essentials of health and safety at work:** *guidance for small firms;* HSE.

* **Guide to the classification, packaging and labelling of dangerous substances regulations 1984:** HS(R)22.

* **Articles and substances used at work:** the legal duties of designers, manufacturers, importers and suppliers and erectors and installers; IND(G) 1(L) Rev.

Guidance notes

* **Articles and substances for use at work:** guidance for designers, manufacturers, importers, suppliers, erectors and installers; GN: GS8.

Other useful sources

* **The Health and Safety Directory 198-/8-:** City Financial Kluwer.

* **Safety Practitioners Yearbook 198-:** Institution of Occupational Safety and Health; 222 Uppington Road, Leicester LE5 0QG.

30: Workplace health and safety services

THE NEED FOR SERVICES

If employers are going to be able to meet their obligations under health and safety legislation they need to have access to professional advice and services. This means employing directly or making use of a variety of specialists such as occupational health doctors and nurses, occupational hygienists and professional safety advisers. Some of the tasks of health and safety services include: identification of sources of health and safety risk and advice about their control; advice about compliance with legal requirements; monitoring the employer's safety policy; notification and investigation of accidents and cases of occupational diseases; inspection of plant and the equipment; provision of regular information and training and so on.

Employers also need specialist hygiene services to deal with specific environmental problems such as exposure to dust, fumes or use of toxic substances. They may also need medical and/or nursing advice to tackle specific health and safety problems, to offer advice about first aid, fitness for work, job placement or rehabilitation or to provide a programme of routine health surveillance for workers exposed to known sources of health risk. In addition, specific legislation may require a specific health and safety service input – for example, checking hoists and lifting gear, undertaking estimations of substances in blood and urine samples or, in the case of forthcoming Control of Substances Hazardous to Health (COSHH) Regulations, asbestos or noise legislation, and making environmental assessments.

This chapter is designed to help safety representatives and other union officers to assess what sort of health and safety services are needed at workplaces, how such services can be provided by employers and how unions can be involved in their work. As well as explaining why employers need certain kinds of expertise in health and safety – the chapter provides a simple explanation of some of the functions of the main specialists involved and highlights issues for discussion with employers. It has been designed specifically to assist safety representatives in contributing to the health and safety service review process which has been advocated by the Health and Safety Commission (see opposite).

CURRENT PROBLEMS

At present there are only a few specific regulations which require employers to use health and safety specialists and consequently the provision of adequate health and safety services is still limited, on the whole to major companies and the public sector. This is due mainly to failure by employers to understand the essential role of such services and also to the fact that most of the traditional health and safety service 'delivery' systems which have been developed to date, tend to be inappropriate and unworkable for most small and medium sized businesses which now employ the majority of the workforce. The result is that less than a third of all workers are covered by adequate health and safety services and in many areas, provision of medical and hygiene services is virtually non existent.

In most small and medium sized organisations full time 'in-house' provision of services can be ruled out because specialist staff are scarce and resources are not available. Part-time provision tends to be a rarity in the safety field and in occupational health, despite some good work, it has often tended to be no more than an extension of general medical practice onto factory premises. The use of reputable independent consultancies in safety, health and hygiene, on a fee-for-service basis, whilst a possibility for small firms, is rare and often because of the difficulties involved in identifying appropriate consultants. The wider use of NHS services has never been developed but some interesting experiments are now taking place.

Membership of a group service is a possibility – for example safety groups in the construction industry (promoted in the HSC Construction Industry Advisory Committee's Guidance on Health and Safety Services in the Construction Industry: Parts 1 and 2). On the other hand, group occupational health schemes set up in the 1970's have been hard pressed to survive in recent years, being limited to distinct geographical areas – with membership representing a continuing cost for fewer participating firms. Sharing of occupational health services between employers as advocated by the HSC, has never been developed to any significant extent, although use by sub contractors of main contractors' services in industries like construction is one possibility which could be examined.

TUC PROPOSALS

In 1980, in order to highlight the need for new action on health and safety services, the TUC published *Workplace Health and Safety Services: TUC proposals for an Integrated Approach.* This argued the case for regulations and an approved code of practice to require employers to employ or to have access to a range of specialist services appropriate to the control of risks arising from their activities. It gave a description of the role and functions of the four main health and safety disciplines, safety officers, occupational medicine, occupational health nursing and occupational hygiene and made proposals for joint control of health and safety services by employers and unions at the workplace or at local level and through group/industry schemes. Although differing on the need for legislation and on the question of safety services, the recommendation of the 1984 report on Occupational Health and Hygiene Services by the House of Lords Select Committee on Science and Technology (The Gregson Committee) followed the TUC approach to a large extent.

The ILO has also published a Convention (No 161) and Recommendation (171) on Occupational Health Services which the TUC has urged that the UK Government should accept and ratify by introducing new legislation.

HSC INTERIM ADVICE

In order to follow up the Gregson report the HSC has published interim advice to all employers urging them to review their needs for services in consultation with unions and health and safety specialists. The TUC has welcomed this as a useful first step – for, although it is limited mainly to occupational medicine and occupational hygiene, it offers trade union representatives the opportunity of reviewing their employers' needs for services, how such services are to be provided and staffed and how they are to operate on a day to day basis. Safety representatives and other union officers should use this review process therefore to urge employers to prepare detailed written assessments of their health and safety service needs and ways of meeting them, so that, through consultation procedures, these can be used as a basis for negotiating improvements. (If they are to be comprehensive however, it will be necessary to ensure that such reviews also encompass safety services).

At present, there is still little officially published guidance to help smaller firms to assess their health and safety service needs. In 1976, the Health and Safety Executive published a discussion document "Safety Officers: Sample Survey of Role and Functions" which was heavily criticised by a number of bodies and did not lead to the publication of official HSE guidance on safety services. Instead HSE have tended latterly to focus on the role of management in publications such as "Managing Safety: A Review of the Role of Management in Health and Safety" by the Accident Prevention Advisory Unit 1981, "Effective Policies for Health and Safety: A Review Drawn from the Work and Experience of APAU" published in 1980 and "Monitoring Safety" 1985. These are excellent publications which have never been sufficiently publicised. A more traditional approach to occupational health service needs is set out in the HSE Booklet "Guidelines on Occupational Health Services" HS(G) 20 published in 1982. This booklet however, is aimed mainly at the larger enterprise with little discussion of the needs of the smaller firm – so HSE are currently developing new guidance.

The HSE has also published *"Essentials of HSE"* which provides basic health and safety information for small firms.

ASSESSING NEEDS

An employers' needs for health and safety services will vary according to the nature of his undertaking and the risks involved. Some services may have to be provided on a regular basis. Others may only be required on a one-off basis. The outline over page of some of the main functions of safety officers, doctors, and occupational hygienists is designed to assist safety representatives to identify their employers' needs for services in particular workplaces:

WAYS OF MEETING NEEDS

'In-house' services

As stressed previously the option of providing a comprehensive range of services 'in-house' is limited largely to major private employers and to the public sector. In such cases employers should be urged to review the structure and organisation of their

Safety officers

1. Advising management on:

   - the identification of risks and dangers associated with
     – injury or ill health to workers;
     – damage to plant, equipment, and materials; and
     – fire and explosion;

   - improvement of existing working by the introduction of safe systems of work;

   - legal requirements affecting safety, health, hygiene and welfare;

   - provision and use of protective clothing and equipment;

   - safety-suitability of new and hired plant and equipment, and ensuring all appropriate test certificates and technical instructions are obtained;

   - potential hazards before work starts and on safety organisation required;

   - new methods of safe working arising from current technological developments; and

   - appropriate fire and rescue procedures.

2. Carrying out workplace surveys to assess compliance with health and safety standards.

3. Investigating the cause of any accidents or dangerous occurrences and recommending means of preventing their recurrence.

4. Supervising the recording and analysis of information, injuries, ill-health, damage and production losses; assessing accident trends and reviewing overall safety performance.

5. Assisting with training at all levels.

6. Keeping contact with official and professional bodies, eg HSE, EMAS.

7. Liaison with safety representatives and safety committees.

8. Fostering, within the workplace, an understanding that injury prevention and damage control are an integral part of business and operational efficiency.

9. Keeping up to date with recommended codes of practice and new safety literature.

10. Preparing budgets and obtaining approval for funds to implement policies as related to safety, health and welfare.

11. Liaison with client's representatives and subcontractors on health and safety issues.

12. Liaison with employer's insurance company(s).

Occupational health doctors

1. Advising management on:

   - identification of risks to workers' health:

   - assessment of such risks;

   - relevant control measures; and

   - First aid and welfare facilities.

2. Routine health surveillance of workers exposed to hazardous agents, eg:

   - noise;

   - vibration:

   - radiation;

   - biological hazards;

   - toxic substances; and

   - physical and psychological stresses.

3. Routine examination and advice for workers doing jobs which may aggravate an existing ill health condition or whose health status may put others at risk.

4. Offering advice about job placement and rehabilitation – for example following sickness and injury.

5. Providing relevant information and training at all levels – eg health education.

Occupational hygienists

Advising management on the recognition, evaluation and control of environmental factors in the workplace which may adversely affect the health and comfort of people at work. Environmental factors in question include the following.

1. Airborne dusts, fibres, micro-organisms, gases, and vapours that are likely to be inhaled or absorbed onto or through the skin.

2. Noise and vibration affecting worker's hearing or circulation.

3. Ionising and non-ionising radiations.

4. Heat or cold leading to discomfort or stress.

5. Ventilation and other measures and their ability to minimise the effects of any of the above factors.

services to ensure that they cover all relevant areas of expertise and that health and safety staff involved work together effectively as a team (see page 203).

In the majority of cases however health and safety expertise has to be provided from sources outside the employer's own organisation. Even where some 'in-house' services are provided, this option may also be necessary to tackle special problems *eg* occupational hygiene monitoring, or advice about special hazards such as ionising radiation, microbiological risks etc. A number of options are available and these are discussed below.

Group occupational health schemes

These are relatively few in number but provide mainly medical and nursing services to participating firms in a distinct geographical area on a subscription basis.

Group safety schemes

These are concentrated mainly in the construction industry and involve sharing the services of a qualified safety officer between a number of employers usually involved in the same industry.

NHS services

There are a limited number of consultants in the NHS in Occupational Medicine but these are concerned mainly with occupational health needs of NHS staff and do not offer extensive services to employers generally. There are also a limited number of General Practitioners with qualifications in occupational health. When assessing what services the NHS can offer in specific cases contact should be made with the District Health Authority or local Family Practitioner Committee.

Consultancies

There are a wide variety of organisations offering medical, safety and hygiene services to employers. Some are relatively small – sometimes based on individual specialists. Some are larger organisations operating on a fee-for-service basis. A number are based on university departments. Wherever such services are used it is important to assess their professional competence and past record (see page 203).

Employers and trade associations

A number of employer and trade associations provide services and advice to member companies. These can vary from specialist medical and scientific services to general information and guidance on common hazards in specific sectors.

Sharing services

This option has not been developed to any significant extent – but is a possibility, for example for sub-contractors who can be required within contract conditions to use a main contractor's

services or provide equivalent cover from other sources. There is also scope for exploring ways of sharing the services of safety officers and safety representatives to provide basic health and safety assessment and advice in workplaces within the same industry or locality.

Joint industry schemes

In a number of areas, for example agriculture and the rubber industry, the TUC has proposed the setting up of new jointly controlled schemes under HSC Industry Advisory Committees. These would cover particular industry sectors and act as clearing houses for health and safety service needs and promote and co-ordinate health and safety service activity sharing information and research findings wherever possible.

ROLE AND FUNCTIONS OF HEALTH AND SAFETY SERVICES: SOME KEY POINTS

1: Prevention

The primary function of health and safety services must be prevention of injury and damage to workers' health. Whilst this might sound obvious, it contrasts starkly with the fact that only a minority of occupational health services appear to place primary emphasis on preventive activities. It is often said that occupational medicine is concerned with the effects of work on health and the effects of health on work. The fact that so much scarce and highly work-qualified medical manpower is devoted to routine medical examination suggests that, in practice, occupational medicine is heavily biased towards the latter.

The principal task of occupational health staff in any service must be the recognition, evaluation, and elimination at source, of occupational health hazards whether they be physical accident hazards, ergonomic problems, noise, vibration, radiation, heat, light, and so on, chemical, biological, psychological (mental stress, fatigue etc). The question therefore which should always be uppermost in the mind of the occupational physician or nurse is, is the job 'fit for the worker? – Is the worker fit for the job?', is then a relevant but subsidiary consideration.

2: Planning

Doctors, nurses, hygienists and safety officers also have a key role to play in eliminating risks to health at the planning stage. The requirement under the HSW Act for employers to devise safe systems at work; the requirement for manufacturers and suppliers to ensure adequate research and to make available full information on their products; and the requirement for employers to consult with safety representatives before new plant, processes or materials are introduced, all mean that occupational health personnel have a key role in planning for health and safety at the design stage.

In the TUC's experience, however, in only a minority of services is such a role developed to any significant extent.

3: Monitoring the workplace

Although the main aim of occupational health and safety services should be to eliminate hazards in the workplace before they arise, occupational health staff must also be involved in recognising, monitoring and controlling existing hazards. A major part of the work of occupational health doctors and nurses should be regular inspection and initial assessment of environmental conditions (noise, dust, thermal conditions, exposure to atmospheric pollutants, contact with chemicals micro-organisms and so on). The primary importance of this should be stressed as strongly as possible. Only when such monitoring has been carried out does clinical observation and medical screening of the workforce assume any real relevance.

4: Health surveillance

Failure in the past to link the results of environmental and clinical monitoring has been a major source of weakness in past occupational health practice. Sometimes scarce medical resources are devoted to extensive routine medical examinations and, whilst this can be of value in helping to detect general health problems or refer patients to NHS services, it may not necessarily help to identify and tackle harmful influences in the workplace. Health screening and surveillance must be used selectively to tackle specific occupational ill health problems or provide a check on the efficacy of control measures.

5: Record keeping

A blanket approach to routine medical examinations of workers – for example in pre-placement medical examination – is unlikely to be of great value in controlling health risks. Equally medical surveillance without adequate and standardised systems of record-keeping is likely to be of limited value. New requirements in the Control of Substances Hazardous to Health Regulations on the keeping and use of occupational health records and the results of hygiene monitoring mean that a much more systematic approach has to be adopted.

6: Research

Employers' health and safety services also need to promote co-operation in joint research projects – for example between HSE, EMAS, academic, trade and research organisation etc, in order to assess and monitor health and safety problems in workplaces and industries with similar hazards.

Such projects can help avoid duplication of effort and generalise useful experience and lessons gained in specific situations. Trade union representatives need to be closely involved – for example in advising on research methods, eg implementation of screening procedures – or areas in which new research should be carried out. The legal basis for such involvement already exists, since the provisions of the Safety Representatives and Safety Committees Regulations entitle trade union representatives to be informed about the conduct and results of occupational health research in their place of work.

7: Fitness for work

In the area of rehabilitation and adjustment to work, it needs to be remembered that one of the main purposes of medical examination must be to see whether any special provisions need to be made in order to help persons involved adjust to the demands of their work. This can be necessary as a result of permanent or temporary handicaps which arise as a result of injury or illness – or where an individual's capacity for work may vary with age and other physical and psychological factors. It is essential that in these cases medical examination and the advice of occupational health doctors and nurses should be available for those workers for whom it may be necessary to arrange either alternative work or adjustments in their work regime, as well as continued medical surveillance, up to the time of full resumption of normal work.

It needs to be remembered however, that problems of adjustment to work need to be discussed between occupational health personnel and patients in an atmosphere of confidentiality and mutual trust. It is essential that if problems of adjustment to work are to be handled in the patient's (as opposed to the employer's) interest, that the disclosure by workers of difficulties in coping with their work does not lead to transfer, down-grading or even redundancy. Where adjustments are necessary, the employer should be pressed to arrange for alternative and comparable employment or suitable retraining and the need for any such action, agreed between doctor and patient, should only be proceeded with after adequate discussion between management and trade union representatives.

8: First aid

Another important function of health and safety services is giving general advice on first aid and treatment services in the workplace. Safety representatives should remember that the role of occupational health services in the treatment of injuries or ill health, should, with the exception of relatively small health problems, be limited to first aid and emergency treatment only. It is not really part of the functions of occupational health staff to provide treatment services which are normally available under the NHS eg via a worker's own General Practitioner. Occupational health personnel do have a major role too however, in supervision of statutory first aid requirements, training of first aiders and advising on provision of medical treatment and first aid facilities in occupational health services. This can include assessing factors such as potential hazards of particular situations, the proximity and suitability of relevant NHS casualty services and the need for close integration where necessary between workplace first aid provision and NHS services.

9: Health education and counselling

Health and safety staff have an important role in providing information to workers on hazards at the workplace. But in addition to purely occupational health education, the work of the occupational health doctor or nurse can make a valuable contribution to developing a wider understanding of health problems, particularly in relation to discussion of problems such as diet, personal hygiene, exercise, smoking, weight problems and so on. The availability within the workplace of health counselling can do much to promote a greater awareness of health problems and enable occupational health personnel to refer patients to their own doctors for further advice and treatment where necessary. (Further advice on alcohol problems is available in the TUC booklet *Problem Drinking: TUC Guidelines for a workplace policy*).

Workplace health counselling can also act as a focus for the work of mobile screening facilities, for example the programmes which have been mounted for early detection of breast and cervical cancer. It is TUC policy that there should be a national screening service for these two particular diseases in liaison with workplace occupational health services, and that more use should be made of the workplace as the focus for the provision of health education and health counselling services for women, for example workplace based ante-natal care. In this way occupational health provision at the workplace can make a major contribution to tackling general health problems throughout the community.

OCCUPATIONAL HEALTH NURSING

Trade unionists should also remember that there is considerable scope for enlarging the role and functions of suitably qualified occupational health nurses. In many cases the skills of occupational health nurses are underutilised. But given sufficient scope, they can provide a permanent focus for occupational health activity in the workplace or in group schemes – drawing on other sources of expertise in medicine and hygiene and related services as and when necessary – although obviously suitable training and experience are necessary.

THE NEED FOR A 'TEAM' APPROACH

Finally, it must be remembered that health and safety services should function as a 'team'. This

means a re-examination of the traditional view that occupational health is the province of doctors and nurses, and safety and welfare that of other disciplines. The health and safety of workers is too important and complex a subject for such compartmentalisation. Each discipline has a contribution to make in all areas of the subject. Medical, nursing, safety and hygiene personnel need therefore to work as part of a co-ordinated effort in the identification, control or elimination of occupational health and safety hazards. The prevention of occupational ill health is not uniquely a medical problem. Workers can become ill as a result of exposure to toxic substances, physical agents or dangerous stresses. So once sources of health risk have been identified, the question of prevention is primarily a matter of engineering control, organisational arrangements and protective measures.

Within this process, the role of occupational medicine is one of diagnosis, assessment, and monitoring and the skills required are not just clinical but involve toxicological and epidemiological expertise as well. This emphasises the limited value of considering the role of occupational medicine and occupational health nursing in isolation from health and safety services in general.

In many areas where occupational health and hygiene services are under-developed or non-existent, safety services can play a major role in the identification and control of known health risks. Similarly because they deal with the effects of accidents, occupational physicians and nurses will inevitably become involved in advising about accident prevention. These examples show the need to understand the disciplines of occupational medicine and occupational health nursing, hygiene, safety, etc., as interconnected resources to be combined effectively in a general strategy of prevention.

QUALIFICATIONS

It is important for safety representatives to be able to assess whether health and safety staff have appropriate training and qualifications. Some of the main qualifications in each discipline are outlined below – but remember experience too is just as important.

- **Safety adviser:** Fellow, Member or Associate Member of the Institution of Occupational Safety and Health (IOSH) (these are under review at present) – from 1989, membership of IOSH will depend on obtaining the Certificate or Diploma of the National Examination Board in Occupational Safety and Health (NEBOSH).

- **Occupational medicine:** Fellow, Member or Associate of the Faculty of Occupational Medicine of the Royal College of Physicians.

- **Occupational health nurse:** Holder of the Occupational Health Nursing Certificate of the Royal College of Nursing.
- **Occupational hygienist:** Certificate, Diploma, BSC and MSC degrees in occupational hygiene.

DIRECTION, ACCOUNTABILITY, AND CONTROL OF SERVICES

Given the major role which health and safety staff play in protecting workers from injury and health damage, it is important that safety representatives ensure that they have an effective voice in determining how health and safety services operate. For example health and safety staff, whether employed directly or engaged from outside organisations, must operate independently of the employer. This means they must be accountable to joint employer/union bodies such as workplace or industry health and safety committees.

Often health and safety staff are seen as having an ambiguous role and in some cases they can be seen as part of management and do not enjoy the complete trust of the workforce. For example, to the extent that employers regard the company doctor as their employee and expect co-operation in such questions as sickness absence, compensation claims and disclosure of confidential information about individual workers, this will serve to undermine confidence placed in their services by workers and their representatives. Even where doctors pursue professional objectives diligently, they can still suffer from isolation, lack of knowledge and pressures from management.

This means that certain mechanisms of accountability and control are very important:

- the appointment or dismissal of occupational health and safety staff should be subject to joint agreement between employers and unions;
- the activities and work programmes of health and safety services should be subject to periodic review and agreement;
- in the case of group services, trade union influence should be exerted through representation at the level of an administrative board;
- targets for the improvement of health and safety should be agreed using appropriate industrial relations procedures;
- trade unionists should have the right to receive regular reports from occupational health and safety personnel to enable them to monitor progress towards these targets; and
- trade unionists should also have the right to call in or seek advice from either their own or the employer's occupational health and safety staff wherever necessary.

Above all it needs to be remembered by both management and safety representatives that it is the task of occupational health and safety personnel to identify and evaluate risks and to advise, but it is the responsibility of trade unionists and employers, on the basis of that advice, to reach agreement on how such risks are to be eliminated or controlled.

CHECKLIST: HEALTH AND SAFETY SERVICES

Safety

How does your employer obtain advice and services in the following areas?

1. Workplace health and safety inspection?
2. Advice about legal requirements – including changes in legislation?
3. Accident investigation and analysis?
4. Evaluation of information from manufacturers and suppliers?
5. Advice about safe systems of work?
6. Health and safety training and provision of information?
7. Advice about protective clothing and equipment?

Occupational hygiene

Are specialist hygiene services required to identify, evaluate and advise on the control of the following?

1. Airborne dust, fibres, micro-organisms, gases and vapours that are likely to be inhaled or absorbed on to or through the skin?
2. Noise and vibration affecting workers' hearing or circulation?
3. Ionising and non-ionising radiations?
4. Heat or cold leading to discomfort or stress?
5. Ventilation and other control measures and their ability to minimise the effects of any of the above factors?

Medical services

Are any of the following medical services required?

1. Advice about medical aspects of systems of work?
2. Routine health surveillance of workers at risk from harmful factors above?
3. Preplacement medical examinations?
4. Regular assessment of fitness for certain jobs?
5. Advice about rehabilitation and adaptation to work?
6. Advice about first aid?
7. Health education and health counselling?
8. Medical record keeping?

Health and safety service 'delivery' systems

How does your employer provide the above services?

1. In-house health and safety department – (safety officer based)?

2. In-house occupational health department (doctor/ based)?

3. Group scheme?

4. Services of a trade or employers' organisation?

5. Consultancy, *eg* University or Polytechnic department?

6. Sharing services of other employers?

7. What other specialist services may be required, *eg.*

   - radiation protection?

   - ergonomics?

   - microbiological control?

Relationships and style of work

Are safety representatives consulted (for example via the safety committee) about the following:

1. Services required and qualifications of health and safety staff?

2. How services will be provided?

3. Health and safety service work programmes, and targets?

4. Reports by health and safety staff?

5. Do health and safety staff work together as a team?

6. How much of their time is spent on accident and ill health prevention?

IMPROVING SERVICES

Prepare a list of current health and safety service needs and ways services can be provided or improved. Make a report, discuss it with fellow union representatives and compare it with your employer's review assessment.

FURTHER INFORMATION

TUC publications

- **Workplace health and safety services:** TUC proposals for an integrated approach; TUC Publications.

- **Problem Drinking:** TUC guidelines for workplace policy; TUC Publications.

HSE publications on occupational health services

- **Occupational health services – the way ahead:** HSE, 1980.

- **Guidelines for occupational health services:** HMSO: HS(G)20.

- **Health surveillance by routine procedures:** HSE; Guidance Note MS 18.

- **Pre-employment health screening:** HSE Guidance Note MS 20.

- **Guidelines on occupational health services in the health service:** Health Services Advisory Committee, 1984.

- **Guidelines for occupational health services in the oil industry:** Oil Industry Advisory Committee, 1987.

- **Review your occupational health needs:** HSE Employers' Guide.

- **Review your occupational health needs:** HSE Employers' checklist; HSE.

HSE advice on safety services

- **CONIAC Guidance on health and safety advisory services for the construction industry:**

    Part 1: the need for advice and the services available;

    Part 2: the safety adviser: selection, training and professional standards;

    available from HMSO.

- **Professional training and qualification in occupational health and safety:** HSE discussion paper; June 1983.

- **Safety officers, sample survey of role and functions:** HSC discussion document, 1976.

- **APAU papers and discussion documents:**

  Monitoring Safety 1985;

  Managing Safety: A review of the role of management in health and safety, 1981;

  Effective policies for health and safety: a review drawn from the work and experience of APAU, 1980.

Appendices

South West:
Inter City House, Mitchel Lane, Victoria Street, Bristol BS1 6AN. 0272 290681

South:
Priestley House, Priestley Road, Basingstoke RG24 9NW. 0256 473181

South East:
3 East Grinstead House, London Road, West Sussex RH19 1RR. 0342 26922

London (North):
Maritime House, 1 Linton Road, Barking, Essex IG11 8HF. 01-594 5522

London (South):
1 Long Lane, London SE1 4PG. 01-407 8911

East Anglia:
39 Baddow Road, Chelmsford, Essex CM2 0HL. 0245 284661

Northern Home Counties:
14 Cardiff Road, Luton, Beds LU1 1PP. 0582 459775

East Midlands:
Belgrave House, 1 Greyfriars, Northampton NN1 2BS. 0604 21233

West Midlands:
McLaren Building, 2 Masshouse Circus, Queensway, Birmingham B4 7NP. 021-200 2299

Wales:
Brunel House, 2 Fitzalan Road, Cardiff CF2 1SH. 0222 437777

Marches:
The Marches House, Midway, Newcastle-under-Lyme, Staffs ST5 1DT. 0782 717181

North Midlands:
Birkbeck House, Trinity Square, Nottingham NG1 4AU. 0602 470712

South Yorkshire:
Sovereign House, 40 Silver Street, Sheffield S1 2ES. 0742 739081

West and North Yorkshire:
8 St Paul's Street, Leeds LS1 2LE. 0532 446191

Greater Manchester:
Quay House, Quay Street, Manchester M3 3JB. 061-831 7111

Merseyside:
The Triad, Stanley Road, Bootle L20 3PG. 051-922 7211

North West:
Victoria House, Ormskirk Road, Preston PR1 1HH, 0772 59321

North East:
Arden House, Regent Centre, Gosforth, Newcastle-upon-Tyne NE3 3JM. 091-285 9682

Scotland (East):
Belford House, 59 Belford Road, Edinburgh EH4 3UE. 031-225 1313

Scotland (West):
314 St Vincent Street, Glasgow G3 8XG. 041-248 2760

How to obtain free HSE publications

For free HSE literature and information about HSE priced publications contact one of the HSE public enquiry points between 10 am and 3 pm Monday to Friday:

- HSE, Baynards House, 1 Chepstow Place, Westbourne Grove, London W2 4TF. 01-243 6000

- HSE, Broad Lane, Sheffield, S3 7HQ. 0742-752539

- HSE, St Hugh's House, Stanley Precinct, Bootle, Merseyside L20 3QY. 051-951 4381

  Many free leaflets are also available from HSE area offices.

  A complete list of HSE publications – "Publications in Series" — is published twice yearly. This, and bibliographies on agriculture, chemicals and construction, are available free from the public enquiry points.

How to obtain priced publications

Most priced publications produced by HSE are available at government bookshops, or on request from any good bookseller. More specialist publications can be obtained from HSE's sales point at St Hugh's House, Bootle.

When ordering priced publications quote the International Standard Book Number (ISBN) if possible. The ones held by HSE have an ISBN starting with 07176.

Full ordering details are given in the HSE's Publications in Series free booklet.

A list of HMSO Government bookshops is given below:

HMSO Publications Centre (mail and telephone orders only)

- PO Box 276, London SW8 5DT

- Telephone orders 01-622 3316

- General enquiries 01-211 5656 (queuing system in operation for both numbers)

HMSO Bookshops

- 49 High Holborn, London WC1V 6HB. 01-211 5656 (counter service only)

- 258 Broad Street, Birmingham B1 2HE. 021-643 3740

- Southey House, 33 Wine Street, Bristol BS1 2BQ. 0272 264306

- 9-21 Princess Street, Manchester M60 8AS. 061-834 7201

- 80 Chichester Street, Belfast BT1 4JY. 0232 238451

- 71 Lothian Road, Edinburgh EH3 9AZ. 031-228 4181

HMSO's accredited agents
(see Yellow Pages)

Through good booksellers

3: TUC PUBLICATIONS

Below are listed TUC publications which give information and guidance to trade union negotiators and health and safety representatives on how to identify and deal with health and safety issues.

Hand-books and leaflets

- **Workplace health and safety services:** *proposals for legislation to require employers to use health and safety services;* 74pp, 80p (4/81).

- **From dust to dust:** *dust at work has been the largest occupational killer from which trade union representatives must seek to protect workers;* 25pp, (5/84).

- **Government cuts put workers' health and safety at risk:** *a Campaign report on the effects of cuts in the Health and Safety Executive on the nation's workers;* 22pp, 60p (11/83).

- **Government cuts . . .:** *action brief for trade union representatives on the shop floor of the effect of cuts in the HSE;* 17pp, 20p (11/3).

- **Lighten the load:** *a bad back is no joke and this TUC brief on manual handling at work shows how to avoid one;* 36pp (8/88).

- **Asbestos in the workplace:** *the dangers of asbestos at the work place and how they can be prevented;* 16pp, 20p (3/85).

- **TUC handbook on dust at work:** *detailed guidelines on how to tackle dust problems at work;* 68pp, £1.25 (2/86).

- **Know your rights** – health and safety at work: *highlights key role of trade unions in securing health and safety improvements in the workplace;* every safety representative should have a copy; 21pp, 80p (8/86).

- **Say 'No' to noise:** *a handy brief for on-the-spot reference in the workplace;* 12pp, 15p (9/81).

- **TUC guidelines on visual display units:** *you need to read this if your employer is thinking of installing VDUs;* 80pp, £1.00 (3/86).

- **Health and safety in the office:** *each year 5,000 serious injuries occur in the office;* 17pp, 25p (3/86).

- **Noise at work:** *sets out a basic noise strategy including controlling noise at source;* 104pp, £1.50 (9/86).

- **Protecting young people at work:** *practical advice on how to ensure the health and safety of young people at work;* 38pp, £1.00 (5/86).

- **Problem drinking:** *TUC guidelines for a workplace policy;* 25pp, 80p (12/86).

- **Cleared for take-off?:** a TUC Report on air safety; 45pp; £5.00 (6/88).

Working papers

The following documents are available from TUC Publications, price £1 incl p&p unless otherwise stated.

- **A review of the Fire Precautions Act** — *TUC evidence on the Home Office Consultative Document.*

- **Workplace health and safety services** — *TUC guidance on health and safety services which employers should provide at work.*

- **Health and safety in small firms** — *the case against deregulation.*

- **Preventing violence to staff** — *Conference Report.*

- **Preventing violence to staff** — *Progress Report.*

- **AIDS: TUC evidence to Social Services Committee;** £3.00.

- **Health and safety at work** — the way forward: *1987 Congress Statement.*

- **TUC environment policy file.**

- **Ionising radiation** — dose limitation: *TUC submission to the National Radiological Protection Board.*

- **Prevention of accidents to children:** *TUC comments on Health Safety Commission recommendations.*

- **Restrictions on employment of young people, and removal of sex discrimination:** *TUC remarks on Government plans.*

- **Extension of YTS health and safety regulations:** *TUC opinion on HSC proposals.*

- **Health and safety information for employees:** *TUC comments on HSC recommendations.*

- **Control of substances hazardous to health** — (COSHH) Regulations: *progress report.*

Posters

- Noticeboard size posters on: *Safety Representatives, Dust, HSE,* and *Noise* – SAE for each poster (or set of four).

Health and Safety "Bulletin"

- Produced on a regular basis giving up-to-date information on a range of health and safety issues available on subscription £10.00 (4 issues).

Postage

- Unless otherwise stated, postage is payable at the following rates and must be included with your order:

- up to 5 items, 20p per item;

- up to 10 items, 15p per item;

- 11 items and over, 10p per item;

Bulk prices inclusive of postage are available on request. All orders should be sent to Publications Department, TUC, Congress House, Great Russell Street, London WC1B 3LS.

This statement was adopted by the 119th Annual Trades Union Congress, Blackpool, September 7-11 1987

1: Commitment to prevention

The prevention of accidental death, injury or health damage to working people must be accepted as a matter of absolute priority by Government, employers and the trade union Movement. At present nearly 700 workers die every year in accidents at work, over 275,000 are injured and there are some 900 notified deaths from prescribed industrial diseases. The true extent of occupational ill health however is very much greater but remains largely uncharted. As many as 50,000 people are expected to die over the next ten years from past exposure to asbestos alone. Chronic conditions such as tenosynovitis, back injury and deafness drastically affect the quality of life of millions of workers. The burden of pain, grief, suffering and economic loss which this imposes on the victims, their friends, relatives and the community at large, is totally unacceptable.

Success in the control of risks to workers' health and safety is an important barometer of social and economic advance. The TUC considers that it is a prime responsibility of Government to take all necessary steps to promote a continuing improvement in health and safety performance by ensuring that employers meet their obligations. Such improvement depends first and foremost on the commitment by Government of adequate staff and financial resources to enable the Health and Safety Commission (HSC) and the Health and Safety Executive (HSE) to carry out their responsibilities under the Health and Safety at Work (HSW) Act.

2: TUC strategy

The trade union Movement has a central role to play in securing the protection of people from the hazards of their work. The TUC therefore, will continue to pursue and develop its general strategy for the improvement of occupational safety and health. Four key elements in this strategy are:

a) securing the effective involvement of unions in health and safety issues – at national, industry and workplace levels; for example through well understood and effective procedures for consultation;

b) defining problems and priorities – for example by the promotion of research;

c) securing improved health and safety standards in legislation; codes and guidance; and

d) ensuring compliance by employers with such standards and the adoption of safe systems of work – through the development of health and safety policies and services at the workplace and effective enforcement of standards by an adequately staffed inspectorate.

3: Factors affecting progress since 1974

The HSW Act was widely regarded as the 'jewel in the crown' of the last Labour administration. It laid the basis for a major advance in occupational safety and health by creating a new legal framework, by reorganising the various health and safety inspectorates by extending legal protection to eight million workers previously outside the scope of health and safety law and by increasing the involvement of trade unions, for example at the workplace through the safety representatives and safety committees system and nationally through the advisory committees of the Health and Safety Commission (HSC). In turn the HSC provided a new means of generating improved legislation and standards.

At the time they were introduced, these changes led to a new level of preventative activity in workplaces throughout Britain – leading to physical and organisational changes which greatly benefited working people and improved protection for the public from the hazards of work activity.

These achievements and the promise of further progress however have since been undermined both directly and indirectly as a result of the policies of the present administration – particularly cuts in resources allocated to health and safety, privatisation and attacks on local authorities. Meanwhile, not only has the climate for improving health and safety at work deteriorated due to fragmentation of the industrial structure but the Government has encouraged companies to become 'leaner and fitter' thus giving the green light to unscrupulous employers to place less emphasis on health and safety matters. The result has been a disastrous rise in accident rates in many major branches of industry (see Annex, Table 1).

In this situation the TUC has fought to limit the effects of these attacks in order to preserve the gains secured under the HSW Act. The task now facing the trade union Movement is to halt the downward slide and to create a new momentum of improvement.

4: Developing the role of the Health and Safety Commission (HSC)

Effective consultation arrangements are of fundamental importance to the development of improved health and safety standards. The new consultative structures established by the HSW Act through the HSC and its advisory committees have provided much greater opportunities for the trade union Movement to influence the development of health and safety policy. There are now 18 advisory committees involving over 100 TUC representatives. Industry Advisory Committees (IACs) are now an important source of authoritative standards. The TUC will continue to press for the establishment of further advisory committees – including new IACs for all major sectors – and will continue to service and co-ordinate the work of trade union representatives in these committees in order to secure improved standards and to promote new initiatives to protect workers' health and safety – for example by promoting training and research and tackling the hazards of new technologies. The authority and influence of the IAC's must be expanded and they must be asked to develop and publish health and safety strategies for their industries. They must also be given greater resources as well as oversight of the work of the HSE within the sectors which they cover.

The TUC is continuing to review and to develop its consultation procedures on health and safety including consulting unions on specific issues, co-ordinating responses to HSC consultative documents, providing feedback via the TUC Health and Safety Bulletin and reporting annually to Congress.

5: HSC/E resources

Since 1979, the total number of HSE inspectors has been cut by 119. The number of Factory inspectors in the field has been cut by 116. The HSE's staff complement as a whole is at least 25 per cent below the target of 4,400 total staff (including 1,050 factory inspectors) which was agreed by both sides of Parliament when the HSW Act was introduced in 1974. Cuts in HSE staff have reduced the frequency of inspectors' visits to workplaces; have reduced research and scientific support activity; and have restricted the provision of information and advice and the development of new regulations, codes and guidance. At present, resources for the whole of the HSC/E in 1986/87 are limited to £96 million. A substantial increase in resources is necessary.

- Grant-in-aid to the HSC/E must be immediately increased to £200 million.

- An emergency recruitment programme must be put in hand to restore HSE to pre-1979 staff levels and to meet the staff targets agreed in 1974 – with a medium term objective of securing a doubling of the Factory Inspectorate in the next five years.

- In addition to expanding the number of inspectors in the field, there must be a balanced expansion of HSE support services and key parts of the Executive such as the National Industry Groups, the Directorate of Information and Advisory Services, the Accident and Prevention Advisory Unit and HSE's Medical and Research and Laboratory Services Divisions. Pay and conditions of HSE staff must be improved in order to attract and retain sufficient numbers of specialist staff in key areas such as engineering, occupational hygiene and toxicology.

- New staff resources must be found immediately to enable the Executive to carry out new work arising from compliance with EEC and International requirements and from new pending legislation covering hazards such as noise, toxic substances, micro-organisms, radiation, gas safety, diving, dangerous pathogens, road tanker safety, major hazards, pesticides and asbestos.

There must be a corresponding increase in local authority health and safety resources with closer co-operation between local authorities and HSE.

6: The importance of new legislation

Of central importance in the Commissions' work is the continuing development of new regulations, codes and guidance. Much new and improved health and safety legislation has been introduced since 1975 and major packages of legislation dealing with important issues such as toxic substances, noise, asbestos, and manual handling, are in the pipeline. These and further projects must be brought forward as quickly as possible with an expansion of HSE staff resources to ensure their full implementation. The development of effective health and safety legislation is of central importance to the improvement of working conditions and the control of occupational risk. For this reason care must be taken to ensure that duties in new legislation are clear and unambiguous and that there is no weakening of the provisions of existing health and safety law. The TUC is opposed to any suggestion that Section 1(2) of the HSW Act should be repealed since this section establishes the important principle that new measures to be introduced under the act must be ". . . designed to maintain or improve the standards of health, safety and welfare established by or under . . ." existing health and safety legislation.

7: The need for increased inspection and tougher enforcement

Without regular inspection of all workplaces by an independent enforcement authority, there can be no guarantee that legal and other standards designed to protect workers' health and safety will be widely observed in practice. The proposals contained in Chapter 6 of the HSC's "Plan for Work 1985/86 and onwards" are rejected by the TUC as an unacceptable departure from this key principle. These proposals should now be withdrawn.

Priority must be given instead to:

- more frequent visits by inspectors to workplaces – including a return to the principle of at least one visit to every workplace once every four years or following a major injury;

- stronger and more effective enforcement – including a more vigorous prosecution policy by the HSE's Inspectorates, for example an increase in the amount of inspector time spent on inspection work, more exemplary prosecutions and more cases prosecuted through the higher courts;

- an increase in the presently deplorable level of fines imposed by the courts, and the imposition of custodial sentences in cases where individual managers or directors show wilful disregard for the lives of their employees; and

- greater publicity for those found guilty of breaches of health and safety legislation.

Emerging evidence suggests that reduction in frequency of visits to workplaces, lack of enforcements by inspectors and very low penalties have together lessened the impact of the HSW Act on employers and management. A tougher enforcement policy is urgently required – particularly in sectors characterised by small firms and high accident rates.

8: Abolition of Crown Immunity

In the light of mounting public pressure, the Government has been forced to accept the need to abolish Crown Immunity in the NHS. The TUC welcomes this move, although it is now long overdue. Crown Immunity has led to lower levels of compliance with health and safety legislation in many key areas of employment including not only the NHS, but the Prison Service, the Civil Service and Government establishments generally. It is an anachronism and serves to undermine workers' legal protection from risks to their health and safety. The removal of Crown Immunity in the NHS must now be followed up by its removal in all other areas and fresh resources must be provided to enable health and safety standards to be improved in the sectors affected. Removal of Crown Immunity in the NHS shows that the alleged constitutional difficulties involved are by no means insuperable but have been used by the Government as a smokescreen for avoiding the resource implications of having to comply with health and safety standards that apply in all other workplaces. The TUC will now step up its campaign to ensure that Crown Immunity is abolished in all other sectors.

9: Deregulation – the wrong starting point

The TUC is totally opposed to the Government's stated policy of deregulation in the health and safety field in order to remove alleged 'burdens' on employers. In particular the TUC is opposed to the Government's intention to raise the threshold for employers' written safety policies from five employees to 20. Such a move could have a major impact on the health and safety of up to a quarter of Britain's workforce. If the Government now exempts small businesses from having to prepare even a simple written plan on how they are going to tackle health and safety, one more incentive for them to think through their approach to protecting their workers will have been removed. And if accidents and health damage increase as a result, responsibility for this will fall directly on the Government. The TUC urges all unions and employers' organisations covering small firms sectors to campaign to prevent this move.

The real burden faced by small firms is lack of resources and expertise to cope with complex health and safety issues. Health and safety legislation should not be regarded as a 'burden' but rather an essential means of assisting employers to tackle some of the real problems which they face, namely uncontrolled hazards, accidents, injuries and health damage to their workforce. Rather than cutting health and safety legislation, the Government should be reversing cuts in the HSE which have reduced the frequency and effectiveness of inspectors' visits to workplaces, and they should increase information and advisory services available to employers.

10: Statutory health and safety services

Employers need professional advice if they are to meet their responsibilities under health and safety legislation. At present, widespread use of health and safety services is only to be found in large companies and parts of the public sector. Given the failure of the voluntary approach to the provision of such services, new legislation must be introduced as soon as possible to ratify ILO Convention 161 on Occupational Health Services and to require all employers to provide or make use of professional services appropriate to the control of risks in their undertakings.

- Employers must be required to review their health and safety service needs in consultation with union representatives.

- Professional health and safety staff (including appropriately qualified occupational health doctors and nurses, hygienists and professional safety advisers) must be appointed by, and be accountable to joint health and safety committees.

- New agencies and approved group schemes, established under similar joint union/employer control and operating on a regional or industry basis, must be set up to provide and share health and safety expertise throughout the working community.

- New experiments must be undertaken to find ways of providing basic health and safety assessment of small workplaces.

- HSC IACs must have a central role in the development and operation of health and safety services in their industries.

- Those employers not providing adequate 'in house' services, or not participating in group schemes, must be required to contribute on a pay roll levy basis to jointly controlled health and safety service funds to be used to finance the provision of services from approved sources.

- The HSC must be allocated extra resources to establish a national health and safety services development unit to oversee this work in close co-operation with the IACs and to set up new units at local level to co-ordinate and promote effective use of professional health and safety services by employers.

11: Tackling health and safety in small firms

Given that the overwhelming proportion of Britain's workforce is now employed in small and medium sized firms in which health and safety performance is relatively poor, new and imaginative action is urgently needed if the aims of the HSW Act are to be made a reality for the majority of people at work. The main responsibility for developing such action lies with Government – particularly by ensuring the allocation of sufficient resources for the HSC/E and by promoting new systems to meet small firms' needs for professional health and safety advice and services.

In the past, strategic thinking about health and safety has tended to focus on the larger enterprise. Given the changing structure of employment, there must now be a new emphasis on the need to tackle the special problems faced by those who are employed in small work units. For example, besides enhancing the advisory role of the HSE, the development organisations should be required to provide comprehensive health and safety assesment and advice for new companies as part of their business development role. Closer co-operation is also needed between all public agencies, including local authorities, in order to identify businesses which fail to notify the HSE of their existence.

12: Accounting for health and safety in company reports

In order to promote a more systematic approach by employers to protecting the health and safety of their employees, Section 79 of the HSW Act should be implemented forthwith. This section was originally designed to require directors of companies to give specified information in their annual company reports in order to declare a record of their stewardship of the health and safety of their employees for the past year. The Companies Act was amended in 1975 to allow for this but Section 79 was never implemented. The TUC believes that this Section is an important provision which would inform workers about their employers' health and safety performance. It would also call to account those employers who fail to meet their responsibilities. Companies should be required to declare for example, details of notifiable accidents and diseases, as well as details of enforcement notices and prosecutions and details of health and safety services provided for their employees. Similar requirements must also apply to employers in the public sector.

13: Action to reduce accident rates

New industrial wide HSC/E initiatives are necessary if unacceptably high accident rates in agriculture, construction and parts of manufacturing are to be reduced. Incidence rates for major injuries in

manufacturing and construction have risen by 24.5 and 41.8 per cent respectively in the period 1979-85. This deterioration in safety performance is directly attributable to cuts by Government in health and safety thus enabling employers to reduce attention paid to health and safety issues. It is also associated with the spread of small firms, self employment and subcontracting which has accompanied recent decline and fragmentation in Britain's industrial structure. In addition to more vigorous action by the HSE, a series of top level enquiries should be set up into safety in the above sectors in conjunction with relevant IACs and joint bodies.

14: Specific areas of risk

As technology and awareness of health and safety issues develop, the boundaries of health and safety continue to expand – demanding further research, the development of new standards and fresh approaches to prevention. For example it is recognised increasingly that women face particular health and safety problems because of their dual role in society, their position within the workforce and the potentially harmful effects of many of the work tasks which they have to undertake – for example working with new technologies.

Evidence continues to emerge which raises concern about the extent and consequences of hazards to human reproduction from a wide range of physical, chemical, biological and psychological factors encountered at work. These can affect both men and women and include both ionising and non ionising radiations, teratogenic and mutagenic substances and stress.

Microbiological hazards pose a growing risk to workers' for example AIDS, Hepatitis B, and dangerous pathogens encountered in certain occupations including medicine, laboratories, agriculture, sewerage and waste disposal. In addition to developing a widespread programme of information about these hazards, new action is needed to ensure that safe work procedures are followed in all jobs where workers may be at risk.

New initiatives are urgently needed to tackle occupational stress – including the harmful effects of shiftwork. With this in mind the TUC remains firmly opposed to the Government's removal of restrictions on women's hours of work and favours a new legislative framework to tackle stress including early extension of controls on night work to both men and women.

Urgent action is also needed to tackle the problem of injury as a result of violent assault faced by many workers whose jobs bring them into contact with members of the public.

Responsibility for the health and safety of seafarers should be transferred to the Health and Safety Executive.

Transport accidents at workplaces continue to account for almost a quarter of all fatal accidents. New action is needed to tackle transport safety issues including an examination of steps which can be taken to improve safety for those who drive vehicles on the road as part of their job.

15: Planning for health and safety at the design stage

Waiting for evidence of harm to emerge before taking action to prevent accidents or damage to workers' health from new sources of risk is entirely unacceptable. Recent proposals and changes in health and safety legislation – including: strengthening Section 6 of the HSW Act;

regulations on the notification of new substances; and Control of Substances Hazardous to Health Regulations – have all re-emphasised the need for risks from plant, equipment, articles and substances to be identified and controlled at the design and planning stage and for full information to be made available to end users. The response to legal requirements in this area however has been poor. Further action is necessary, for example:

- improving the professional training of engineers, designers and technical staff in health and safety;

- new enforcement and publicity initiatives by the HSE amongst manufacturers and suppliers; and

- greater consultation with unions by manufacturers and suppliers about health and safety aspects of plant, equipment and substances for use at work.

16: Expanding occupational health research

It is estimated that at present more than 10,000 people die every year as a result of work related health damage. If this toll is to be curbed, occupational health problems must be properly identified, and assessed. To do this, the HSC must be able to develop a comprehensive programme of research and scientific support. The HSC research budget for 1985-86 has been restricted to £14.8m. This has meant that a number of important research projects have had to be shelved. Increased research effort is needed to identify new occupational health problems and sources of potential health risk. New health related legislation such as the COSHH regulations will also increase the quantity and quality of occupational health and hygiene data. If this is to be used effectively however there must be an increase in scientific services and support provided by the HSE — for example in assessing and collating exposure data and undertaking epidemiological studies.

Research resources must be increased and there must also be greater opportunities, through agreed procedures at the workplace and nationally, for unions to influence the scope and direction of research activity and to help identify unmet research needs particularly in relation to occupational health issues.

17: Controlling risks to the public and to the environment

The control of workplace risks must be accompanied by effective control of risks to the public and the environment generally from work activity – including the control of major hazards and the adoption of best practicable environmental options for the control of pollution. Trade unions have a major role to play here and further steps must be taken to extend trade union involvement in environmental issues, responsibility for which within Government remains fragmented and poorly co-ordinated. The Government must give top priority to establishing a permanent advisory body on environmental protection working in close co-operation with the HSC. They must also extend public accountability and involvement in major areas of environmental concern – for example radioactive waste and hazardous waste management.

18: Protecting young people at work

Further steps must be taken to protect the health and safety of young people employed on Government training schemes such as the YTS.

- Young people should only be sent to workplaces which can demonstrate a high level of health and safety control.

- All proposed training placements should be subject to a comprehensive health and safety assessment and there should be effective monitoring by HSE Inspectors.

- All trainees must have appropriate health and safety training and adequate supervision.

- There should be full implementation of the TUC's guidelines *Protecting Young People at Work* which are designed to ensure the health and safety of all young workers – whether they are part of a Government training scheme or are in full time training or employment.

19: Strengthening the role of safety representatives and safety committees

The introduction of the Safety Representatives and Safety Committees Regulations in 1978, gave important and legally guaranteed rights and functions to workplace trade union representatives including the right of safety representatives to:

- represent their members on health and safety matters;

- be consulted by employers;

- inspect the workplace;

- investigate potential hazards, accidents and complaints;

- receive information and assistance;

- require safety committees to be set up; and

- receive time off with pay to carry out their functions and to undergo TUC or union approved training.

The implementation of the Regulations has led to a radical change in approach and philosophy amongst unions in tackling health and safety issues – and as a result, workers and their representatives have been able to exercise far greater influence over working conditions.

There is evidence however that, in the present political and economic climate, some of the initial impetus generated by the Regulations is being lost. Further steps must now be taken to maintain and increase the authority of safety representatives and safety committees. In particular a number of specific improvements should now be made to the Safety Representatives and Safety Committees Regulations:

a)   to strengthen the rights of safety representatives to participate in planning decisions and at the commencement of new production operations; and to strengthen the requirement for employers and HSE inspectors to provide safety representatives with information about hazards and relevant control measures;

b)   to require employers to agree effective 'fast lane' procedures to enable safety representatives to secure rapid improvements in working conditions where necessary or to take emergency action where there is serious danger of injury or damage to health and to amend Section 7 of the HSW Act to give the right to any employee to refuse to undertake dangerous work;

c)   to develop the role of safety representatives within safety committees in order to give them a much stronger decision making role in the workplace – for example agreeing health and safety programmes and targets for improvement and monitoring the work of health and safety specialists; and

d) to extend the powers granted in the Regulations to the Musicians Union and Equity to all other unions to enable their officials to legally exercise the functions of safety representatives in small, scattered or isolated workplaces or in situations where the workforce and/or nature of work is continuously changing. This kind of approach to the provision of safety representatives is necessary to enable unions in industries such as agriculture and construction to cope with the growing fragmentation of the workforce – for example through the growth of small businesses, self employment and subcontracting.

In addition to campaigning for these changes, the TUC will continue to expand its health and safety materials for safety representatives and to undertake new initiatives to raise awareness of safety representatives' rights and functions. In the present climate, the TUC considers this work essential in order to help demonstrate the practical relevance of trade unionism to people at work. The TUC will continue to promote and co-ordinate the provision of health and safety services to unions and to give priority to finding ways of meeting safety representatives' needs for authoritative information and advice.

20: The growing international dimension

The growing internationalisation of systems and standards in occupational health and safety offers new opportunities to harmonise approaches to the control of workplace and environmental risks and to extend the benefits of health and safety regulations to workers in all countries. This is essential if hazards which are no longer acceptable in developed countries are not to be exported to newly industrialised nations.

Within the European Economic Community there has been considerable expansion in activity in developing EEC Directives which in turn have led directly to the introduction of new and improved health and safety legislation in this country. The TUC recognises the benefits of such international co-operation, particularly in avoiding duplication of effort in research and standard setting. The TUC also believes that there are great possibilities for expanding international co-operation – for example by increased contact between labour inspectorates, by co-operation within international bodies such as the ILO and the WHO and the establishment of international inspection teams. There is also a need for more sophisticated systems of international literature search and comparison of epidemiological data to assess information that has been gathered from research work carried out throughout the world.

The TUC will continue to support and participate in the work of the International Confederation of Free Trade Unions, the European Trade Union Confederation, the European Commission, the International Labour Organisation, the Organisation for Economic Co-operation and Development, the International Standards Organisation and other similar bodies concerned with health and safety at work. The TUC believes that Britain can benefit from the experience of other countries and in turn can contribute to that experience. The TUC takes the view therefore, that in addition to increasing its own contribution to international work in this area, the United Kingdom Government must undertake to implement and ratify (and where necessary go beyond) all relevant international standards and conventions concerning occupational safety and health.

21: Continuing commitment

Securing a continuing improvement in health and safety at work is one of the most important challenges currently facing the trade union Movement. Further progress however cannot be taken for granted and will not be achieved without the active participation and support of trade unionists in all occupations and at all levels. As a result of TUC and union action, major advances in health and safety have been achieved through the introduction of the HSW Act and the Safety Representatives and Safety Committees Regulations which in their turn have helped to generate a new level of activity and understanding of health and safety issues both at the workplace and beyond. At the same time, in the current climate of Government cuts and industrial decline, a number of factors have been working against health and safety. Renewed momentum is necessary therefore if current difficulties are to be overcome and further advances are to be achieved. This requires fresh action and commitment – particularly on the part of Government which has overall responsibility for providing resources for the development and enforcement of effective health and safety standards. The lines of action set out in this statement indicate clearly the next steps which must be taken if further progress is to be made over the next ten years in preventing accidents and health damage caused through work activity. The TUC calls on all those committed to improving health and safety at work to support and campaign for these policies.

Annex

Table 1: **Fatal and major injuries incidence rates* 1981-85**
(Information taken from Factory Inspectorate Annual reports 1981-85)

Standard Industrial Classification SIC Order	*Fatal and Major Injuries Incidence Rates* *per 100,000 employees*					**Increase**
	1981	1982	1983	1984	1985	1981-5
III Food, drink and tobacco	80.1	89.4	92.0	101.5	105.7	32%
V Chemicals & Allied Industries	77.1	87.2	99.9	98.4	104.3	35%
VII Mechanical Engineering	60.9	66.2	68.1	77.8	77.4	27%
XI Vehicles	56.6	49.7	57.1	60.0	65.6	16%
XII Metal Goods not elsewhere specified	86.1	96.1	99.3	115.7	123.1	43%
XIII Textiles	57.3	68.5	74.9	81.2	88.2	54%
XVI Bricks, Pottery, Glass, Cement etc	94.8	118.9	120.8	150.9	138.3	46%
XVII Timber, furniture etc	123.2	145.2	165.5	182.0	181.1	47%
XX Construction	163.7	203.7	220.7	234.2	231.8	42%

Table 2: **Factory inspectors in HSE 1978-86**
(Source: Hansard Written Answers November 6, 1986).

As of April 1	1978	1979	1980	1981	1982	1983	1984	1985	1986	*Decrease 1981-85*	*Decrease 1980-86*
Factory Inspectors in HSE as a whole	695	742	759	735	678	654	627	652	623	11.3%	17.9%
Factory Inspectors in HM Factory Inspectorate (HMFI)	642	688	702	682	620	589	564	589	560	13.6%	20.2%
Factory Inspectors in HMFI (Field only)	619	656	664	638	594	563	539	559	540	12.4%	18.7%